VOLUME FOUR OF THE

YALE EDITION OF THE

UNPUBLISHED WRITINGS

OF GERTRUDE STEIN

under the general editorship

of Carl Van Vechten

with an advisory committee

of Donald C. Gallup, Donald

Sutherland, and Thornton Wilder

THE YALE EDITION OF THE

UNPUBLISHED WRITINGS OF GERTRUDE STEIN

Two: Gertrude Stein and Her Brother

Mrs. Reynolds and Five Earlier Novelettes

Bee Time Vine and Other Pieces (1913–1927)

As Fine as Melanctha (1914–1930)

AS FINE AS MELANCTHA

(1914–1930)

BY GERTRUDE STEIN

with a Foreword by Natalie Clifford Barney

NEW HAVEN: YALE UNIVERSITY PRESS

London: Geoffrey Cumberlege, Oxford University Press

1954

CONTENTS

v

This is a tentative approach to Gertrude Stein and to a variety of her writing as yet unpublished.

The title of this fourth volume is to be *As Fine as Melanctha*, which, in itself, is an appreciation that cannot be surpassed.

How did this title come about?

An editor asked Miss Stein to write something as fine as her story "Melanctha" from *Three Lives;* and so she did. Did she?

I have not yet received the manuscript of the book I have been asked to preface, and because a book may not need a preface but a preface certainly needs a book, I have in the meantime been given *carte blanche* to write whatever I like. Therefore, leaving the future readers to their diverse impressions, I prefer to relate my personal experience and points of contact and discord with this author, whose companionship I delighted in and now cherish.

In recalling so magnetic a personality, how not, first of all, evoke this magnet to which so many adhered? For she attracted and influenced not only writers but painters, musicians, and least but not last, disciples. She used to declare "I don't mind meeting anyone once," but she rarely kept to so strict a limitation. Although the most affirmative person I ever met, she was a keen and responsive listener.

"Life is as others spoil it for us," concluded a beautiful friend of mine who had become a derelict through her fatalism. How many spoilt lives came to Gertrude with their misfortunes, due to some inextricable situation or sentimental rut? She, instead of offering helpless sympathy, often helped them out, by changing an *idée fixe* or obsession into a fresh start in a new direction.

As an appreciative pupil of William James, her study in re-
actions also proved salutary to the *spoilers* of lives. In these she
sometimes detected a genius for deceit which she would aid them
to confess, or she would indicate means to liberate them of their
victims, since as Henry James—was it not?—wisely remarked,
"There is only one thing worse than a tyrant and that is a tyrant's
victim."

Even more interested in cases than in their cures, many served
as characters in her plays and stories. Some of them may even discover themselves in this very book . . . that is, if they are sufficiently initiated into Miss Stein's game of blindman's buff, or
blindman's bluff, in which the reader is blindfolded—obscurity
being the better part of discretion as to who is who. At other
times she issued works of a most penetrating and acute quality,
filled with subtle analysis, like *Things as They Are*.

Even I, who am not in the habit of consulting anybody about
my dilemmas, once brought a problem of mine to the willing
and experienced ear of Gertrude. In a moment, in a word, she
diagnosed the complaint: "Consanguinity."

She never appeared to hesitate or reflect or take aim, but invariably hit the mark.

OUR WALKS

Often in the evening we would walk together; I, greeted at
the door of 5 rue Christine by Gertrude's staunch presence, pleasant touch of hand, well-rounded voice always ready to chuckle.
Our talks and walks led us far from war paths. For generally having no axe to grind nor anyone to execute with it, we felt de-
tached and free to wander in our quiet old quarter where, while
exercising her poodle, "Basket," we naturally fell into thought
and step. Basket, unleashed, ran ahead, a white blur, the ghost of
a dog in the moonlit side streets:

> Where ghosts and shadows mingle—
> As lovers, lost when single.

The night's enchantment made our conversation as light, iri-
descent and bouncing as soap bubbles, but as easily exploded

when touched upon—so I'll touch on none of them for you, that a bubble may remain a bubble! And perhaps we never said *"d'impérissables choses."* *

We also met during Gertrude Stein's lionized winter of 1934–35 in New York, and walked into one of its flashing, diamond-sharp days, where what one touches brings a spark to the finger tips.

Witnessing with apprehension Gertrude's independent crossing of streets without a qualm, I asked her why she never wavered on the edge of curbstones, as I did, with one foot forward and one foot backward, waiting for a propitious crowd and signal.

"All these people, including the nice taxi drivers, recognize and are careful of me." So saying, she set forth, her longish skirt flapping sail-like in a sea breeze, and landed across 59th Street in the park, as confidently as the Israelites over the isthmus of the Red Sea—while we, not daring to follow in her wake, risked being engulfed.

She accepted her fame as a tribute, long on the way but due, and enjoyed it thoroughly. Only once, in Paris—and indeed the last time I saw her—did the recognition of a cameraman displease her, for he waylaid her just as we were entering Rumpelmeyer's pâtisserie. In order to satisfy her need for the cake, and the photographer's wish, she was photographed by him, through the plate-glass window, eating the chosen one. Her eagerness was partly caused by a disappointing lunch we had just experienced at Prunier's, where each sort of sea food we ordered—prompted by appetites accrued by our recent wartime privations and still existing restrictions—was denied us, until at last (this was in 1946), driven to despair of a bettered world, Gertrude dropped her head between her hands and shook it from side to side; and not until we reached that rue de Rivoli pâtisserie did her spirits and appetite revive and meet with a partial compensation.

THEIR CAKES

The discovery of cakes had always been a peacetime pursuit of Gertrude and Alice. Meeting them by chance at Aix-les-Bains,

* Baudelaire.

I enquired why they happened to be on this opposite bank of the
Lac du Bourget, and was informed of a new sort of cake created
in one of the villages on a mountain beyond. But first obliged to
go on other errands, they descended from the lofty seat of their
old Ford car—Alice bejeweled as an idol and Gertrude with the
air of an Indian divinity. As they disappeared around a corner,
not without causing wonderment, the only appropriate offering
seemed to me one of those long, hose-stemmed lotus flowers of
dark pink, which I purchased and stuck between the spokes of
Gertrude's steering wheel, with a card of explanation: "A wand to
lead you on."

Another meeting with this inseparable couple took place in
their *jardin de curé* at Bilignin, on another summer afternoon. It
somewhat resembled the dust jacket Cecil Beaton designed for
Gertrude Stein's *Wars I Have Seen,* only a huge parasol replaced
the parachutes and we sat peacefully on gaily striped canvas
chairs. The four of us—for Romaine Brooks had come along
with me—and Basket, all curves and capers, lent a circus effect to
the scene. As China tea was being served, Alice placed on the
round outdoor table a fluffy confection of hers, probably a coco-
nut layer cake which only Americans know how to make—and
eat. Its white icing, edged with ornamental pink, matched Basket's
like coating and incidental pinks. Gertrude sat in the favorite
position in which Picasso portrayed her, clothed in rough attire,
with moccasined feet, knees far apart, reminiscent of the gypsy
queen under her tent in my old Bar Harbor days.

Meanwhile Romaine, contemplating our group and finding it
"paintable," wished to start a picture of it then and there, before
the light or her inspiration should fade. But I, the disturbing element of the party, because of a clock in my mind and in duty
bound to pleasures, insisted that Romaine and I were due elsewhere. So this picture of us all was left unpainted: *mea culpa!*

Gertrude's and Alice's flair for cakes makes me conclude
that while poets are left to starve in garrets—or, as here in France,
in *chambres de bonnes*—living only in the past and future, with
the hope of an aftermath of fame, an author such as Gertrude
Stein, admitting of nothing but a "continuous present," must be

sustained on sweetmeats and timely success, this being the surest way of taking the cake and of eating and having it too.

FAITH IN HERSELF

Her belief in herself never failed her. Even when still a child, she and her brother Leo used to discuss who would prove to be their family's genius. Leo thought himself that predestined genius; but Gertrude, turning to us—her two visitors were that afternoon Madame de Clermont-Tonnerre and myself—emphatically declared: "But, as you know, it turned out to be me!"

Indeed, such a faith in oneself "passeth understanding," and what a poor thing is understanding, compared to such a faith!

As faith is far more exalting than reason, she once deplored Ezra Pound's becoming "the village explainer," which led so great a poet, and discoverer of poets, to his present standstill.

HER LECTURE AT OXFORD

From the crest of Gertrude Stein's tidal wave of success, she was persuaded by Harold Acton to lecture to a class of students at Oxford University, and she managed to hold them spellbound without a single concession to meet their understanding. Her lecture soared above their heads as they sensed something that surpassed them, but which freed neither their laughter nor their judgment, so that nothing was left to them but to applaud uproariously.

She afterwards consented to meet them on the level, and both their questions and her answers were reported, inspiring and inspired.

WITH OUR G.I.S

This same democratic spirit made her popular with our G.I.s of the second World War. They also gathered something unique from her presence amongst them, and so she led them, as a sort of *vivandière de l'esprit*, from war into peace, and to realize their own, instead of their collective, existence. But in some cases this change was hard to bring about, loath as they were to be "sep-arated from," no longer "club together, be part of, belong to," etc. This fact was brought even to my notice in Florence by a big G.I. who confessed to me that "the urge to join his com-rades was so strong he couldn't even stop a moment to brush his teeth"! The disbanding of the herd instinct—to rebecome indi-vidual and perhaps a nobody instead of a company, to be left to the responsibility of oneself instead of leaving it to a chief in command with everything settled for you (death included), to take off a uniform to become uniform—all this was more than some of them could stand.

And how not feel homesick for their regiment when forced homeward, perhaps to intrude on a family, or face hostile busi-nessmen? At such a moment Gertrude Stein met them with her invigorating affirmations and cheered them on.

It must have been about this period that she was photographed against our Stars and Stripes.

BECOMING SINGULAR

Patriotic as Gertrude Stein seemed, she certainly dispelled our discouraging axiom that "one man's as good as another." No one has ever dared to say this of the American woman!

From her *Making of Americans*, I translated into French some of her most significant pages on our "progress in becoming singu-lar." These pages were read—between wars—in my salon, at meetings destined to bring about a better *entente* between French, English, and American authors.

On my "Friday" celebrating Gertrude Stein, Mina Loy ad-dressed them by explaining her admiration for this innovator who "swept the literary circus clear for future performances."

Many examples, including her own, were read to this effect—and a zeal for translating seized upon many of us from then on.

My *Aventures de l'esprit*, published in 1929, mentions these reunions as well as my literary adventures, including letters to me from Pierre Louys, Gabriel d'Annunzio, Marcel Proust, Rilke, Max Jacob, Paul Valéry, etc. This book Gertrude wanted to see translated for America, for it gives an incomplete but authentic résumé of our best period, and of those who made it so—and Gertrude Stein was included in this period and the forming of her own. How she stood her ground, never (unless to influence or appreciate) infringing on the ground of others. Indeed she made no allowances that "he who runs may read," and was heedless whether, having read, he ran.

We doubt if she ever thought of her readers at all.

In going over my impressions of her—*de vive voix, de vive mémoire*—in these fragmentary evidences, I find that I have somewhat replaced the essential by the superficial. I suppose that to want to enjoy and know such a personage without going into her more original ambitions and works is like seizing chance reflections from a water-mirror regardless of its depth; this is what I find myself doing here, and avoiding the significance of her undersea mysteries. Yet I have tried to dive deeper, and only touched rock bottom to be ejected up again to the surface, suffocating with too much salt water, in search of too rare a pearl.

Being a writer of *pensées*, I like to find a thought as in a nut- or seashell, but while I make for a point, Gertrude seems to proceed by avoiding it. And this, I am told, in order to create an atmosphere, "a picture," not through connections but disconnections. And her rotative system consists in getting at a subject by going not for but around it and, in snowball fashion, gathering up everything she meets on her rounds.

She also has a marked preference for "similarity" as opposed to "contrast"—a method which has long proved effective in rituals and incantations. As for her repetitions, they seem to me just a way of marking time before finding out what to say next, and remind me of those long sermons bringing about a retarded comprehension to audiences under the mixed fumes of incense and music. But I also remember how glad we were, as children, on the "merry-go-round," of a second and third chance to catch onto the golden ring.

And did not the child-woman, Mélisande, by saying "*Je ne suis pas heureuse*" (which is human), gain an echo's magic by repeating it—aided by Debussy's accompaniment?

HER SYSTEM OF "HIDE AND GO SEEK"

Is not Gertrude Stein's example most stimulating, until she goes too far in the practice of it? Systems are apt to run away with their inventors, or someone else catches onto them and uses them to better effect. While, as in this instance, the inventor remains either monotonous or bewildering. Here Gertrude warns us that "Bewildering is a word that carried no weight." But what of monotonous? And why must she, who can be so startlingly inventive, risk misleading us through such a wilderness of words?

If her meaning were only obscured by density, as in Joyce's *Finnegans Wake* or Ezra Pound's *Cantos*, I could be all for it— as for other breakers of routine, such as Rémy de Gourmont's "dissociation of ideas"; but I cannot see where so simple a dissociation of words from their subject leads us.

However I suppose that there comes a transition period in civilization, where words as well as ideas need to be divorced in order to regain a new vitality and freer associations.

And indeed one must not be too bent on understanding or one misses essential results. So I must either play this writer's "hide and go seek" or stand by my preference for her more comprehensible publications.

Still envying her knights errant: Thornton Wilder, Scott Fitzgerald, Hemingway, Carl Van Vechten, Bernard Faÿ, Max White, etc., for being initiated and able to spin, undazed, around her circles, closing us out from

> Thoughts hardly to be packed
> Into a narrow act,
> Fancies that broke through language to escape.*

Yet why must her fancies prove so discouraging? But we must be patient with geniuses, as they are most patient with themselves, and follow themselves even where we cannot follow them.

STRUGGLING TOWARDS A CONCLUSION

> My idle hands are stained with ink,
> And still I don't know what I think!

* Robert Browning.

and this remains my state of mind even now, when the manuscript shipped across the ocean for my introduction has at last arrived.

Must I confess, as once, much to the amusement of Paul Valéry, *"J'ai peur de lire"*—and should I not all the more fear to read, lest my comment result in a betrayal either of so near a neighbor or of myself?

How shirk such a responsibility, which Carl Van Vechten and Donald Gallup so imprudently entrusted to me? By arguing that a long preface would misrepresent a book of short stories— and especially of these stories without a story! Besides agreeing with whoever first apologized for writing at too great a length— not having taken the pains to make it short. I have always had a predilection for what is short, and especially novels and long stories often seem to me much longer than life and far less interesting.

UP AGAINST VOLUME FOUR

But here is that big white block of a manuscript awaiting my hazardous inscriptions—as though this fourth cornerstone of Gertrude Stein's unpublished works were not better without. Even so must I, after so much hesitation vainly expressed to the sponsors of these posthumous works, pursue? And now, as I start turning over this typewritten manuscript, Gertrude sympathetically comes out of it to meet me with such consoling phrases as

Nobody knows what I am trying to do but I do and I know when I succeed. . . .

She knew how to and when to and why to. . . .

What can be expected of paragraphs and sentences by the time I am done. . . .

That is a sentence but two words cannot make a preface. . . .

It was exasperating, we were patient, we said it again and meant everything. . . .

I have often remarked that invention—and there is a great deal of invention—I have often remarked that invention concerns itself with inventing, and I, I feel no responsibility . . .

Are not such phrases self-explanatory? But it is hard not to resent a method which allows its author to write so many dull pages on purpose. And then again one is suddenly awakened to re-markable remarks, such as

A sentence speaks loudly. . . .
A noun is nature personified. . . .
How many saints are irreligious? . . .
I feel the value of religions. All religions. . . .

And such glimpses into her unwritten novels:

Always she knew she would be everything—he always knew he was becoming. . . .
She is his second life. . . .
How can you be so radiantly far? . . .
Hurry to me restfully. . . .
Eclipsing my feeling . . .
I did not think I ever could be cross again with love. . . .
How dearly is she me, how dearly is she me, how dearly how very dearly am I she. . . .

And what a fresh beauty in such definitions as

Civilisation begins with a rose. . . .
This is the flower of my leaf. . . . .

And what fun she must have had with

I have invented many titles and I have invented many sub-titles.
Please prepare the bed for Mrs. Henry. . . . **Dear** dear this is a title!

MY ATTEMPTS AT IMITATION

I wondered if I could make up Steinean sentences, and suc-ceed in breaking sense away from sense. It's hard to get something to mean nothing and nothing to mean something. I have tried, and this is the result:

Did I like it? Did I like liking it? Or did I dislike liking it or

did I dislike it or dislike disliking it? Or did I dislike liking to dislike it? Or did I like disliking to like it?

You see it's harder than one thinks not to make sense. And
we are never sure of being foolproof. For example:

Did Tom fool? Did Tomfoolery fool? Did fool foolery fool
Tom?

I have written a whole page full of this sort of thing, but
feel it would be inappropriate to quote more of it here. For
enough is already more than enough of this sort of juggling with
words.

"ENTER THESE ENCHANTED WOODS"

I have examined many of the leaves of this forest of words
and lost myself in their midst, missing not only my way but hers.
Perhaps there are signs and paths through it which I fail to sense,
so I prefer to stay on its border and hunt for the wild flowers
amongst the leaves, leaving her knights errant to penetrate its
mysteries. The spirit of them invites trespassers more adventurous
than I have proved.

"Enter these enchanted woods, ye who dare." *

Alice B. Toklas having intimated to me, in her mild but per-
suasive way, to cease beating around the bush and picking up only
the chance plums that fall from it, I have read steadily through
"Did Nelly and Lilly Love You." Though I can't make out
whether they did or didn't—the chances being two against one
they didn't.

I like this kind of novel, but that's perhaps because I don't like
novels. This chapter contains none of the usual or unusual subjects, intrigues, or relations and sequences, nor a climax to a more
or less fictitious end. Certain words acting as highlights lead the
way, but to no conclusions, or to conclusions left to the reader
and interchangeable enough to suit more cases than one, more
love affairs than one, and to more marriages giving no clue. If
clue there be, it is left to our discretion: the clue is perhaps you.
Our approach remains that of the eavesdropper on situations to
which we have not been initiated. At least this discretion spares

* George Meredith.

us the embarrassing complicity through which we have too often witnessed the love scenes in book, play, and film—especially in those moving pictures where the sexually starved feed their emotions on the hero and heroine's uniting in that culminating, inevitable and prolonged kiss [a kiss which should, in natural sequence, precipitate the couple off to bed].

The subjects of this book are divertingly different: in "A Third" it must be very interesting for the three concerned, that is if no one of the three remains the third.

"Equally so. A Description of all the Incidents which I have Observed in Traveling and on my Return" leaves open the question "Whether one receives more letters at home or abroad?"—one of the determining questions as to whether to travel or not to travel.

The portrait of "Miss Cruttwell" was taken from the life of a real person, but she is treated so that no one would recognize her—not even Miss Cruttwell.

In "No," if *Yes Is for a Very Young Man*, "No" should be for a very old and wise one!

"The Background of a Detective Story"—if the best detective story is the one whose mystery remains complete and the crime undiscovered, this one should win!

In "One Sentence," how well its author has imitated the cacklings of "An elderly couple talking talking much much or much talking too much to much!"

And "She means nothing wrong but the love of talking is so strong in her that I think it necessary to check it whenever I can."

"A little example does make it thin it makes it very colored very colored white."

What "One Sentence" says has as much relation to speech as when a parrot first tries to vocalize parts of a conversation just overheard!

It is obvious that in "A History of Having a Great Many Times Not Continued to Be Friends," her friendships ceased from the causes already detected in their beginning.

Other pieces are so much less comprehensible that I can make neither head nor tail of them, but nevertheless feel something like the first principles of life interestingly astir in their middle.

Then again I find many treasures in this version of *As Fine as Melanctha*—as though she, Melanctha, had fled from giving herself a rival self, but not without leaving behind for us her jewel case, containing such gems as—but these, as the rest, I must now leave her readers to discover. With my apology for detaining them—if I have detained them—so long.

NATALIE CLIFFORD BARNEY

Paris
17 January 1954

SUBJECT-CASES: THE BACKGROUND OF A DETECTIVE STORY

1923

SUBJECT-CASES: THE BACKGROUND OF A DETECTIVE STORY

In case of this.
A story.
Subjects and places.
In place of this.
A story.
Subjects and traces.
In face of this.
A story.
Subjects and places.
In place of this and in place of this.
A story.
Subject places.
In place of this.
A story.
When the work when the work and when the work when should he work.
In place of this and in place of this and in place of this places.
Subject.
Places.
Subjects places.
In face of this how hardly in place of this, how hardly in place of this, places, how hardly in place of this, how hardly to place in face of this, subject cases, to place in case of this, to place this subject in case of this in place of this. Subject cases in place of this.
To watch. Prepare two. Prepare to watch in that way. To watch anyway. Anyway to watch.
Lighter than in there. No lighter than in there.
Subjects and cases. In case of this.
What else can you do.
What else do you see.
What else do you see.
Leave the letters at the door and more and more very nearly there do they have noises established. Let the letters be left to me

by them very often. In this way I know this tendency.

Now exactly.

If as an objection if it is an objection if it is objected that it is
due to this that they have it to do, if it is an objection that they
do do this if this is an objection, this is the object of this attention.
He can we think. This is in building. Now now now have a cow
have a cow.

Concentrate.

If in this way preparations may be undertaken. To undertake
preparations. Comparative preparations. To comparative preparations.

Four heads are his specialty but it is mouths we want mouths
and noses.

Sit and sit smell and smell. Go to hell go to hell.

Action and to reaction. To serve notice as well. Deserve to
notice as well. Notice it as well. To deserve to notice it as well.
It serves very well. It is of service to notice it as well. It is of
much service to deserve to notice it. Very much. Very well. To
notice it as well. To notice it as well. To deserve to notice it as
well.

If the agitation is passed. Agitated, for in the sense of because
of this agitation, clearly and repressed agitation, repressed as to
being agitated and very needful of the adjoining pleasure. To join
in pleasure. To an addition of pleasurable agitation, to such an admission admit that admitted it is admitted it is submitted, to submit
agitation, agitate for admission, to agitate to admit, to submit, to
the pleasurable to the pleasure of joining in that pleasure, to join in
that pleasure. To agitate to be agitated, to agitate the joining in that
pleasure to the adjoining pleasure, to submit to this as an admission,
to admit this to submit to this, to submit this agitation so that it is
admitted that there is an addition to the adjoining pleasure, to
join in this pleasure, to submit this altogether with the admission
of the agitation to join in this pleasure. Altogether to join in this
admission. To submit this to the joining in this pleasure altogether.
Altogether to join in this adjoining pleasure, to submit to this
joining in this pleasure to admit this as an agitation to join to be
joined in this as an adjoining pleasure, to submit this to admit to
this, to admit and to join to join in this as in an adjoining pleasure.
An adjoining pleasure is admitted and it is as it is submitted to

have been the beginning of the agitation and agitating this and joining to this and this then and for this adjoining pleasure.

Accidental work, no accidental work. No accidental work in a parlor. For accidental work. Not for accidental work not for accidental work in a parlor. Accidentally or is it in accidentally earning. Calmer than that. By accident. By an accidentally earned and by anticipating by accidentally anticipating earning interest in more and more separated parlors admitted it is to be admitted and then to be admitted to admit that very accidentally that very indeed very nearly and accidentally earned and to be earned very nearly accidentally earned and to be admitted and to be nearly in and to be admitted and to be admittedly nearly and accidentally admitted. Do not hesitate to brush by to brush by to brush by by accident, and to brush accidentally too.

A considerable factor it is a considerable factor in this way, this is a considerable factor, to share in this, it is a considerable factor to have a share in this and once again following and in once again following and in following and in a share of this and in following and in once again sharing, this is a considerable factor in this, it is a considerable factor in this to share in this. And once again more than once a considerable share in this more than once and a considerable factor in this, it is a considerable factor to share in this.

Plenty of this in the place of this and in place of this plenty of this in place of this. The fairly well seen formation to fairly well see to fairly well to have to see fairly well, to see to it fairly well, fairly well seen information, to fairly well see and to inform to informally see very well to it and to plentifully see and to fairly well see and to see plentifully and in place and in this place and to place and to place more there, plentifully, and formally and for that and for that to be seen fairly well seen to be fairly well and informally more and plentifully more plentifully fairly fur-nished with the information additionally. To add this as informa-tion and to be authorised informally.

Just a station in justice to this station, just to state and adjust it, just to state it in justice to state it to state it in justice to it, to adjust it, and to do justice to it and to be adjusted for it, for it and by advising justice for it, to advise to do justice to it, due to it, justice due to it, to adjust more than to just advisedly obstruct it, justice do it do and do justice to it, do and do do justice to it, to advise to adjust it to this and to that, and to do justice to this adjustment and advisedly defer to the justice of it and to defer the justice of it. Is it just and does the justice done to it decide the justness of it and does the adjustment of it determine the judgment to be made for it. Determined to abide by the judgment of it and to have had justice done to it and to justify the advisedly judicious information just given with it. Indeed with it and for it indeed for it and by it indeed by it and with it indeed with it and for it. Justify the judgment given of it. Indeed justify just the judgment and the judgment was given with it. Indeed this judgment of it. Just to justify and to judge and to judge and to advisedly justify this judgment of it. To advisedly judge just this in the judgment of it. To advise the justification of it. To justify it.

Antedate. This is antedated. To be antedated. This is to be antedated. Confederate, to confederate. Is it to confederate state that it is antedated. To confederate to state that it is antedated. Too confederate to state that it is antedated. In this state in such a state in such a state to compensate. It is a compensation it is in compensation to antedate it is a compensation to antedate to antedate as a compensation. Compensate for this. To compensate and to antedate. To confederate and to antedate. To antedate and to compensate. Compensation and confederation. To antedate as a compensation and as a confederation to antedate, to confederate to antedate. To antedate is to confederate. To refute it to refute in refutation. A refutation. To dilate upon it. To dilate upon a refutation. To presume to antedate and the presumption is that it is to be attenuated that to antedate is an attenuation. To anticipate and to antedate or as if in a confederation. To antedate is to confederate. In anticipation to antedate in anticipation, to confederate to antedate in anticipation. Or as a preconception or in indication or in anticipation or for confederation or as to or as in presumption of an intention. To antedate in anticipation, to confederate or as a confederation. To compensate. Compensation. To antedate in compensation. To compensate and to antedate. To confederate and to antedate and to antedate is to confederate. And resistance, resistance is anticipate. To anticipate compensation and confederation. To anticipate and to antedate, to antedate and to participate.

Understood as periodical. To be understood as periodical. Periodically fastened. Unfastened. Take it for granted that there is an addition, take it for granted that there is addition take it for granted there is addition. Addition antedated. Take it for granted that the addition is antedated. Take for granted an antedated addition. Presently presently and presently. A perfect letter-writer.

If not what, change in cases change in case a case of it in exchange. Exacting an exchange for it. Exactly in exchanging in case of it. In exactly exchanging because by it, exactly changing. In changing because of it. Because of it. In changing because of it in exchanging for it, and then what. In exchange. Now and then and to suit and to boot. In exchange are objects colored by water. Ejaculation and rooms. In exchanging for in exchanging. In exchanging for an exchanging and in exchanging for changing. In exchanging for rooms. In place of in exchanging. Exchange very nearly to change.

Last at last how many directions are there at last. By this mail at this sale what direction was it at the last. At least. By mail and in detail and for sale in how many directions unasked and in what direction. In what direction do they last. It is classed. It is to be passed as if it were to be unasked. A direction is unasked and by mail and at last and for sale and in the past and in detail fastened and unfastened. In reconsideration. Let it be Saturday. In reconsideration and at last and to last. Did in a direction being intended to be at last as a last indication, did a direction intending to at last be unasked, did it indeed the direction at last did it indeed the indication as at last, did it indeed as an indication and as a direction did it indeed determine it as at last and as at by mail and as at in a sale and as at as indicated in its detail, did it as direction was it as an indication was the direction asked or was it unasked. In as an indication in a direction as direction and in proceeding, in proceeding and in establishing by mail what is in the sale and when there will be divested when it will be divested of all indication as to this detail. Let there then be reasonably a history of habitations. In this way mail sale detail indication direction and a history of habitation at the last may be in a way as if it were to make. To be arousing, this to be connected and antedated by a house and houses, by houses and homes, by homes and indications given of directions given of directions given and indications given and establishment. It is established and it is meant it is established and to prevent the direction from being asked and in a direction and on this evening and antedated as to it evening.

Ineradicable to remain, to possess and to see movements when movements are approachable approachable as if it were undoubted. May be doubted. It might be without doubt. Ineradicable to remain. What is it. In as it were intentional. And to be presentable. Bows and smiles. Organisation and in time. It is not only in its interest which is in its interests. Intact, it is to be in its own delight and night, no names of praises are mentioned. To appraise means to come to a decision as to values. Traces of unity and an exact enfeeblement. To carry minutes to an extreme. May it be said of a little minute as of a little week. Exact aggrandisement and reunion. To duplicate resonances. Enjoyable governing, and mantling in that way roses and revision. Reversion makes revision stronger. And in combination, combine mistakes with mistaken. Not to be mistaken. If any one. Not to be mistaken for any one. Dividing, division, rapidity, encroaching, to transmit and to reverse. Reversibly speaking. To maintain. Did it necessitate that others wore this. To exclude pieces. A conspiracy to exclude pieces for it. Not a piece. No not pieces and inhabitants and dwelling. Not to dwell upon it and in a manner of speaking houses.

If it were to if it were to as if it were to take steps and to as if it were to come down and to step as if it were to step down and not a crown, a dog and Putnam, if in an engagement to hold the heat in place, in place of plenty of places, in a way to say repeatedly. To withdraw and to amass, to add and to vary, to interline, to obviate and to ferry, to ferry across the weight of there there need be no vagueness as to hair. If the hair is cut, what, cut, if the air is cut, and to say it with flowers, not too rapidly and outstanding. An outstanding obligation. Please and pleases. Not creditably as a circumstance and no sales needed. The futility of a policy of irritation and many majors do. Born in this way it is to be born in this way and may there be antedated purses. Not any one mentions the name of anything. It is easy to very easy to, it is very easy to and very easily too.

It was succeeded by, it was before this, it was unnecessary to

mention too many and in any case two more and so to speak it
was Wednesday and in a made way. When and where are obelisks
washed and arches. When in that case more than in there. As intentional as that and eyes, eyes are mentioned to be singular or
more than singular. In this way readiness comes readily. Markets
too and after glasses, markets are too and after that as to glasses.
It can be driven here and there and with some care and in that
manner care is shown and not in the same as sound. To sound and
to sound, to see to it. If inclination is exhausted attentively if inclination is exhausted and attentively and if inclination is tested
refuse testy, if inclination is exhausted attentively, attentively remarked, and an inclination to it. Measured to measure and fit to
fit. Not a ship. Shipping so to speak reshipping and so to speak
reshipping in addition. In addition to this shipping and regaining
and gaining and to not surprise suddenly. Not to surprise by sudden ability and so commonplace, and so so to speak common sense
and so so to speak maximum and so to speak also so to speak furnish. To furnish this. To furnish this and to very nearly and very
fairly, is juxtaposition the same as in case of maneuver. Maneuver
is a word and a paragraph and a sentence, in a sentence, and in a
paragraph a word has this connection. To be connected with antedating organs for this, canadians can carve wood for purposes of
deception. This makes a street not noticeable as indeed two can
be more often seen than one. One has no separation there as an
allowance and no corals. Corals are again stylish. Bow to them. In
this way anything can seem to be read. Not so very funny. It is
not so very funny, it is not as it might be said of it not actually
famous. Can antedating be so nearly and so nearly has it in the
sense of nicely, has it been very near. Blue in green and white in
blue green in glass and all seen through the medium of energy
and precision. Action and reaction being equal and opposite when
all is said exactly what is it that has been referred to. References.
Begin now. As if to mount in a way from one to another. All smile.

Even and calculable, incalculable. Even and and incalculable,
evenly and incalculably culpably, and inculpably, and even and
uneven and calculable. Was there a background and was there a
ground for deers. Incalculably around and around. Around yes
and incalculable yes and inculpated yes and calculable. Calculable

yes and inculpated yes and around yes and altogether found altogether yes. Inculpated yes and calculably yes calculable yes and
inculpated yes. Yes a ground, yes a ground for mails yes, antedated and referred to and an instance of reaction. Action and reaction being equal a restraint is unequal. Unequal to this. In calculable and antedated and ministrations, ministered to and admin-
istered for and mentioned as a door. Best not say yes and no and
do as you are told. In that as neglected, expected and directed, in
that as directed expected and neglected, in that as directed in that as
neglected, in constructions profoundly modified by unexpectedly
balancing, balance to rest. Is it antedated if it was to be said so. Act
quickly and measure them for clothes. Does it seem as if it were to
be the same to be wealthy and thin. Thin it as a hem, a hem does not
need wishing. In just such a way does willingness make it uppermost. Uppermost eradicates explanation and impediment. It is
uppermost. In this settled distinction all can really share. And it
will do.

Young among. If that is said so. Mount and amount. If that
is said so. If that is so and the amount and if the amount and young
among and if the amount and it is said to be so, if among the
young it is said to be so if the amount is said to be so, if the amount
is said to be so among the young, among a number there are if it
is said so, a number among the young, and the amount and the
amount might mount, it is said to be so. Among the young it is
said to be so. The amount is said to be so. It is said that might
mount to this amount. It is said to be so. It is said to be so and so.
It amounts to that. It amounts to this that it is said to be so.

Added to it no not added to it or if indeed as in speaking additionally and abominably, as if additionally speaking and an article
if it is as indicated, if an article what as it is to be chosen. If in reading, reading and writing as it may be speaking reading and writing if it as it may be it may be as it is to be sent. Sent away. It is
not intended that it is to be sent in this way. And then, and if then
and when, when if there is to be more and some more some do
more, more and more, some do, more and more, if as follows, if as
it follows, by this means and really rise, not too exactly placated
as if no settled masons sit. Masonry settles in this instance and
collapses too. Two and two make parlors. Parlors are as if started.

Mention parlors. Parlors are none none are in parlors, parlors are known and unknown and peculiar. Peculiarly to satisfy to satisfy a peculiarity. Can be seen can be seen in collaboration it can be seen to have been done in collaboration, collaboration and collusion, collusion and carefulness and carefulness and harmony and harmony and distance and distance and determination and determination and selections and selections and elaboration and elaboration and initiation and initiation and able to be seen it is to be seen that collaboration that there is collaboration that in collusion that there has been collusion that distance that as to distance that every indication that there is every indication that no pleasure is perceived. To perceive a perception, in a way perception is more as money is, if it is as it is does union make for strength and does it does it unify action. All to go and all to stay all to stay and all to go and all to say so, all say all are to stay and all do say so. All are to go. If there are changes, if there are to be changes if there are to be exchange of ounces, ounces have meant that and this there and here. Appear to hear, and to appear to hear. Here. Ounces and pounds and miles and miles and miles and ounces and miles and pounds and pounds and ounces and miles. In a way peculiarly. And parlors are in that way announcements.

It especially precluded violence why especially preclude violence why was violence especially to be precluded why is violence to be especially precluded. Naturally not naturally violence is naturally not especially precluded and systematically reversed, the reverse of systematically especially to preclude violence. Esther and aim and in and aid, esteem it an aid, to esteem it to be an aid and to estimate it as an aim and as an aid. Net result, an effort as in consideration. Considerably antagonised. Was it sixty and if sixty was it fifty for sixty. Sixty for fifty makes not more than three thousand. Fifteen for three thousand makes less than or more than two hundred and for four, to be surprised by and at Jane and Julia and a likely looking colored girl. To apply for it to apply for it as if an application suddenly was as related. Related to what, to what was it to be related, it was as it was to be related it was related to this and related to that and antedated as in commencing and as to antedating, as to antedating and as to in commencing to announce as managerial that which holds more and more. It holds more and more. And if it holds more and more. And if as it holds more and more, if as it is holding this much and more than this, if in this way as it is beheld, it is not in this way to be fancied, fancying nests this, nest and nest, and to see and to that search, saturday and solemnly, when is it attributable to an edge to money, to an agglomeration as if not inhabited. To have a history and not to deny extracts as extraordinarily and houses as seen to be scattered and in many cases not clearly separated, so estimated as an estimation, as indeed as if it has to be thoughtfully fed. Fairly well sawed as if it were to be fairly well noised, noised about, about and nearly for this as an integral may it be said integrally may it be claimed and in the special and in the especial solidity concerning solidity there is no repetition. To be sold. Further. Farther and farther. In this way farther and no farther and laterally as it may be. It may be. As it is fair to state as it is fairly an interstate, to understate, shouting makes for silence. When and when and when there. When there. When there is more than there is for more than there is. There is more than there is for this and for more than for this and before this is to be over-stated. In any pleasure pleasurably speaking in any antedating and in antedating making more than samples, making more than their samples securely and securing and as to security, for security.

The history and beaming, the first article antedating making more than examples. The history and this as in a measure terminating and conforming to the agitating blandishment as inaugurated. The inauguration is as it is never to be presently presented, authoritatively. In this measure in a way it was to be all rejoined. Rejoin articles and regions. They spent their past time as pastime. As pastime some gratitude differs from others. In there in the meantime how are they all to say how do you do how glad we all are to see you and we are not at all not prepared to see all of you. Mellow and mallow very mellow, and mallow as it is known to taste. A considerable instance of a foreground. In the foreground there usually are to be found grass and colors colors as if it were as if they were to be worn. Worn can be used in the sense of to be worn out and to be worn as about. Out and about and ante-dating and bowing, bowing to this as a suggestion and also to that and moreover as to discretion, indicated as discretionary and

illustration. Illustrated not angularly not angrily nor even for-
biddingly, not forbidden nor to be left over and as addressed addressed to them. In this way mistakes occur and delicacy varies
with and at variance, and at variance and to say so, to say so and
next to and nearly there. Next to and nearly there and registered
as if lingering. Linger longer Lucy.

A guide to guide and with a guide. For guidance, for their
guidance and by their guiding and with and all and to their and
you and man and riddance, to be as it is to be to be not as to con-
venience and purposes. The purposes are there, two and more
articles and to and for buildings, inhabited buildings differ from
uninhabited buildings in certain respects. Respect and respected
to respect, and to respect, and as expected and as it is to be expected it is to be respected and it is to be expected. It is to be expected and as it is to be respected it is to be respected as it is to
be expected. It is to be expected. It is expected. And in that and to
wait and to wait and in that and and to wait. Weight, and to wait
and in that and and to wait. And to wait. Not to be as to have it
to say not to be permanently and permanently. Not to be permanently not to say so not to say so and permanently and beyond
thirds. One third and their thirds. Their thirds. Beyond thirds
and their thirds. Permanently and beyond thirds, not permanently
and beyond thirds.

Not a guess and guessing, not to guess not to be guessing,
guess and guess and guess again, not a good guess. To guess. Fortune and as comfortably, this night is as important as any other
night and as comfortable fortunately. Fortunately as fortunately,
as fortunate it was fortunate, it was very fortunate, fortunately.
This night was as important as any other night fortunately. Fortune and a fortune, and for a fortune and fortunately. It was very
fortunate. Parlor, to be as if it were more than it might be if a
little quickly, to be quietly and quickly to be as if it might still
have to be as quickly as it might still more than and not more than
that and equally and equably, equably speaking as if unequally
preferred. Preferences, accepted as parlors as parlors are private.
Privately. Private not used as uneasiness, uneasily felt, to be more
than as if it mattered. Mattered too much, it mattered too much
and very nearly, not as if to be closeted, closeted connects again.

Closet to connect again and to closet or a closet, to further it as an estimate. To and to name to as a to countenance, and to be as if to and as a price, inquire, if a parlor really, and really, and there, to be, as well, let us as well, not to let, not to be let, not to let it be, not and narrow and to carry not to carry not to carry it away. Any day.

Monsieur Mansard and the architect of Versailles. Is Monsieur Mansard contemptible or not. The architecture of Versailles do I lie do I lie. The architecture of Versailles, to build it high to build it high. The architecture of Versailles. By and by by and by. Not to express address, egress, Negress Negress. Negress egress, address express, humbly apologise. And how to how to, and how to how to. Humbly indeed, apologies. Requesting the presidents to urge upon their governments and the governments of certain nations the immediate necessity of elaborating and restoring the expression of thanks verbally and moreover educating the administration of planning. To plan to. In this way each of them comes away. And now then. What do they seed broadcast, they seed broadcast the respect for colored glass. White and rose-color preferably. When opaque white and blue. Red white and blue all out but you. In season in the season in this season and an outburst, in season and in the season and in this season. Chances many chances, and some chances some chances are taken and other chances are not taken. Antedate and a plate, and to placate and to antedate. Other chances which are not taken are those of which being reminded it can be recognised it would not have been judicious to attempt the undertaking. A great many people reason justly. And not very trenchantly. To advise and to advise, it is advisable to entangle to disentangle, to disentangle one arbitrary decision after another. Another and another. The coral remains the same. Just now it is an attraction. To attract and to attract. To attract to the attraction without indication without any indication of the nature of the attraction. Be beset. To be so beset. To be so beset and so beset. Finally.

Not poppies for poppies to poppies as poppies, turns to poppies, pansies turn into poppies, as poppies, to poppies for poppies in poppies into poppies, and so as to turn and so as to return, it was returned and the following was closed inclosed, closed in, and as to a lot of it, it was so to say the group to be seen and heard, and as to reading and as to illiterate if it sprang away, if it sprang and sprang in that sense sprang, a few months suffice and twice, it was to be definitely dissolved and so to obtain an interest as interest and in their interest. It is intended to interest to be of interest and to introduce the approach to that as a parlor. When they arrive and they examine they observe the depth the length and the breadth and the pleasures of purchase, then in order not to compare, they come and declare what can be declared ostentatiously, what can be declared to be in order. Everything in order, in that order in order that there is no value. There is no value in our having been right. Alright. To ground a ground and on the ground, to be as if it were to be found here and there. To be defended, if it means, no, no, and if it means yes and no, and if it means no not at all and if it means in order to excuse. Excuses made, and to be as if to be made. Excuses made, to have to have excuses made. To excuse the recognition of and the interest in and the description of and the delight in and the request for and the determination to and the denial of and the attribution to and the defence of and the interruption for and the disappearance of and the declaration with, and the combination with and the distribution of and the negligence for and the abstention from. Why abstention and smell, very well why smell and smelling and very willing and very much sought for. Can a declaration that a door as a door, and as in question, as in a question, this as in question, to question this. To miss and to miss. Amiss and amiss. Not too much to-day. Any day. For a day. To call for a day. To call for a day. Joiner, a joiner was once a carpenter. A carpenter was once a carpenter and to carpet is to cover. To cover as a cover. A cover is not embroidery. And so women appear and disappear readily. Favor, and as to flavor, to know very well that they ate very well.

Plentifully it may plentifully pay. They can absolutely say, as to display, to display and absolutely say, plentifully pay, it may pay, as to display, as to plentifully pay, as to absolutely say, to say to pay to display, for pay, to say, as display, to plentifully display, to absolutely say, to adequately pay. As to a parlor, alright as to a parlor, for a parlor, for the parlor, to adequately attend to the preparation and transportation and singing, transport as it were, from port to port from door to door from the door, away from the door. In so much as it is plainer, in so very much as it is so very much plainer, as if in a history as historically known, to be known and a tone, to be thrown and as it shone, to loan as to a loan, as to lean, as to lend, as to lend as to advise as to advise as to be seen as it is to be seen and to be as if in relation to a parlor. How can it be said to have been so. And so. And so. To see, as if to say it severely. Severity if described is as an index to a silver set. Silver set of course. Of course and restlessness and easily, very easily as a settlement. A settlement means an exchange. An exchange of this for this, and exchange for this of this. Of and for because and why, when and shall and it and all, all and more and asked and ended and defended. In a way to be defended. Necessarily closed. Admirably adhered to, indefatigably circumstanced. And a reference to it as antedated. To be restated. Restate, in this way north and south and east and west are directions. In this way north and south and east and west each one is in that direction. Directly it was furnished it was furnished for them. A name is always astonishing.

Articles, are to, close to, articles as protests may, to be pronounced to be protesting or merely said to be providentially, providentially common rose or odors. Proving it as it may come to be no bother, no bother if at all. In this way before and also afterwards, afterwards as if in this not being in any way different contemplation authorises authority others as in their authenticity, remind to remind, reminding and reminding it considered as protesting and as in no way catalogued, catalogued uniquely, universally tinged, tinged with this and that and more nearly reluctant. Unions and safety and firstly and intermittently and if there is a monopoly, monopoly and not cowardice, in wishes in organised wishes, to wish to wish and formerly, formerly it was very well understood, formally to be personally and not in any way responsible. Can it be said to be in this way not proven but established that not even indications make it plentiful in the sense of having been adapted to change and conditions, adapted to change and conditions, in this way it is very well known that establishments are not at all are not all found at all found and in this way, days and ways, understand it to be said, they know colors to be another subject and more exactly.

Attach to it to attach to it, as attached, and when it is attached, and lessening, to lessen, as it lessened, lessened and to be avoided, as to avoid, avoiding evidently and not to be planned and carried there. To carry as an extra, extraordinarily and just as soon, just as soon too. If it is to be absently and urgently replenished and not undertaken not to be undertaken it is not to be undertaken, not to collect parlors in parlors. Parlors and in a pet in anger and not angry and plentifully papered. It is no longer necessary to use paper. Antedated and so forth. In repeating and four followed when they were sitting there. Where. No one knows as certainly as formerly. Informally has been mentioned and so has pursuit, pursuit and in pursuit and in pursuance, in this way in pursuance of their intention. Can it be ascertained how incompletely and repeatedly and heatedly a parlor contains the elements of enjoyment. To enjoy and relish to relish and refashion to refashion and entertain, to entertain and to vindicate, to vindicate and to indicate and to indicate. As indicated. It was as indicated. To be indicated. So many thousands have thousands. So many thousands have so many thousands. And as thousands. And as thousands are to be considered indeed to be as considered as many thousands are to be as many thousands and as considered and as many thousands. As many thousands have as many thousands. Many thousands have many thousands as many thousands. To be considered to have. Have to be considered to have and to have and to have to be considered and to have to as as to have indeed to have. Have. Have to have and to be considered to have. This is the best yet and matters in hand and the matter in hand and to the matter in hand is to be added intensity and reiteration. Reiteration is said to have been said for them. Parlors and parlors and for their parlors and in their parlors and to the parlor, to the parlor into the parlor for the parlor and in fact for it and in fact more than a fact. A fact is a fact. It is a fact, and facing and replacing, in replacing, to replace, to replace here and there, and so much. In so much and so quoted and as quoted and so forth and for the most of it, for almost all of it and so and in that way not investigated. As to investigating reasonably preparing, preparing to do

so. Do so and do so and to do so and as it were to be as if it
were to have contributed and furthermore not more than as to
stating. To state. Behind them to state, behind them and not to
wait, behind them and more frequently and as it was very frequently they were merely as to have it attributed. Attributed to
all of it and so satisfactorily as stated. No one heard them, and
no one is to understand distinctness. More of them and in a way
more and more. More and more and more was said to be and all
of it and instead, finally to do so and finally do so.

In that little while for a while and for a while to while away,
for a little while and for a while for that while and to while away
and for that and for a while and for that while and to cause it
to and because of it, for a little while and for that while and for
that while. A while. In a little while, for that little while or for
that little and a while for that little while and for that little while.
To cause it, for example to cause and to close and to be close and
to be closely and for a while and too closely to as one may have
said for a while and indeed for that while, formerly a while,
formerly for a while and as one may have it said to have it said
in a way said to have had it to have in that way had it as if once
in a while as if once in every little while, once and once in a while,
as if once every once in a while and as to have it and as to as to
have and as to have had it once in a while once in once in a while
and as if too closely to be close to be close to it once in a while
every once in a while, and as one while and as for one while and
for one while for a while.

Every now and then and when, when every now and then
and where, where have they heard it. Who told them to who told
them and who told them to and when and where every now and
then. To startle as if to start and when to separate, to separate
and to sort and to assort, no one knows how clearly it shows how
very clearly it shows and where it shows and to expose it and to
reconsider it and afterwards to expose it weigh it and the weight
of it for the weight of it and by its weight by the weight of it,
what is its weight. When is it important and why do advantages
accrue. To accrue and advantages to accrue need to have it re-
established. To reestablish is separately useful and to be used
what is to be used and why do they mean to say yes and yes.

Yes and yes, guess, press, address an address as address, address can be useful more than a meaning or many folds, fold and folding to follow, if the praise of it if in praise if it is in praise of it, to praise it, and praise in that way very presently and to present it as a present or as present. It is present, and better pleased than before. Before and more, more than that before, more of it than before, more than that of it and they say it changes, as change, as to change for them to change and to exchange, exchange parlors for parlors. To exchange and to be in a parlor and to change from being in that parlor to being in another parlor, in this sense to change a parlor and to exchange to feel funnily, very funnily to feel that there is more advantage than there was than there would have been than they would have had.

Instead of dwelling upon it, instead of selling instead of planning not to introduce more than they meant to have considered, it is very well to be considered in that way. To be considerably in their way, to have it considered and to be ready to consider it and commenting and as for consideration can it have the same ceremonial certainty for this and for that and considerably felt as if it were in consideration for all of this. And this as if to please and this and please, moderately to venture, at a venture and in moderation and in moderation and to settle quickly into a place that has this particular satisfactory quality. Quality and equality, equality and irritation, irritation and installation to install everything. Everything and if as wishes if they wish, to wish and to present wishes presently. And to furnish it as well and not leave it there, then too and nearly as if it had been an offer. It was offered to them. If inappreciably there is a difference as to delivery, and notably not at that time it was not as an interruption but not in any way to please themselves. So thirdly it can be as it was to be if it had had to be antedated and in this as it is and was not to be shown. Not at all shown to them and not found there not to be shown to them and not further to be shown then to them.

Indicated vindicated, it was and it was as it was, it was as it was, and indicated to be indicated, to be vindicated, to be vindicated to be indicated as usual, usually, usually as to choose, usually to choose, to choose and organised when and why and organised, if in outline, to outline to more as if it were an inclination, incline to it, able to be and to rebound to their credit. To and from and from there and to them, and moreover suitable suited to this as situated and not partly, not partly and situated and partly and partly this. Partly this and very and when can when did it where did it and for the time and in time and may it be traced. It was traced literally traced, traced as to invitation not an invitation. Not and not and not in choice, not a choice, not chosen not to just chose, chose and to have as chosen, not to have as not and as it was chosen, and those, to be counted one to count and account, one and two and to count and as to a count, as to a count, cups and saucers and put it away. Close, close to it, close and not to close, fully state what, fully state what is what. To fully state and to fully compare, compare and compare, in this way all of it is passed in a review, as in a review, as in a pretence to oranges. Pretended to, they pretended to. Silly and not silly not to nor evenly not to, not to show, not to be shown to be accurately defined. What is a definition, it is a definition, definitely and more sheltered than ever. If it is exactly stated that to be drawn blinds can be drawn, doors can be made, windows can be entitled bay windows and all parts of a parlor are copied by them and not at all. May they have it settled, may it be is it able to be and in question, is it in question. To question, a question, come again soon. More of a question. Come again soon, to be questioned, and come again soon, with them and by themselves, come again very soon and come again and as to very nearly very nearly to be coming out and going in there, very nearly to be going in and very nearly going in there. Not as it would have been added, added to.

Protected and partly protected after six months of protection after being with an object, helped, protected, helped and protected, protracted help for themselves and either or for this, in the exchange of helping themselves, protecting themselves and adhering to, adhering as if as it were protected by and very near by, very nearly by means of not nearly as newly as before, sent to them without mentioning the permission, permitting it, as a permit and if it can be helped, can it be helped. Partly and partly this, settled for them it was settled for them partly for this they parted it and in question it was in question. By nearly all of it having had and in not vacating as if it were valued, valuable as it can be. To be as valuable as it can be. Sizes, as to their seeing to it, seeing to it as if it were traced to them, traced to them as if it were inclined to be doubted. May be they do but do they have doubts about it. May be they do. In doubt, when there is a doubt, can they be in doubt, and rectify, rectify antedating, antedating yesterday. In a day more than that in that and to defer to that. Deferred and referred and to refer, as to reference to it, as to a reference to it, referring and delighted to refer, to refer more than to refer to it more than it was to be expected that they would need it to refer to. Obliged to stand still. Standing more than that and standing more than that. To change for it in exchange for it. Not violently as exactly for that situation. Situated where.

They as well very very well, and as well, largely readily and if they might as well tell. Collectedly, as to collectedly, very nearly to be as to selections, and in order to be for their sake. Connectedly tracing, a trace can be so much for their interest in their interest. Afterwards and known, known to be afterwards and settled known to be further and it does matter in that way as if returning in returning that. Much of it fairly and nearly, fairly well, and afterwards as if in connection with and fairly well managed and as to an understanding, no not depreciated, appreciated and fairly well and connectedly speaking, connectedly speaking and they thank you. To and to them and so much for the use of a parlor. In return, in in them, in the return and none of this is not for much of it and when much of it, and when can it be correct. To correct, and four four are more than if they call out the same as they have said that they did. Come faster than that. Have to have it come to have to have it come so many times, time and time again.

As stated or as stated. Finders keepers, and kept as found, found that it was kept and to be kept, found as to be kept. Finding or to be finding it, and to be finding it and to be keeping it, or to be keeping it and to be keeping it. If they mind, do they mind, do they mind and if they mind, if they mind, if they mind and they do find, if they find if they mind, find and mind or mind or find. Find or mind. Find or find or find. So indeed so indeed a

parlor settles that. So indeed and so indeed and so indeed and a
parlor settles that and so indeed a parlor and so indeed a parlor
settles that. A parlor. Indeed, and as to a parlor. Indeed as to the
parlor. A parlor settled that.

Makes music. He was in love with his wife. He makes music.
He was in love with his wife. A long gay book. Oh see. Thieves
see see to see. See to see, season this season for only this season, in
season, for a reason, for this reason, he was in love with his wife
and see to see, for this reason, in season, and in season, see to see
and to see, unrelated, tell it to them, related, tell it to them to be
related to tell it to them, to relate it that is if to tell it to them, to
tell it, relate it, tell it to them. Practically well, very well, practically, and practically, so that is thereby when it is obligingly
feeling for it. To feel for it and so by themselves and so to say by
themselves, so in a capacity, capes and capes, come for this, see
to see, and come for this, come and come, and come for this, come
for this and to come for this, so near that it may be said as if it
were so nearly as stamps, not stamping but just and especially so
nearly retained. To retain means permission to find it more than
convenient. Conveniently is that word and absurd. To be added
and in addition. A long gay book. To stay. A long gay book. A
day. In a day. To-day. To stay. After six months and after six
months. To introduce them in a parlor. A long gay book, I took.
You took, the long gay book. Along. Thank you very much.

Usually one, unusually two, unusual too, usually too, use one,
and if too, use one, and if one, used to use one, and if two, not any
use to use two, and if two, there were two, and they used to use
two. They used to they used to use two, they had no use for
those two, they had not used the two, they did not use two, they
did not they never used to. They can see them as they fall, they
can see them as if at all as if they were at all there. They can use
them as they do they can use them as they used to, they can
use them as they do, they do not use them at all, they have no use
for them at all, they were there as if they were used to it too.
They never used to they always used to they were used to they
were never of any use to they did not care to and the circumstances, can it be useful in that way, in the way. Two thirds too,
two and two thirds to two and two thirds and to depreciate the

difficulties and incidentally prosper. Prosperity clauses, incidentally and not at all and difficulties and definitely and praiseworthy and have they happened to incidentally, it happens that
definitely it is antedated. Too in a memorandum, to and two
again. Again, men and mention, again women and two, too and
two, to a seat, and the other way too and in that other way to
and to that farther there, come again here. So that as in so that in,
in and by that, buy that, buy that, come to be and as to a parlor.
This makes it in the way on the way by the way.

Indicated and also ransacked and so much as to all of it as
precarious, as to unlimited and in no need of parcels. Parcels in
place of sights, in sight, to be flattered, and to be flattered so that
there is more and their name, so they name the direction for the
parlor. It is undeniable that in this direction it is as reliable that
coming to meet all of them coming and if in a parlor there is
more than recently was flattering. To be flattering too. All tie
they all tie, and a variety, in their variety as to a very seldom and
related, as to relating, relating this to a difference from all of the
same all the same and not relating and not so nervous, not so
nervous nearly, nearly this as they say. Later they came they
came later. Economical and there, here and there and a slip, a
slip of the central baggage as baggage and what did they manage,
they managed it as well as ever. Hardly ever. Readily, going
back to that. Under the circumstances. In the large building they
already had they had already they had it ready, as to the large
building it was already it was as ready it was to be ready they
were to be ready, readily, to change to that, readily, in change
for that, readily and to exchange to change more than that and
to be attached to readily attached to be readily attached to be
more than that as if in attaching, that to the space ready for it.
And so forth. And so for it. So for it and so to see so. Up and down
steadily as if when a knighthood is in flower. I effect an exchange,
in effect. Was and expose, was expose, and to show, and to show
and settle as if so carefully attending, in tendency, able shall it
spend and too more. Consenting. A parlor for consent. And detri-
ment. If not having advanced and as across it, to plan an opposition
to this and more so as standing. It was as standing in the relation of
here and of here. Hear. Shall they speak of it. To it and more than

was accounted for to be considerable. Considerably too. And so if there can have been all of it to announce and stating and so much more as if a parlor has in it what. What was it. Commenced allowing as if to manage as it was. It was. So near. So much can the rest not actually. Actually as to that. Thank you and come again. And in speaking.

CHAPTER II

Exploration.
The party prepares to depart and starts to leave having first put everything in order as a preface. They and their companions install themselves and look over everything. This once one, and at once over and in addition all the material of which they can be careful is carefully placed in the safest place. Alternately they are carefully looked over and arranged and not replaced. It is preferable even if there is not much space not to put anything where it can not be easily found. With this in view everything is accomplished and no one is mistaken. Mistaken for something unexpectedly, unexpectedly to mistake, to misstate to make a mistake. In the meanwhile they note that everything is in order and they verify their collections immediately. Immediately entertain. And so forth. To entertain and so forth and ultimately finish, finish which is in a way taken for granted. In the beginning not, not to and to and to go and at hand everything was at hand. In plenty of time. And as preparation. And valuable. And for divisions and at most, all most, almost, congratulate, prepare and all about it. Practicably, every one practically, as practicable and as practicable. And so forth. Whether, and whether to go. Or whether to go. Or whether to go. And as to it. Indeed stretches as to it and so have they had hold of the half of all of it. In the meantime what is the floor for. For that. And all three. All three, all of them and all of them allowing allowing for it. To show. All there for three for three all there. All there for three, for three and four all there for three and for three and four and all there, for three and for four. Therefor they were there.
Settle to a second and as secondly, settle to a second and three, four, and not as undertaken finally. They met and to try indeed

and to untie and to have energetically all of it as in the circumstances they do need to. They do not need to. Indeed not to have it as nearly as it can be left, left to them altogether left to them. Windows are nearly round. If in plenty of time, have it as in leading them there. And almost all and why, not so very much too much and so and there and so. As parting any way. In there as at all and they have met and come as long as they are there. Not provided, and as for the rest, not arranged and as for the rest, not at all to rest, not more than the rest and they have not only agreed but they have been thoroughly and formerly and farther behind. In no case was there any right to provide and provided they needed the road a road connecting in connection. So easily can in between, so easily can there be that and all of it conspicuously directed. In that direction. They met with orderly and dutiful appearance and delivery. And all that can be further attended to is further attended to. A plan and all of it so arranged that in spite of inconveniences no disturbances can occur. Could they go away. Having come have they any interest in what is happening all of it makes an end to an itinerary and all of it shows that nevertheless they recommence. In a way they do. Stretches and so and stretches and so. So and so very readily. To begin as has been practically particularly tolerably acquired. And so forth. Now not as an exhibition but more so than cemented. And after all two years are plentifully arranged as to bridges. If three bridges are said to be so, and is it fairly clear. Weather and they say so. So much reminds them and antedating and once more and parlors and twice more and more and come more and more often and come more often and to come more often. Or to come more often. In all of that and when a part of that and by having that parted parted in two, two and partly four for this they said they were practically shining. When all of it makes it able to be traced, trace it anyway, anyway there is a trace of it and they will originally follow as followed. No one must disagree not enough if all of them agree. They agree. Alright. They agree. Agreeable.

In sight and by sight, and insight in sight and by sight. They knew them by sight. They kept them in sight. To keep it as quiet as it is it has been necessary to sit down to get up and to walk around. By sight, they can tell it at sight. Unsuitable in every

way they say. To suit them in this way. Next to it nothing is
nearly offered. In offering as an offering. Offering for them. They
have to balance it as they can. So next to that and so next to that.
It is so and next to that. And next to it. In a way to resume and the
preparation is, measurements for them measurements by them. In
a measure, they can as a measure, they will as they measure, they
have to measure, and as they can be advantageously so soon, ready
as soon, they can be ready very soon. By any perplexity, fully and
as for instance it may be, and may be that. Quarrels may be conducted they conduct them to their seat. Beginning again when.
And beginning again. To be beginning, fancy, as to a change in
any instance. In this instance. Not repeatedly. Conducting not
repeatedly. Beginning again and when. For instance. In this case.
As intended and in this case and more intentional. Not more so
intentionally. No circumstances warrant the use of all of it and
so many say so and very nearly all of it is mentioned systematically
and in no way has there been there and there and there were there
then there and there. They and their intention. Not more than
helping. So many have it as they may say attested.

They will attend to that. Intend to and nervously too and adjoining. When it is joined so that there is no reason for felt and
it is infelicitous, there is an absolute standard. In their fashion. A
background and leisurely approached by them in the meantime.
Not mentioned as care, to care, by their care, in their care, as care,
come carefully and see farther and never interfere. To interfere
and to prepare and to endow and to share it with them. As in
speaking. Hearsay. By hearsay. As in speaking and by hearsay. In
speaking and by hearsay. Carefully to see farther and to acceptably organise. Organise a victory.

Planned as to use. In next to nothing and of course. Shall they
reduce it day by day. Shall they, do they will they pay. As to in
general. They do not care about generals or anything. In general.
They do not care about the general or anything. Or in general. As
a general. Or in general. Generally. They do not care about a
general or anything. They do not care about a general or about
anything. They do not care about generals or about anything. Not
in general. The reason for this and this is a reason and their reason
and for that reason. Reasonably. Reasonably speaking to address as

their address. Their address is this. For all of them and not particularly, for all of them and particularly, particularly for all of them.
It is particularly for all of them. This is particularly for all of them.
They and before, before or, and before or before. Do they do do
they do, they do do, how do they do, how do they do it, do they
do it as they do it and is it done. It is done. As it is done. A parlor.
In the meantime. From it, away from it, not away from it, in it,
and in it, and in it. And so they were there and they can very
nearly estimate have as an estimate, decide to estimate, remember
an estimation, in their estimation, to seem, having had in no and
at no time and as a share and as their share there. So nearly have
they had an understanding and a division and for this and their
account on their account and as an indulgence to indulge themselves very nearly here. Here and there and to all and they have
to be met as they come and they are to come, come here. Seeing to
it makes of it, seeing to it as it is seen to and to be seen, never
decide, they decide and tried they tried and have it as if they had
it. They had it and for it when was there when did they intend,
when have they any avoidance of a feeling of inquietude. Correct
and correct, as correct. It is as correct as it is. Corrected and corrected. To be corrected as it is corrected. It is to be either corrected or entirely corrected. Have you finished with it. Or have
they had it finished for them. As it is finished it is to be nearly
finally and as in preparation. A preparation for in preparation for,
their preparation, they have prepared it and they may do they
prepare and may they repair this. If there is any attention, attending and in offering. They offer what they have offered and it has
been offered to them.

   In plenty of time, there is plenty of time and as there is plenty
of time and as they are in plenty of time, there are plenty of occasions and indeed yes. They have seen no reason to hurry. In a
hurry, they have not meant to be in a hurry. Hurry. As to this
and as to the difference, there is a difference, there is this difference there is no difference, indifference and in no way not in their
way, any way not as a way. To weigh, they know, to weigh they
know, underweigh they know, to proceed, they know, under-
weight they know, to concede they know, to have it and they
know and they know that they have to have it.

Leaving it at night, as it is right, leaving it as it is right, very right, they are right, they may and they may, as it has been their habit they may and they might have as they may have. May and may, might and they might. If they might. Measurements of them as is necessary when an expedition has returned. Have they returned. If they will be neither here nor there. Here nor there. Will be. If they and if they and they and so much it is as they and they and not at all as they. Remember their claim to it and that they are very willing to be as if it were and so them. Very well and very well. The sixth in the series.

Imagine comfort imagine the comfort of it, imagine and the comfort of it, imagine it and the comfort of it, imagine it for the comfort of it, to imagine it and to imagine the comfort of it and to imagine the comfort in it, imaginable the comfort as comfort and imaginable as in the comfort the comfort there is in it. Unimaginable that there is comfort in it and the comfort of it and in their and at once and so at once and in their and at their suggesttion and in their and for them and in their reception of it. To extend, to extend, to blend, to extend to extend, and to send to send and to send, as if to send as if to extend, as if to extend. Prepare, kindly prepare the parlor. The parlor is prepared. Kindly antedate it, it is antedated, kindly attend to it, it is attended to, they are so kind, they know that kind, they are that kind, they are so kind. Will they be so kind, will they be as kind, are they more than kind.

Incidents as they might close up and go away. Incidents and wonderful wood and incidents and wonderfully and incidents and incidentally and for instance. As an instance they their insistence, they may, formerly, as formerly, they may have, fundamentally, as they may have had, intermediate, and in the meantime, as they may have had to do. As they may have had to to do. As they may formerly have had it to do, and as they may have it to do immediately as they may have an immediate necessity to determine not to do it. As they may have come to some decision and as in deciding they may have closed up at once and gone away for the holiday. Not indeed carpeting, as carpeting it is laid on the floor. Actually carpets, as actually carpets, no one needs this. They have carpets actually laid on the floor. In this way around and around.

At once if at once, if they are there at once, it will happen at once, it will be happening at once, all at once, it will all be happening at once and at once, at once, can they at once, can they and at once, at once, as at once. All at once and can they be there at once. Can they all be there and at once. Have it at once and at once. They have it at once, they have had to have it at once. And at once. They and with their and with them they and for them with them with their, whether, whether they were there were they there and whether they were there at once. Whether they were there at once. As they, were they, as they were, were they there, whether they were whether they were there, whether they were there whether they were there once, whether they were once there, whether they were there at once, when they were there, they were there at once, as they were there they were there once, they were there at once, as they were there, and as they were there at once, more than once, as they were there once, as they were there more than once, and at once they were there, after two years two days, as soon as they were there, they were there as soon as they were to be there. As they were there they were there soon, they were there as soon as they were to be there, at once, as soon, at once and as soon, as soon and as soon as they were to be there.

If they do not move if they are sensitive if they are sensitive if they do not move, going, as going, if they are sensitive and as it can have been illustrated, if they do not move, going and as it can be illustrated, as it can be illustrated. If they are sensitive.

As it can be illustrated if they do not move as it can be illustrated. Come together, as they can be illustrated and as they come together and as they can be illustrated. The illustration of it as an illustration of it, and illustrate, to illustrate, as illustrated. As illustrated, for this illustration and as more illustration of it. For the illustration, as an illustration, for illustration, as it is illustrated. As it is illustrated it is fairly well illustrated and as an illustration it is considered a good illustration. Action and in action, they are satisfied as they have to have it as they are to have it. No more than that any way. In any way. As there is more than that in a way. In a way as in case of it, more in case of it than before and the finishing touches. The finish may make it shine, a bottle of wine to make it shine and two little niggers to squeeze her. Finishing touches as to the best way of establishing it as at present. Presentable and presented. For the permanent use of joining. As many as that.

Fairly hilly, they should not have and as it was fairly hilly, they should have and fairly hilly. As fairly hilly as fairly hilly and as they should have. Meanwhile in the meanwhile and not at that time and particularly, as they particularly as they very particularly and as it is fairly hilly, in the meantime their establishment to establish entertain and rest. The rest as for the rest in the meantime as the establishing and as established in the meantime and no reason, for no reason and because of the reasonable request, request them to, to request it of them and as requested. It was as requested. A request, they request, as to that request, when they need to go there and not at all as it is not only not requested but not even investigated. Do they establish and as an evidence as the evidence as to the evidence and for it as evidence and evidently more than ever and evidently more than ever as it is evident. It is more evident than ever. Not than ever. In the meanwhile in the meantime as in the meantime there is established definitely established and not requested and not evidently not very evidently and as evidence and in evidence and for evidence as to the establishment as to their being established and as being as an established thing, it is to be so much in evidence. Believe them. Evidently they do. As it is to be kept up and as it is to be kept up and as it is to be kept up. To keep it up so that to keep it up, it was their request it was there by request it was to be kept up at their request. To keep it up and as it necessarily means this, it necessarily has meant that as it was being established and in earnest and as an evidence and in evidence. More in evidence it was more in evidence.

Not very hilly yes and will they discharge their obligations to themselves and to their other friends. Their obligations are there and they see to it. If in obliging themselves to do so to discharge their obligations there are no complications and no further pleasures, farther and farther and then in no wise and then as to the way of spending themselves, they spend themselves repeatedly.

It is like this. If they have said yes, if they have said yes and no, if they have said they have said so, if they have at all said, that this is said to be originally the same they would not have said that they said that this was originally the same. The afternoon passed pleasantly and on the return a great many saw them. It was not at all hilly and it not being at all hilly it made them more certain that they were easily between hills. As hills are even, evenly, as hills are evenly, and more evenly even more evenly as more hills are even more than evenly, as more hilly as hills are more evenly hilly, it is very hilly. It is even more hilly, it is easily seen that it is even more than hilly. Nevertheless and nevertheless than there are more copies of it, more than to copy it. Tissue paper, tissue paper fairly certain to be inherited. Tissue paper is not as useful as oiled paper and oiled paper is often left about. Left and about. Tissue paper and oiled paper and left and about. It is often left and it is often left about. They meant to use the center as well as the left, the left center, they meant to be left in the center as well as to be left. They meant to be left in the center and they meant to be left and to be left in the center and they were left in the center. To stand up to sit down and to walk around.

So Nice, a town.

Treat and retreat seat and reseat receipt and seat and able able to be seated, suitable, suitable as a seat.

A seat, to be seated on a seat. Reseat, to be reseated, to be seated, to be on a seat. A seat, to be seated. Reseat. To be reseated, to be seated. A seat. To sit on a seat. To be sitting on a seat. Sitting sit, seated, seat. The seat, this seat, and sitting and seated. Reseated, as seated, a seat.

As scenes.

As seen.

Or as seen.

Or as meant.

Or as to mean.

Fairly finish it as seen.

Subject-cases makes a dressing, subject-cases or as pressing, subject-cases or as seen, subject-cases have to mean, as sent. They sent it in that way. Distress. No distress. Yes, very nearly yes, intended as intended, reliable as to being so reliable, in question,

as there is no proceeding, in fact or very nearly. Designed for
this. In the meantime as meanwhile, in fact, so they can have it.
Have as you can, antedating, exactly, more than so, and as if it
were not unsuitable. No more as when there can be no more so
there can be, more so that there may be more so that there may
be. As more. No hurry.

And more as soon.

Or in as wanted.

Can it be or ordered ahead.

Not fairly sorry not so much nearly as that.

For nearly as that.

That is the end of it.

NO

1915

Left.
Left.
Pretty.
I
had
pretty
a
good
pretty
like it
room
pretty
all
and
I fire
chairs
pretty
silver
good
left.

We went and looked. It was easy to do. If you measured. Then they set a wood instead of placing iron. They did not mean iron. It was too expensive. We asked everybody.

We had eleven men and seven of them were all they liked. singing. He did not sing. We called him that.

That was finished. After that glazing. This means glass. It came quicker. More quickly than otherwise. We went away. Not yet. We chose painting. We timed that and we changed everything. It was exasperating we were patient we said it again and meant everything. It was finely, finally finely done. Not finely done. We were pleased.

When we wanted silver. We wanted steadier fire, we even did not want money. Then we placed an order. This was satisfactory. Anybody can sit.

Not as before.

I can tell a pail.

It is in my room.

When we went to see two we found apricots. Dear things.
We did not say dear thing.

I am so disappointed.

Papa.

I like to look at both sides of the table.

He came to say that it did not pay.

It must be brisk.

Now the narrative.

If a cloud settles on a bank and an ell is a measure and nonsense
is vigorous he gives advice.

Farther.

He gives advice.

He says that it is best to ask in question.

Suppose we estimate an end, not suddenly suppose we do accept honey, leave it to me. He does not leave it to him. He asks
many.

This is the way.

They came together.

Not to be polite.

Please it in trust.

He said he was surprised.

Nonsense. It is very simple. You must take a risk. If you chime
in you are not feeble. You are feeble by fall. You are certainly
willing. Then comes this question. Not by this time.

I speak feelingly.

Does he speak feelingly by an intention to say puns. The name
is the same.

I was placid.

If it is dangerous to believe water it is not so dangerous to stir.
Danger is in lights. This is not where we mingle.

I was bolder than that.

I was grieved that he sat. Not because I was in the least inclined to further his religion. Nearly enough was scattered.

Humming.

I felt in the same butter.

Now I change the subject, I will change to a description of our leisure.

She can sew.

I don't know what good that does.

If quiet is still then a hoarse voice is mine.

Believe me.

She had a little more then. She did not burn.

We cannot displace another.

It was so sad but since her eyes rolled we were in query. We did not doubt. we said we were sorry. We said we had another. We said we were sorry.

I will describe anybody.

Of quarreling.

I do not believe whether a fire and a cleaning thing is outside. I do not believe a fire. We cannot fear.

Cleaning.

Thousands of times.

When we had a chance to choose we chose two. That meant that each one changed their mind and recognised it. It was so dear.

Now what can I read about. I can read about the Maoriland Bush.

I have counted twenty-six men being in a boat. I don't mean that I have counted actual men I mean that I have seen it in gold. I have counted them quickly because after all it is a very small space. It would be unwise to think about commencing to have more.

And then cold weather.

I wrote that it was cold, that it was not a pleasant thought.

I also said that I had no trouble in getting my money.

To another I said that it was cold and that I was sorry that I had not thought of any way of his arranging to leave London.

The way to express feeling is to say that you are glad that you have heard something about Mabel.

In order to visit every day you must pass very close to a house because otherwise there is a remark to the effect that there have been times which have not come to be regretted.

This afternoon they asked us to have coffee.

I am not disappointed in beds. It is strange that nearly each one had a way of leaving the coal. There was more coal. I hope I have not paid for it.

I cannot think of a dog.

Supposing we had a surprise at Christmas and had two little dogs.

Do I know whether I want a big dog or another kind. I know I do not want restlessness nor do I want a dog to be attractive enough to induce staining. This seems the best way to settle the matter. We will wait.

I don't think this is so good.

A cape invests even a negligee with an air of pseudo formality. I washed my hair.

I do not wish to remember the third thing. Yes I do. It would be a great help. It really isn't necessary. In any case I made a list.

I do not wish to get excited.

In asking Mr. Tonnel if he knew where I could get fire irons I did not make a mistake in language. He answered pleasantly.

We have tried there.

It does make a difference if your nails are cut.

I do believe witches.

When some one said December and meant December, when he said successes, then gleams and then he was certain. I believed him. I said so myself.

I had said so in finishing.

Mrs. Nortel came this morning. I told her I knew all about it. I said that I was reading the paper. I said it politely. I said she should go away. I did not mention her mother. I said I had wishes. I did not drag it about. I did not mean to be perfervid.

Then there was the explanation about mediocre telephoning I can just hear his voice.

Needless to say there were three of them. One opened the door. More than that there were five of them. Two went out. Then it was not ridiculous. It was not cheery. After all if one has been earning a great deal of money there is some disappointment.

He said that if he were young and did not have kidney disease he would not have hesitated to do as he did. They were pale. That does not mean color. That does not mean spirits. That does not mean a discussion. That does not mean parallel cases. It is easy to say I am feeble. It is hard to say by a boy. It is very easy to be persuaded. It is cold in a room.

I do not mean this here.

I am surprised at my ending.

When they came to-night they explained that their first visit would be here. We came then.

I do not wish to describe even then.

Kissling went and had a sweater an American sweater given him and some money. He was unexpected. It is hard work. I hope to expect it.

A communication.

When they get through starting they are about. Not above there. Not appealing.

I am so neglectful.

A glass of water.

I should have told you that between pages when there is no intermission and it is on top there's a space.

Is there any way to arrange it to make a space.

That meant a space and you see you didn't leave it.

That's a title.

You won't get angry. If you copy a thing you have just done recently you always make quantities of mistakes.

Just why isn't it.

He does ask too much. He always did that. He couldn't help associating selections. He selected hymn.

I don't want to talk about it.

When he asks me I'll say all five.

I had a great deal of unpleasantness. A dog.

I had a great deal of unpleasantness. A dog. I said yes. I did not say I wanted it. I said was it difficult. I said a cushion. I asked. It did matter.

I asked and I believed that I was especially prepared. I was especially prepared to be patient. I do not like a water proof. That doesn't make any difference. I do not like a water proof. We made a great mistake.

It is raining.

I was disappointed.

I was not disappointed by appearances. She said she reminded her of Sarah Whitney.

What is the reason that every one means to like us. I don't mean every one. Each one says that he pleases. Each one says that he pleases us. I don't mean to be realistic.

Why does every one say that they can find time. Give me new faces new faces or faces. Every one makes it a reproach to him that he is seen. How can he help it. All the soldiers have gone to the war. He offered a large bouquet of roses. To Whom. To Eve. It was refused. He said he would come in a minute.

Why is it painful for us to refuse favors. We are so accustomed to be exact. We are so careful. We have so suddenly had smiling, we are so learned, we are alright.

I meant to-day.

To-day was the difference in intentions. Twenty five hundred. Five thousand. Terms. Louder receptions. Piles of balls. Not an obus in the biceps. I should be strange with an index a chief finger and a thumb. This was so stamped.

Every one of us is proud.

An evening with a dog.

Fancy striding.

I was not disappointed.

I will not change the two for anything. They have to be that one.

I did not mean that I wanted that cushion. You understood me very well.

I was cold and there was a fire.

Black silk satin.

This is a very good one.

License.

Parts.

Screech.

Louise laughed.

This evening they mentioned boats. I would not allow it.

A formal pleasure.

I was thinking that I did not know if I would like to have a dog. It is troublesome. It is troublesome not to know sometimes. I was so scolded.

Monday.

Vacation.

I am not thinking about it.

I am thinking about Friday Saturday and Sunday.

I was successful.

These narrations.

Please consider an s.

It is not polite to answer it.

Three.

Not all in one night.

A long sentence.

A long sentence begins with b.

By climbing and relieving points, by climbing up high and saying I am coming, incidentally by blowing division, division between knees and knees the long plain assault with fears and a new name, Blanche yes Blanche, not excitedly. This is a longer pretence.

I do like expressions.

What is a soldier.

I answered that in grammar.

Please be teased. She said it was a mistake and that I would have to recount that in learning about Monday.

A long drawer.

When Alfred came and saw a bullet he pulled at the tree and he said leave it there. He met an announcement. He said I knew your brother. He was dangerous. He said he would have gone anywhere.

Why are places so soon having 50 sheets. Because they were not washed. Lots of goods have been left. Some said that they had no use for meddling. I wish I was wise.

Believing thousands is not tiresome.

I was so pleased. They were so pleased to see no catches to the windows. You would not think of that as important. He was so pleased because when he left they said remember me again. Lots of them had messages. A great quantity of little religions poured in on them. Crowds of soliciting showed pain. Better be at rest. Leave out mutton. This was not a command. It was not healthy. No body was better. I don't want to hear him again.

This is not a mistake or an injunction, it is a hard pencil and mother mutters. Please be pardoned anybody. I do not mean to seam.

Leave us.

Pour out crowds.

She coughed.

It was exercise.

I answered better.

I meant it all.

I set a place. I lit a light. It is easy.

Not again.

Or again.

What is water.

Water is robust or air.

I don't think that's funny.

Do not be disappointed.

Leave please.

Oh search.

Nature claims.

I wish to repeat that unduly vexed and exactly irritated makes it seem likely that he will believe for a month. More than that, urged, he will be extremely angry. He will say that he always knew everything suddenly and that authority has been so obliging that if he went Saturday and came Saturday and needed Saturday he would be equally celebrated. I am so tired of lenders. They are so kind. Yes I know that kind. I don't like that kind.

This was said.

Nearly left.

I am going to change my name.

Please me.

A long comma.

I chanced one day to express my delight in recent changes and occurrences and I predicted that certainly a thankful shelter would be made by grey paper. Grey paper is the tone of my room. White flowers in plenty. I chanced to say that I respected this. I predicted moreover that leaves were falling fast. I said that. Then suddenly before I felt myself labored I expressed a resolution. This is it. To make a pleasant home. To arouse feeling. To purchase linen. To have recourse to some blotter. This meant that we had it made. Not beautifully made. We are satisfied. Most of this is charity. A little of it is romance. We do not select darkness. We have many friends.

It might be better to undertake more. It might be naturally taken for granted that each one alone is happy. He is not. He is reminded of a bell. It isn't really a bell it is a cord. It is not the same thing. It does both doors. After that light. More than that plenty of ferrying. It is not secondarily a universe this which makes so much natural pleasure. We feel it all.

I went too far.

Do not doubt me.

I whimsy you.

Any day practically any day. I call it.

You don't.

Don't be so sleepy.

Go on.

I will.

I hear it.

I answer.

We are together.

I only went down to see.

It does make a nice cake.

Four of them came this evening. Five of them came this evening but that was not important. What is important is white stockings. Mention the age and send back some more and say you want to be worn. Worn out. Every one tired. Disappointments. Black satin. Large papers and sacks. I do not say description. I say annoyance. She moved. Poor forever. Lot.

No.

Sanction.

Seas or baths.

Letters and lessons.

Battle and hopping.

Lieutenant and extra.

Struggle and mentioning.

Expense and able to be beside himself.

Stretching.

Listen to regrets.
Necklace.
Paper pears.
I knew it.
No too.
No not at all.
Risk it.

I wish to imitate perfectly what is meant by audience allowance, Saturday and treasure. I wish to be read by any number of
letters. I wish to be beside myself and yearning with indelible
chattering and with leaning by the side of black stairs. I do not like
color. I do not like more sentences. I do not like pears. I eat pears
and I state they're better green. Green in Mallorca.

To bury boats.
To bury boats.
Is to meet feet.
To meet feet.
To meet feet miraculous.
I made a mistake.
When I tie I try.
I try to do better.
Felt it.
I was disappointed.
Hands.

I made a mistake. Not a mistake. I said something. I made a
mistake. Hands. Hands are photographable.

Come to me.
Not a color.
We are going to get some more.
Tuesday was expected to be a rough day.
Pleasant.
It is pleasant.
I don't like to mention shades.
Pleasant.
Letters.
I see a resemblance between papers.
Not all the same.
Go to bed.

I don't see it.
He is.
I want to describe leather buttons.
Not equally.
Was he disappointed.
He was.
Of course you can't have it.
Please please me.
I am so unhappy.
He is not crazy.
I don't say for excitements.
Please be understood.
Don't fancy it.
Don't fancy there is anything new or behind.
Don't be disappointed.
Don't regret looking anywhere for money.
Don't regret peace.
Don't be mournful.
Don't have a fashion.
Don't leave out Mary.
Please me.
Do please me.
I find it all.
I find it all so.
They meant to break them.
She is satisfied.

All the children are well James Fred and Emma. Our daughter Frederika has been suffering but owing to her recovery she is better.

I explained that last time.
Writing.
Everything on the table.
Cards.
April.
January.
I know he won't come.
Let us think of all of us.
Please me.

Sleep sweetly and long and be rested.
Is my song.
Disappointed.
Animals.
Charm.
Change.
Lambs.
Release.
Ploughs.
I don't say so.
Climbs.
Persons.
Exactitude.
Limbs.
No
I hear her.
No second place.
Rubber.
Politely.
This is not an excuse.
The result.
In time.
Time.
Not naughty.
Stop it.
Was it.
Go on.
It is such a change.
I don't believe it.
Merchandise.
I want to go on.
I know what I want I want a narrative based on that.
Not after.
Rough.
Neck.
Spell it.
Ask.
Rind.

Excellently.
Continue.
Bless us.
I change.
Slaps.

Nearly behind Barcelona and a little way they fed a house that was near there. They made a plan and they authorized the street and nearly near there behind summer they believed what, now answer. It was bought. Decorator.

I go in.
Tender.
Buy nothing.
This was a story they call it Maria.
Papers.
Papers made me feel.
Tall.
I said believe me I am praised.
What if he did.
Russia.
Oh I was so glad.
Happy farm.
Ferny.
Sew.
Buttons.
On.
Gloves.
Space.
Do
Sew
Buttons
On
Gloves.
It's too easily used.
I don't care.
Write to them for brown.
There should be shouldn't there
Do you like my two little stories.
Hush.

This is a nice story with a happy ending.
Work.
Harden.
Neglect.
Coverings.
Long distance.
Please me.
He does please me.
He pleases me.
Long distance.
Coverings.
Thank you for a birthday.
Soup.
Soup.
Soup.
Thank you for that.
Soup.
Better.
Any presents.
Please me.
Water.
Or.
Dog.
Fish.
Not that.
Fish.
I said yes.
Plainly.
Another day.
I know what I want.
I want riches.
Not butter.
Did we say butter.
Fish.
Not riches.

We are so pleased with Jenny. We mention it whenever any locked ceremony makes economy.

Plenty of appeal.

Defense of boxes.
Identification.
Pursuit.
Long glances.
Did he go.
Where is he.
His age.
I don't know.
Shame.
I bless you.
Curl.
Flower.
Taught.
Plate.
Engineer.
Will you go home.
They say our home.
Pleases us.
It is descriptive.
And rejoicing.
And by that
We mean
Industry.
Why in hands.
Sweet potatoes were a failure.
I am not delighted.
I
Wish.
I
Could.
Draw.
You.
Fairer.
I
Wish
I
Could.
This is a nice story with a happy ending.

Go on.

I

Do

Make

Nice

Things.

Done for.

Baby bottle.

I'll tell you what is the trouble. It is this. We that is I do. I make it morning. It is by that time apparent that I, to-morrow surprise. What. Elegance. I do so thoroughly instead see plenty of expectation. This is a change from suddenness.

I am going to tell this story.

I do not believe in reflections.

Don't praise me.

I am so disappointed.

Then the worst of it was determination. I was determined to succeed.

I met everybody before mentioned and I strangled that thought. Then I proceeded to cry. It was very simple. I meant to be famous. What is memory. It is the illusion of mind. I did not marry money.

Do not be merry.

I am going to tell more for it.

Daisy Done For.

I am sorry.

I mention.

I mention it so often.

I don't care.

I don't believe in astonishment.

I don't get a note.

I said to a lady I am astonished to see you. I mentioned yesterday that there would be further intentions and now what do I see an early plight.

To-morrow.

To-morrow.

Yesterday

Afternoon.

Clearly.
I imagine.
That
Reasonable
Surroundings.
Make for beauty.
I am serious.
I shall satisfy.
Do please.
Be there still.
Be still.
Oh likely.
Very likely.
I am going to mention this.
It was remarkable to see five.
Four followed. Not five.
Plenty of preparation was needed.
I don't care.
I don't believe in stamps.
Plenty of people mention it.
I don't do it again.
It is. Or enough.
Not nearly.
Carelessly.
This is not the truth.
I do not misstate it.
I do not believe it nor do I incur it.
It was so changeful.
Do I tell this as a story.
Leaning.
Not this, does not suggest that or burden.
It is an indelible pencil.
Lots of places.
Lots of places are scarce.
Scarcely.
All open.
Please don't.
Please do it. Gertrude doesn't like to be frightened.

All towels are European.
Not yet.
Be plentiful.
All joy.
Immerse.
Help from the colonies.
Policing the Turk.
Daisy.
Delay.
I do not believe or matter.
Shelling.
Shelling.
Buy that.
Opportunity.
No Doubt.

I want to tell about Uhde. He was the individual who came here and had no hair. This does not manage to reclaim him. I do not like it. I did.

He came frequently and he had tall ones who were obedient. To what. To standing. They did not stand then. This is not a misery. He was put off. I shall be ill.

When he came again and was merry it was not a joke.
I purposely say it.
I cannot see shooting.
We all saw it.
By this time.
Whether.
Black meadow. So dear.
Please be ready.
Cloth.
It was a change.
I want to tell another.
Day.
By time.
Better.
Not.
Behind.
All.

Wednesday.
I come to class.
Clash.
Feather.
February.
Whether.
School.
Does it.
Mischief.
Chief.
Properly spelt.
Out.
Right
Sun
I return in again.
Buy.
Not it.
Are we unprincipled
No.
To be.
Sew up.
Clamor.
Shoulder.
Wheat
Brown
Toes
Particular state.
Eyes.
Ties.
Leaf.
Did he say leaf.
Let it.
It is much.
More.
Wide.
Than
Shine.
Shine up.

What
Ever
Did
You
Say
That
For.
I have been foolish excitable and irritable.
He waited for similar necessities.
Cook
And a brother
The feeling in high places comes from their being no motion.
If you are high up and there is no motion it stands to reason that
it is unnatural. I am afraid and there is reason for it. The kind of
a way that I leave it, I don't really leave it, makes me realise that
I could see why I do it.
A white wall is settled.
I didn't mention it.
A whole list.
First
Clear
By
There
Told
Joins
Seat
Pole.
Either
Night Holy
Upper
Traces
Middle
When
Strip
Houses
Up
When
Reels

Called
Shall
Lion
Well
Buy that.
Louder
Clear it.
I made it.
It was the first time that I noticed the best one.
I do not see their faults.
Please pardon me.
I am reverent.
I rejoice.
I blame them.
I speedily suck.
It was a pleasure.
Such a pleasure.
Train.
Trains.
I do not wish to be influenced.
All day.
It's a joke.
Spend
That
Time
Will
Be
Spent.
Not
There.
He wished it.
She wished it.
Ball
Tower
Watch
Quilt
Satin
Lest

Nine
Breathe
Puddle
Stack
Bar
Relief
Did he do it.
Day
Sour.
Was it.
Alright.
I don't mean it.
Anyway.
You wish.
Look.
Here
Another.
Afternoon.
Will.
Suit.
Ten.
Days.
We are going.
At least.
Not yesterday.
Not after.
All.
Do be there.
I do.
Astounding.
Miss.
Ten.
Not astounding.
The party.
All of it.
I make that sound.
Remember chances.
I don't.

I really don't care.
I believe in mother.
Look
Here.
I don't wish to be thought careless.
No I won't fill it up.
It is a new expression of lingering. It is barely nice. It is all,
nearly all spoken. It makes me think. I do not believe he is dead.
Oh Lord no.
Well
Very well.
This time.
Buy that.
By that.
I did finish.
I was torn.
I shall steal.
I mean to go.
I do tread.
I have fans.
I do believe they will like it.
I don't know the noise.
No not plants.
Extreme.
Application.
I don't mean to say that every one is mistaken. I do not pur-
pose to smell millions. I do not say feeble. Plenty of velvet knit
brightness and calm and expectation and power and ministry and
celebration. I was so pleased with it.
I don't believe they will refuse.
They will think that it is quite new.
They will not like washing it.
Watching and watching.
Others.
Come to it.
They really are.
I think there was a little of that feeling.
I come all the time.

They don't.

What difference does it make to them. If it takes them a little more ungently it isn't because they are vanishing. It is that a little naturally that is it. Indignation.

She will be pleased.

Who is it.

I mustn't ever put that in my mouth.

I could seat persons.

Where.

In between.

The Line.

The Lines.

I could seat persons there.

It was pretty.

I was placed there.

I am so sorry.

I said it.

I made a mistake.

What is a disillusioned American.

He is one who writes it to that statement.

What is it.

It is this.

Hold.

Enough.

He says it. He says any way.

Any way.

These years.

Those years.

It doesn't make any difference.

To whom.

I ask it.

I please.

I please whom.

Outside.

Or

Outside

Her

Plain.

Plant.
Cover
Cover me.
I could shout.
I do not.
Beside that.
I maintain
What
It is.
Is it.
Selfish.
Is it
Bewildering.
No it isn't.
It isn't bewildering.
Baby mine
All the time
Be Light
Nestle tight
Shall giggle
With
Splendor
and
Courage
and beauty
and
goodness.
Daisy dine
You are mine
For
Thee
To
See
Mastery
Shall be
Cheerful
What
Husbands

Shall
It
Sew it.
That's a wonder
I expect to close.
Knit it.
Not
Knit it.
I expect to close
By and by
It is
An instance
Of
Darkness.
It is darker.
I shall see around
By then
Do be quiet
Do be
Received
Do be
All of it.
This isn't quick.

I meant to pass away water and milk and lettuce I did. I made a mistake. I was foolish. I had plenty of opportunities. Chances. I tried some. They were severe. Prunes and apples and butter. We were to write for it. Did we. We exclaimed. Fine. I want to be good and happy and cheerful and not blameworthy or peevish in short I want to be good and industrious and patient and loving and earnest devoted equable goodnatured and pious. Besides I want to be here. I want to see. I want to make dresses. I want to knit and to sew and to make that fire. I want to change places. I want to be told what to say. I want to be vaccinated. I am not thinking of it. Do not tease me.

There is still one thing to do. It will cause me to be happy. I mean to do it. No one can surprise me. This is it. It is to draw daisies.

I don't do it again.

Little words.
Surprising.
She did not.
Mention
Eleven
Curtains
Or
Cushions.
By that time.
I was.
Not
Able
To
Delay it.
It passed that way
It passed away.
We were glad
We had bought them.
They were there
To be given
And it was
Very well
Worth the delay.
I don't mind it.
Yes he did it very well.
I don't get as much satisfaction out of it as I did.
This does not mean a change.
It means that they show as well as ever and anyhow I was mis-
taken.
I do
Like
Them
Very much.
All the time.
That is when I notice them.
Which is
When I look at them.
I don't make that a division.

I said it.
Change the name.
How do you do.
They capture too many of them.
No
I am near it.
By this.
Stream.
And I said
That I was nearly there.
All of it marked.
By that.
By it.
I did it shortly.
I am waiting for more.
Exciting.
Leave it.
Leave it
Leave it
But.
Make it for him.
I do not wish to change.
Favorite teasing.
It is so earnest.
And even
And
By cards.
I say it.
I am not disappointed.
Neither is she.
She is a daisy.
I believe a daisy.
I believe what it says.
It is convenient.
And easy.
And pleasant.
And polite
And careful

And beautiful
And regular
And beside that violent
I am not astonished by values.
I am warned by expression.
I do believe in heels.
I have a bold sash.
I collect powder.
I am orderly.
I am so used to it.
I do not speak of lunch.
I am occupied by coal.
I have a liking for dust.
I am clean.
Bathed
Petted
Carpeted
And I refuse oil cloth.
This has a different name on a bench.
This has no meaning.
I do wish I had bees.
They are warm in summer.
It want it winter.
I do not wish for bees.
I have changed my mind.
Open.
Matter.
Days.
Of
Edging.
Edging what.
Edging printing.
This wasn't warred.
By him.
Two
Many
See
It.

Too
Many
Of
Us
Beside
And then
Bother.
Brother.
That is a word
Hold
Hold him.
I hold him.
I hold him then.
Not this.
Over.
It is a noise.
It ought to be bewildering.
No not yet.
By this time.
When
The tea
Not by water.
Wasn't I.
Any
Ready
He gave two.
Not at all.
Do you.
Do you promise.
Do you

It was very likely that he meant to say that if he had not left
that it would have been the day that he did not feel well. He
managed to say that.

Whisper.
Fifteen is a lucky number.
By this.
When she.
Has a stand

She has a standard.
She asks medals.
She is polite and by that means she is prepared to remember
Spain.
I do.
I ask her
She said.
Believe it.
I do.
I am careful.
I have a tender letter.
I expect as much.
What do they do what they intend that they celebrate.
Who is it.
I smile.
I am happy.
I am there.
I am not pale.
I am told.
What am I told.
I am told to be all all but ready.
I am ready.
I am tall.
I am breathing
I am favored
I am beside that penitent.
No
No
She won't.
She will not.
It isn't that.
I don't say that.
By nearly half.
By all then.
All of it.
I made a mistake.
Who pleases
Do they make that noise.

They know how to say it.

They do.

By nearly all of it.

I don't wish to say anything.

I said it I am in the midst of it I am involved in it I am thoroughly rested for it I am nearly like it.

What do I mean.

I mean by that to say that it is better and better and I do not care for another.

No thank you.

That was a funny noise.

I really meant it.

Changing.

I incline to weep.

Not by a long shot.

How

Do

You

See

In

There.

Exclaim

Put it in.

These words.

I was astonished at Robinson Crusoe.

Borrow money.

Buy a mattress.

Borrow money plainer.

This is what they say.

I would not dispute

This is the last time.

I wish I was learned.

This does seem particularly vulgar.

What was it.

We went up the stairs.

She gave us the invitation, she said if she did learn it by that time she would send it, she said it was the best written piece, souvenir of Rousseau. She said it was defended, well defended.

She said it was defended.
Buy a piece.
Of it.
And
Show
More
Places.
We were so glad.
We were.
That
They
Were.
Why is it.
Why is it.
What.
Why didn't you give it to me.
Did it.
Did it did it.
Did it.
Well I guess yes.
Buy that.
I don't.
Have to.
Why.
Because it's mine.
Is it.
Yes it is.
Is it.
I don't say everything included.
Is it.
Yes it is.
I will not be frightened.
I will not be worried.
I will not be heavy.
I will not be sad.
I will not be objected to.
I will not be unreasonable.
I will be polite.

I will be cordial.
I will offer plants.
I will be liked by everybody.
I will be easily ordered about.
I will be pressed to be better.
I will be so easily disturbed.
I will not leave hilly places.
I will not be afraid.
I will give it away.
I do mean to be right and allowed to get home.
I am not afraid to swim.
Swimming is not as usual.
I am certain of this.
No I don't want to.
I don't want to mention it.
I do not.
Brood.
And
Gloom
I will.
Leave it to me.
Perhaps to please me.
A pear.
He asked me.
When did he ask me.
He asked me which I like better.
Do be anxious.
To please.
Do be anxious to please me.
Do be anxious.
To please.
It was a remarkable piece of early training.
He was trained to sing.
He had to mutter.
It was unusual.
When they said a birthday they meant it.
They meant to speak of it.

They really were bewildered.
Calm
To be calm.
Battle.
To be leaving when there is extra happiness.
To be leaving when there is extra implication.
To be leaving.
Or authority.
Or authority when.
Press it.
Press it up.
So.
We were so pleased.
I like it again.
He gave it to him.
By not frowning.
He did not frown.
I must confess I did not understand him.
Able
Shall
Why
Old
Or
They
And mixed.
To
Safer.
Were they.
In
This
Dress.
Was it.
I should recognise splashes.

It was not as funny a story as the one about the girl. She was the daughter of their mother. Making wills for belts is not what he felt when he turned that way. She was so much a better height and by that he knew a wonder. He wondered why he said hush.

He did it. He was beguiling. He said hush hush. I don't do it nicely. He said I do think it is a funnier treasure than that other by the ladder. A funnier treasure than that other.

I am discouraged.

I am treated as if I were prepared to go away.

I am not left by nearly that plate.

We have decided to use glass as a shelf and to support it with a little wood and to believe what we say and not to cover it with anything heavier than toast, that's not it. I mentioned that. We have decided to ask for another brother. Two little dogs which have a color. This will please us. It is more bother. I said I did not wish it. I will ask when I am told that I may.

I think you are right, give Jenny a note book and pencil and have no exceptions except Louis and Jeanette and Claribel. Everybody else must have permission. She is very wrong about the fire. And remind her. That's all. I think this is my very best letter.

I want to stop it.

ONE SENTENCE

1914

To-night bore away.

An elderly couple talking talking much much or much talking too much to much.

A young man deaf deaf too a young man deaf to hear, two hear, a young deaf, holey holey to hear.

Set in. Set in blame to set in an excellent way to be lucky. What is it, it is to have twenty in believing that she said she would go and she did and she did. She said she would not go and she did not go.

Old review. Old review respects render shy not and or lock behind fraying. Fraying. Suppose a fringe has died. A little example does make it thin it makes it very colored very colored white.

She means nothing wrong but the love of talking is so strong in her that I think it necessary to check it whenever I can.

I hope I shall never do so again by talking less.

It was slippery. It was slippery and it was slippery enough so that falling down some are in falling down. Dear me how kind he is to me.

I feel better already.

Before he came I was frightened and so were her two children.

Felix knows I am not fond of early quotations so if I knew it I should not repeat it.

I saw them a long time yesterday and was very tired of them.

How any one says summon.

Why quiet when for.

How excellent does she furnish.

It is a trick.

Miners.

There was a no name the same.

Regency beauty.

What happens to him.

May lay may lay may lay.

Left over.

Beautiful dust or yes.

Spectacles.

This is an answer.
Did you have curtains.
He assured me he was quite well.
I am going there.
I know what I want.
This is going to be only.
A little coffee.
They came and they were speaking of it. They came in and they were loss.
They showed the whites.
They had the same trimming.

I know what I want.

A little railing and closets.
This makes the very best interpreter.
Really a time when everybody loses samples is not the time to stay anyway.
Long hair.
I do not care to wait any longer for your decision.
Of course.
If you have made a mistake that is another matter.
Blowing your nose.
I know perfectly well what I want.
Scenes from childhood, yes.
I have had an awfully happy day.
Three dirty handkerchiefs.
In it.
He thought they were there to welcome him to his home.
He had not all the support he had a right to look for.
They assured her she was not.
It will be nearly a new house.
She was a very pretty little girl with a round face and firm complexion.
She is now about thirty.
She is now very thin and withered.
He is a dear boy and stayed until ten.
The weather is very warm.

She is afraid of catching cold and cotton.
She says Isabella gives inexpressible pleasure.
I heard him acquitted.
I heard him acquitted.
If you are under thirty take my advice and do not go do not go for her.
Somehow I do not extravagantly admire her.
Needless to say they are mercenary.
A past censure is pleasing to the opera.
Really personal silence is more flexible.
She was older age.
He talks with the greatest concern.
He seems most perfectly at ease on the subject.
He seems a pleasant man but a fastener.
Fastening.
He believes him to be charming.
He is now a thin man.
I was much affected.
He is till.
Until.
Separated he will.
They refused not to be dirty.
I believe she is crazy.
He was as he often is extremely disagreeable.
The others I do not know.
What a disagreeable old woman and a safe. She sees combinations. That is false.
We visited yesterday and got in.
He is a good humored pleasant man the most disagreeable little sniffling grumbling one.
It was very necessary for them not to ask me.
She looked very foolish.
She looked very foolish to preserve that.
I told her that I had come to stay some time.
They were heavy and looked better.
She is nearly fifty and has been and very likely is all beautiful and on a very large scale. She is without exception the most rebuking holding unpleasant woman I have seen.

She seems to smile and is flattering and is ever lifting.

He is an ugly insignificant looking little mortal and appears good humored.

It is very likely that he will he will be dead.

He is going to be near her.

She seems as happy as possible.

The children had a full view of his face.

She seemed glad to see us.

A very nice little girl she is.

They did put him out.

He was so different and applauded whenever he could.

It was very disrespectful in them.

Particularly.

It was dreadfully hot.

He was obliged to leave him home.

He told him he loved him.

The house having been lighted up looked very pretty but I was tired and I was wavy.

This is the age for grandchildren to be young and admired.

I suppose by the time there is one I shall be a great beauty.

Alas.

I feel a little mortified by it.

Only a little.

I shall see last night at half past ten.

I find her remarkably determining and she really is beautiful.

There were a good many women.

She is certainly a very handsome woman but I do not think her looks stable.

There were only two women but there were a good many men.

She asked me to come.

I can.

She is fairly pretty.

She is not at her ease.

She has always been a most disagreeable mother.

I am commonly an acquaintance.

I can see it.

There can have been a fire.

There can be curtains.

They have a house opposite.

She is noted for having been unkind to her family, she seems an amiable little woman.

They have four children.

They all eat their meals.

She is a polite silly woman.

He is a haughty disagreeable man. She was covered with laughing. She is very reasonable.

How unfortunate they all are.

I do not admire a very pleasant woman more.

This is an ugly place.

It is a disagreeable place.

I like all of the family.

He is a thin man rather pretty and pleasant.

He is very gentle and kind and apparently amiable and severe and stiff and cold and ten years older.

There is something about her that makes me certain that she is good.

He has not spoken to me since yesterday. He has not even spoken more to me.

I thought he had said he was in the way.

He had fruit brought there all day.

She is really good humored.

He is tall and thin and very sudden and a great smiler. He is very kind and certain to every one. He is to walk to-morrow.

I do believe that they have at last sold me. I can charge it for rolling.

There are ways of pushing a cart.

If they ran over him.

He is more than eighty and he fell off from a horse and was reset almost immediately.

Really a row.

He is charming and amiable. It was a wrestle.

One.

Two.

Three.

Brawny.

Five hundred times a day.

I am not gay.

He is behaving badly as badly.

They hope that he is not married.

She is beautiful and pleasant and is seventeen.

Shoe making.

This is very useful.

I have just finished a shoe only by myself.

I sat.

I went home at night.

She returned them away from the door.

They fry everything in oil.

He will never see him.

She certainly is handsome and for her. She is short and fat and wears lace and shoes. She is doing so by asking. She is giggling.

She has a voice and a face, and she belongs to kissing breakfast or rather dinner.

Plenty of fur.

She did intend to do so later.

It is a beautiful place.

He is going to be confused.

He is a very sensible man and it is a surprise that she fainted and was taken home in a terrible condition and nearly all of them knew the same.

They have ten children. Five are of each kind separately.

There was a behavior that was irremediable. Call it shortly.

He could not stay.

It was very hot.

He was very tired.

I should have been able to be hoarse.

I sleep in a back parlor which is a quiet cool room and I have to go up and down stairs.

There is a needle in her leg.

They tied some things around her neck.

She cried all the time and she was certainly a sample a sample of orange and sheds, shedding.

She looked very supreme.

She is at least six or seven years firmer.

He is not quite twenty.

There is a lovely little girl she has been lovely.

She did read.

She was aloud and very very resisted.

Grapes are quite ripe and are growing very sparsely and there is underbrush and vegetables vegetables with apples.

They were delighted to see us.

He is very good looking and he is pleasing.

He is not particularly disagreeable.

She is fifty seven and old and more piles piles and piles and ordinary ordinary stretches.

He is drinking glasses.

There was no pain.

An effort.

To amuse.

You.

They are pretty and particularly around the mouth and I can say I do of hers.

She never appears excepting for a short time in the evening.

She has plain red hair and is so attentive to her sister.

She goes home to-morrow to my great joy. They are very pretty with beautiful eyes.

He searches for a hundred minutes and than I may admire what has been and is done.

It is a very peculiar circumstance that the odd piece they bring with them. It is the things that they bring with them.

They bring them with them and call it heavenly.

James is very fond of folding.

She was burnt to serve shelters. A tear is in an eye and stirring is simple.

Three days later.

The papers say that she is recovering.

I am unconcerned.

They are not uneasy.

He is thin.

They were two days without eating which they begged to hinder in collecting.

There are bundles of dirty clothes.

There is a great deal of kindness.

There are certainly a people with purses and a change.

Not tall enough.

There is no use in saying that she does read and compare.

There was a fire that is to say everybody went in a way.

Beautiful.

To be beautiful.

There is a general curve that makes one after another.

She had a great deal of trouble.

I feel a good deal disappointed.

Mortified.

I expected her to be prettier and more admired.

There was a little walker and he was so comical and had so great an obligation and was taken because of place in trouble and every one was laughing at him.

She was the mother of four children and running and ran away. He was a lovely man with a lovely family.

A shock is fear.

Remembering a picture only handsomer.

He is a charming man, placid in his manners and very pleasant. He is deaf, his wound is healed and his lungs are affected. He will never recover and I am afraid it takes three hours.

I liked him and I was disappointed in him and I had heard so much about him.

He has some more money and he is an uncle of the only one settled in the place of being civil and good humored and entirely connected with inventing baths.

He took me over this.

He sadly wanted me to go into one.

She is very pretty and interesting.

They have grown frightened and he is a terribly violent man, he has a low obstinacy and he is believed and moreover generous. He is obliged to learn talking.

He is very little and has a nice character.

She is afraid of everything and everybody.

There is no use in being younger for a change and to be

pursued with capable splendor. It was a certain time and perhaps it would be a combination of places.

In having two ladies sleeping there can be terror and horror and all of it.

There is not a time to spoil.

It is a nice little dog.

In not taking any trouble to hold up her head she has to sit down and shudder.

It does make a difference between disappointment and a fine looking girl.

They dance I believe remarkably well but to see tall ugly girls kicking and dancing is displeasing.

He is very ugly and a very good young man, the best part of his house is ivory and the rest beautifully furnished and burnt.

He is eighty three and so methodical and superstitious that he will not mention it for days.

He always crosses a hill before pressure.

He did it for the best and was forty.

How beautiful the time to select a wild wife for a genius.

He says that internal recitation is perfectly healthy but very expressive.

I am going there as I do not like to disappoint her.

She looked very well and she danced very well and really was very much tired.

They would change more yesterday.

I know two peddlers have settled in Oakland but I do not want to know any more about them.

There are sixteen between a table and it is more lively pleasant and glad.

The newspapers say that leaving is the same.

It was unexpected.

A certain time to wear so-called the same coat makes a handsome present show it and when she was seen she said it was just the same as not having had her own.

My dear Mabel. If you have the same and care to you can be certain that it has not been worn since you called it ashore when it was reserved and now if you wish it you can see it is not in any selection in consequence.

Believe me the coat writing and more I think that she will be grateful.

Sick.

Sick.

He is not fur favorite. She has been beautiful.

Believe me that it is not because of my pleasure that I do this.

Uncover.

She and I like.

We like.

Her neck was covered.

She and I like.

All the time.

Isabella's neck did not look well.

She did not look well.

She was covered.

She and I like.

It did her.

It helped me all the time it did her.

Isabella did not look well.

Her figure did not look well.

Her neck was more covered than she or I liked. It helped me all the time and so did it her. It made her stop to order her wickedness and currently speaking there is naturalness and beside pleasure, pleasure.

He is one of the best and most attentive husbands I have ever seen and she is the most beautiful.

Isabella's figure did not look well. She has been beautiful. Her neck was uncovered and she and I were more than alike. She saw me all the time and so did I her and it made her stoop to separate her slenderness.

She is a most flashing looking woman and dances in a most dashing style.

It would be a great disappointment to Isabella.

She has foreseen a daughter.

She is fifty years old.

Seven white ostrich feathers feeling.

One is disappointed.

She heard a good many facing her beauty which I daresay

composed her but she did not hold herself very well. There is no piece of everyone a surprise.

He has grown to be so fat that he is not nearly as good-looking as he was.

I like very much all the birds which have nearly recovered the use of their arm.

I had so many compliments paid to me because of Isabella that I came home conceited. To be handsome shortly because of mats.

A square is a square is cheerful.

I do expect a vest.

It was mine.

The excuse being that he prefers it.

Shameless shameless pills and necklaces and burrs and colored blue. Sell or sold or read a plan.

He and she and some men said there.

Of course there was no conversation except between the rye oats.

Between nine and ten the temple set me down at home.

He heard has just been here.

He went and was very thin which I am sure I do not wonder at.

He got into a crowd while they were ferrying which was enough to deserve anybody. Many families are here. It came in my head last night. Frightened to carry children off to-day. I know I should be very tied away from him. This part of the lawn is very quiet and it is a very anxious current.

He is very handsome, he looks very handsome. She is a very amiable young woman tall and dark and has a point and fortune and I cannot say that he would be to my taste. She is perfectly happy and he is a very disagreeable man.

To show a horse and back, going out and invited in, Mary was afraid of a beard and cried and was obliged. To be sent out of the room.

He is dead.

They hoped their feeling was an only son. How I feel for them. They are composed and very transfixed.

I never saw Isabella look more handsome so handsome.

She has a very pretty house and garden. We stayed until seven came home. Isabella looked beautiful. She had on a hat with yellow flowers and they said that daylight hurried her wonderfully. They were not in search of her husband. She is not handsome but spoken of, well mentioned.

I got very tired of it. They say they make many.

Shut the door.

A birthday is a little less pretentious than a hole and a hole does bloom does bloom fairly, fairly button and alight, alight pleasure, electric gay some and blaming and nevertheless goats.

Miniature painting, miniature painting credit. She is doing a collection too beauty and a craving came in while we were there a chattering good humored and special young fan which is at present sheep shearing.

Tuesday was expected to be a rough day being the one when weather was left with infinite confusion and a boat.

Thanks for the little cigarette case it is charming.

What does a nail do it makes places.

A wild hunt with coffee and buffaloes and little earnest cows.

This is a mix.

Birds for days.

His fortune he has a fortune is a good one to be a wish and whether Isabella longs is the principal objection.

If Isabel is satisfied I must be so.

He is disposed to be lectured and mirth real mirth is calm. Cutting up rhinoceros. This is even a choice and a celebrated relief and moreover all day in consultation and we determined at last to make our consent.

The children remark astonishment they notice that which has a railing around the top. Isabella admires it very much.

He is very near sighted.

Every day.

A watch a watch to tame.

A sealskin shawl yellow and blue and two whites. Grey roses.

She was very pretty.

Isabella is having a fern of her own.

He has accepted in a dignified and proper manner and his feelings hurt by restrictions.

Isabella at a ball. Isabella at a ball refused and I am not sorry for it as she is so young and handsome. I suppose they do not speak there now.

Great nuts.

I am very careful of her. I do not let her stagger or change cards or beam or behave and yet the last perfect resemblance makes no more little pealings than anything.

Ernestine.

How delighted I was to see her.

She is beautiful and looks beautiful.

The please of a copy is in the pearl and white flowers and patience and nearly the best arrangement is two or three months.

I hear that some of the cousins are beginning to not like it, I think it will end by their all losing their hatchets and a pause.

Some girls and are pretty.

Girls are pretty.

Some girls are pretty.

He was found.

Thomas did marry.

He came to consult me.

I did not discourage him and I let him please me.

He was found a few days ago in a hurry and mentioned that he begged and left it to better example.

I really believe her to be a good girl and a druggist and only four came and they seemed pleased.

Thomas informed me that he proposed and has given his father a watch and then it was chipped and if it was silver that is in places there is every reason for an answer to come.

She soon got over it.

The house is beautiful.

If eleven mirrors show it to be delicate and green, delight is permanent.

We got home between five and six in the afternoon and Saturday was the day that was there before the rest.

There was a stream of water and fish were swimming in it, fish and fish and fresh fish.

It was very warm. It was very hot.

Thomas and every one are determined to marry.

I am not clear and this is the reason that when a paper is taken away and a place is put up that I think very well and at others by others not so well. There is not politeness and a little leading.

She is to remain here with us.

Thomas is at all in love.

The family dislike it so that they seem so much suspected and I suspect that he would be.

She has refused tender solicitation.

There are ten in ten times and the tenth time.

To sit up.

I do not think Esther was worthy of the sacrifices that Thomas was not ready to make for her. This is suggested by the way places and places were left together.

Everybody rejoices at his success. He is succeeding he is miserable and ugly and not a very wise young man. He has an extra taste.

He is charming and he is a charming young man.

Escaping escaping permanently.

It took a remarkable red face and a small cigar to measure the size of fifty.

Let us suppose that observations are reclining. It is a pleasant shyness.

I wish that she were a little that she were like more separate happy churches.

This made peas. When the arrangement which necessitated that a whole hand was beside the little after secretion and pussy, pussy pussy.

Three. They had dinner.

Coffee stayed.

Rains hard.

Rains hard and stars.

Stirs cleaning.

It is really not surprising considering the length and nearly more yellow that it does make a month wholesome. A china bell. A silver bell. A bell porcelain.

Living in a different style.

Dislike. I think it is disgusting and perhaps he does think himself reading and paging the rest of the proud good man. This makes it mean that they bring certain excellent broken words.

I was very glad.

Or back.

Terribly noisy.

Our success.

He had to understand music.

A woman who is between forty and fifty has married an oculist.

Any who can can take a great interest.

They do suppose, they have supposed.

They were at one time engaged to be married.

Rose Marie is faded.

The princess is very indignant at being a governess. She says that if she is eighteen to the people she is certainly old enough at seventeen.

Never did the gate have so much to mention between that sermon and the place.

All the same he is particular.

He can change so as to talk and that shows cheerfulness, it does show it.

I really do look wonderfully young.

He is a very ugly man but very signable in his manner.

White satin is very beautiful, gold is very beautiful. Feather and dimness and ahead is very simple. Nothing could be more superb than that sofa.

Nobody knows why he does not go. She is good humored white fat girl with grace and dignity and all about children and very well and so she remained there. She said she could tell her and she would be more delighted to hear about me.

I should have been a very happy woman.

I went afterward and looked at it. It was beautiful. She is not very pretty but her dress was remarkably so. It was black velvet up to her throat with a great many diamonds etcetera. I was tired with my wife. She is regularly parted from her husband and has six youngest daughters and he is a strange good for nothing man. He is uncommonly ugly and those who know him quite advise him. She complains of not seeing a daughter.

She is little with high teeth and a separated elegance.

She encourages more lameness.

It was necessary that her eyes which could go to show that they were should have something to do with arranging little pieces.

She is white and reasonable and makes little balls.

There are various opinions about her. Some mean that nearly all the plates have ten by them and others have more dents.

There is mourning.

We have hopes or really it is a shame that there are so few currants. Even tomatoes and this did make lunch.

Chalk.

I was astonished at her swelling and calling and by the way is there any instance that seems to alter the best lamp. Is it necessary that it resembles a high house.

He is agreeable and charming and poisoned that is to say he is dead. They say that he is in a very good humor and gives an opinion.

She is a very pretty swollen and attractive girl.

I came home at one o'clock.

The old ladies seem to derange in marrying.

This was a mistake.

She is forty five and forty six.

A very pretty and disagreeable woman.

A very young woman. A very young pretty and disagreeable woman.

A very pretty and disagreeable and young woman.

That is some comfort.

That is some more comfort.

She is very good and educated but not pretty.

Chairs are dreadfully humming to me.

A sister and quite fat.

He who is remarkably pleasing is a very languid young man, he measures benches and covers up almost any treasure.

She despised us Paul.

Last night there was finally a dent, it is no use mentioning it is of no use or to mention silver.

I took her.

He is nearly being four.

Under one arm.

Under the other.

Between us.

He took care of her.

She looked rather pale and trembled from head to foot.

She enjoyed herself very much.

They went to swinging and eaten must shells and redolent hurrying and practice.

Who lost his arm.

Jane.

I would bring Fanny.

I think I went away directly.

I was afraid to engage to remaining longer. I thanked kindly and I spread the morning and I trusted that walking and walking and going to bed for the first time in ten days.

I was very angry.

She was moved and my sister and we have been this morning and I have chosen a very pretty paper for my ceiling and room and heard the person say it.

I like a whole lot of chairs.

They do express themselves so badly.

She is coarse and vulgar and her movements are not graceful, she has ugly long teeth. She is not good looking or ugly and she has no particular expression in her countenance.

She did not stay long.

When I met her on the street and she is afraid to bow and I am not afraid to remain not only one-sided but two sided and she makes plenty of little arms and a respectable authority the air more than allowed fills my rain.

A letter which was brought to me by an engraver caused me the greatest agitation.

She is here, she is wretched and really her children are miserably ugly.

They had a son and he lived to be capsized. They were married again.

I must say that I can and can sing.

I like it very much.

He is pleasant and like his mother. He has more memory.

To-day is a lively day and there are curtains.

Of course there are curtains. Inside there are attachments and triangles and little mahogany vases and all kinds of leaves and particularly curtains.

Of course there are curtains.

What is the objection to curtains. Curtains replace colds and towns and wires and almost anything that is bewildering. Curtains show wall paper.

People are running against each other. This makes the even win.

I was very much amused.

I have often traveled.

All the men are after are before cunning.

He cut himself with a piece of glass.

She is very ugly and perhaps there are no parents.

He is very good looking and not in good health.

She has the whole of it and gives fifteen away all in a day.

To be charming and to answer a sister and more in a familiar and regular way makes a period in revolving and makes a sincerely mistaken that is to say a married woman.

He is twenty.

She seemed very glad to see him.

I hear that she cries from morning until night.

What was it that we bought.

We bought a silver service.

The accounts from Paris are not pleasant.

Dear, handsome. All bright. Cup and stranger, little lilacs pudding. I can help coming to see Palma. Palma and glasses.

The accounts from Paris are not pleasant.

There seems to be a great representation of bas reliefs.

I have seen a very interesting but anxious countenance.

Eva was expecting the cooler flowers, plenty of them and yellow but nevertheless making a disposition that shatters car medal solicitude. The best spending is when twelve is five. The best spending is when twelve is well sir five and a half. That encourages a pretty view and a remarkable remarkably little fat.

He told me I had grown very fat. I think the present fashion of being puffy makes me look so.

Nine months three months.

They found Fanny.

Fanny was found.

She has thick lips and some people say that she died from a sore throat.

He is unhappy and would avail himself of a choice which makes marrying a necessity.

Marrying a necessity.

He succeeded in being taken home very angry and saying I am very much pleased with puzzling.

On Tuesday the only person who was a tall man with a bald head disappointed us by slipping.

I never heard anyone play so delightfully in diamonds.

She sings and the sound she brings out are quite mine.

Pansies and colored violets and gold and over black and pink calico.

The second light is good humored and lively and very melancholy and interesting and two sons who were little who do not look as old as when we shook hands, they are very ugly with white skin and a silk curtain.

What is a ship. Nearly seven.

She is a nice girl.

Old Mrs. Henry is dead. She had no religion.

Speak to me Rosy.

Jane and geranium.

I want to say that likely there is an etching.

Marriage. Marriage is, take place.

Mobs like shells.

Candy sticks candy sticks.

Natures which make pencils point to a resemblance to authority.

I very much hope that the marriage will take place.

In walking down the street and noticing that standing still is a certain region the place which is selfish is plainly valuable and ever plastered. This causes two flights of stairs and not even then more than ten.

Suppose a little piece of wood was missing and bronze oak bronze were added the place of the clock is still the middle in the middle.

He sighed.

It would be much pleasanter if when I was so wretched Fanny had grown to be a pretty girl.

You and I are old friends.

In an hour he walked home with me and stayed another hour.

I wished I would stay till Friday.

A brother forty years old and a grandfather has seen one twelve years older than himself.

The mother of twelve children is the mother of ten.

I am growing old.

Twenty five years are so uncomfortable in winter.

My mother leaves on Tuesday.

I mention a hundred years very much.

He has a poor wife.

A son who was shot for a sack.

Back.

When I tell you a thing on a day of whimsies it is just like any day.

Here is finished but you must not put it in any book for a few days.

Quite quite.

God preserve her and make her grey and jealous. This is no sense.

It has always affected me.

She kissed me going in and coming. There was a good deal of description.

She fidgets and wriggles and makes mountains.

I believe she is fidgety.

On Monday I motioned a coal car.

It was condemned with great reason.

She is affectionate.

Here he is.

She fainted and sent me to come in and look at her which she did.

He has curly hair.

Fanny looked very well.

Fanny liked it very much.

There was one room.

He is busy.

He is delighted.

He is not grieved.

He is ready to go.

It is very curious to see eighteen at dinner.

My sister stood at the window.

He does not think they were motionless. He has seen her letters.

He says I am slow.

They are liars selfish and a shadow and married. This is certain.

Her face and her actions are most graceful. I believe there is a wide eye in the house.

He thanked him.

I cannot listen to Romeo and Juliet. That is where they are.

He has a pin for his running.

Three days.

The bananas are very small.

I am glad.

The servants cannot pay and we are growing fat. She has been complaining.

The wedding does take a place and he has said that he hears he is the happiest in the world and that he will keep her for order and that I do not wonder.

She said it quite aloud in an immensely fat ball.

I really think Fanny looks as if she were what she is which is very pretty.

Sitting for an hour and sitting for half an hour.

He did say that he did not know.

It makes it look like a Negro.

I speak to my mother as if she were a Negro.

Roses are red and violets too.

Pinks are sweet and so are you.

Roses red and violets blue.

Wheels shine in wheels.

She looked so pretty. Naturally I was respectable. Mercy shines.

She was dressed in white chamois and really with bunches of roses and a crimson floor and belts. I was altogether satisfied with her appearance.

They are going to be married.

If Henry has a little girl and sounds are the ones they are it is a burst.

She is happy with her husband.

They were obliged to get him out of her room.

We got very tired of it.

We were very tired of it.

We went to a bare room and we liked it very much.

Flood gates and pins all sheltered now.

Do you like that bare boy.

Courtiers enter making witty remarks.

Sorry.

Hammer with it.

A sailor will go mad.

They had persuaded their foolish husbands to stay a week longer than they had intended.

She is buried with her husband.

Agriculture is dreadful.

We liked it very much.

I had not seen them in twenty six years.

I wish that I could believe them.

He is my mother.

Remarkably gentlemanly.

She has been for beauty and dresses.

Her sons are really pretty.

It poured in the evening.

At half past twelve.

I happened to be very hungry.

Ice-water was brought in.

Helen to whom he is married.

The house is very comfortable, they have neglected curtains.

We walked about a good deal in spite of a storm.

I slept in the same bed and we sat in the same room.

It is full of curiosity.

There are more men in the house.

All Friday we came home.

It was a shame to see her who was the prettiest girl in the room.

I find that my house is very comfortable indeed and I am more grateful to Mr. Helen because he left it for me.

They are going to marry a foreign bald headed man.

I feel very well.

I was frightened.

She received me like a sister.

Fanny is as happy as she can possibly be.

I was asleep.

She has a skin like pink satin.

The fat on any arms is really astonishing.

She was tall and pale.

He has very good taste. There is wanting carpets sofas easy chairs backs and dogs. There is nothing to see.

Are you my pigeon english.

Indiscriminate use of feathers by englishwomen is very effective.

My attack on Abbie is like Grants on Lee, Battle of the Wilderness.

Dogs cats and animals.

White pinks.

Gas roses.

Colliding.

The brook is put away with sugar.

He seize, his nails.

Well sir Capri is a fine place.

My coat was shot through and my little horse was killed.

I have been sleeping six nights.

I fear that Louis is a remarkable colonel.

Nobody knows what has become of me. I am counted.

Nobody knows why.

Men are running about.

The Baron and the sailor will go mad.

Nothing at all quite tired me.

To be charming and mild.

They sat together.

To go down a few steps the children were dressed in their best silk clothes.

His energy and marvelous ability.

The picture of his second wife is charming.

An intelligent person who explained everything clearly mentioned a bicycle and a circle.

She is old and ugly.

Twenty five miles, six hours, all the way.

She put cotton in her ears to be deaf. Color color.

It was long before I could persuade myself to get on mine.

They said he hoped I liked it.

He has better taste than anybody.

I went sad.

Nobody need to starve if they have an appetite.

To sleep all the time is a daughter.

Becomes a crime that is an eyeglass in a winter.

I have just been riding by an ugly Christian.

She gets up at five every morning and cooks a dinner.

The present ten have forty six furnaces. He does not seem to be very popular.

She says I was a charming little woman.

I am so warm.

By the time I was cool I was completely so.

There are four of each.

The coat has grown very large but not as much so as I had expected.

She kissed me three times.

The boy could see.

As a colored person so wittily said, Ernest is a name.

A young lady jumped a bridge and strange to say was not drowned.

Four wheels and a Turk.

They had a comfortable little room where no hour passes.

We go to Geneva.

I am all stuck up with wax.

It is really astonishing how everyone is higher higher up melting.

It grew.

Strawberries and milk.

I fell asleep.

We saw four.

Songstresses secrets.

Dance of the emotions.

Do you love me sweetest just as much as if I were English.

Lyrical passages.

Paper coughs.

I can tell now when anything is smelly.

They are agreeable to taste.

We said good-bye at Isabella's gate. We were up at four. Fanny and I and dear Isabella was in terrible grief. We had coffee and it seemed that they all thought I should be afraid of traveling if I knew this.

We were delighted to get into a flat.

We are quite tired of rocks hills and precipices.

Breakfasting in a large town is a nuisance.

He is amiable but can he write can he think does he taste toast. Anyway don't mention it.

Mrs. Chesterfield thinks it a very nice picture. It has legs.

I am delighted with Harris and only wish I had more money to spend. She is a daughter and a most delightful person. She gave me a box and Saturday is a long time.

Wedding wax.

All wax is wedding wax.

I am too sleepy to know what I say, it would be awful to wake up with the clash of that.

However we are pretty safe.

Pretty safe.

Pretty safe.

It is nothing.

Columns and columns and columns a particularly ugly old man.

I am perfectly miserable.

We went in order to drive away thought.

I do not like it I have changed my mind.

He said I spoke French very well. He is a fat good-humored looking man and his voice is disagreeable. The whole thing was over in a half of an hour.

I refuse to be comforted.

She said I had a red face, I said she had red eyes.

I believe he was just as glad as he could be to see me. I certainly took a fan for him.

An elephant of immense size is to be placed on the top.

Water fusses.

I saw anything which made me feel very thick.

He has a long face or rather nose.

To be anxious.

To be melancholy.

This is a bad sunny shot gun.

It is for sale.

She is rather pretty, he is the same little man.

They never speak to each other covered with jewels and extra pieces.

I was out yesterday.

A balloon with a lady in it.

Her head moves when she smiles or speaks.

To have pink, to be long neglected, to have diamonds and roses and clearly little rings to have a face perfectly like a Fanny and me is unpleasant.

Colored pimples extra colored pimples.

It was a time to fish.

Selfish.

It contained three, our two servants. Their cleanliness is extraordinary. They paint twice a year and wash without ceasing.

I covered my face with my pillow and after that ate.

I saw some paintings and a Chinese room.

We are worried to death by sailors.

A lady and a gentleman and their little boy.

I must now write the name.

They call him their hope and they sit on the shell and their lessons are steady and they persuade Spaniards.

I look around to see and if I look around to see I look around
to see.

He has died of a slender complaint and it was just and exact.
He was a person.

She is very ugly having white ways and hair and blue eyes.
She is to be married presently.

To be a nice little girl is extraordinary. My sister was.

It is a very extraordinary worry.

He is short and fat and really handy enough.

To be in a way to stay and settle mother, this makes a plumber.
A plan.

The guesses are coming every Friday night.

To bring two daughters Saturday is civil ceremony.

I hope to meet out of recognition.

I hope if I meet him I shall recognise him.

He was particularly kind to Fanny and to me.

I am most agreeably surprised that Fanny is admired this year.
What is the use of Florence.

I think if he comes to be thin then there is use in feathers.

To sit with her is dangerous for the wind.

They killed and salted some kangaroos.

They have never returned.

She covered her face with a handkerchief and was in such a
state that they were quite frightened. Fanny would not dance all
night.

Eighteen.

Fourteen.

And eighteen fourteen.

He has very good eyes he really has very good eyes.

It would take about a week to finish.

Louise Contadina Sill.

It has been a nice episode in our life.

The plumber's father.

Last night we went to a fine house which was too hot which
is not now a usual thing an unusual thing.

I told him that it is reported that he is married to Fanny.

The poor little man must set out flowers.

Poor Fanny is not asked.

I stood any time.

She told me she has asked thirteen hundred people and they all had come. I was a good deal tired.

To borrow emerald and diamonds and feathers and pink satin is very plain.

There were seventeen hundred people asked.

I ate my supper.

I was in raptures.

Quite recovered.

I don't admire Herbert Kelcey.

They are so haughty.

The child is dead.

I am very anxious about her in the course of the day.

She was eating a little bread and milk.

She really is the best mother that ever lived.

He intends to go soon for ever.

Fanny has just had a letter.

She spells better on Tuesday.

She is to have a procession with ribbons. She is keeping in bed at this moment and on Friday evening at ten we return to Mrs. Holbrook.

Mr. Southey and Mr. Burt gave us their arms.

The weather is very hot.

A cold stove is a steady sun.

Light blue ribbon is Charley's color.

She is very ugly, fair with red eyes.

I think we shall soon hear of his death.

Fanny dined.

Fanny and the boys.

What an indecent thing to do murder and murmur and cry out and hear it is not true. What an indecent thing to do.

Oh joyful surprise.

A purse and a necklace and a quantity of pansies.

Two little bronze figures apart.

Fanny rides.

Four children are very anxious about it, they gather there and are so kind and affectionate and so much improved and softened and so lively and animated and delightful.

He is remarkably agreeable and clever. Somewhat vulgar and having no gentlemen at home the last day or two is a very stupid one and prolix but we have laughed very heartily. He says he does not mind that Miss Shannon is to marry Mr. Herbert James.

He is just her age and she is dead.

Every night there is constant beauty in separate parks.

Brother is a Boccaccio tremble white.

They avoided alliteration and Harriet said she never knew that any one employed it in conversation.

No nuisance is alarming.

A dog measures the distance between an eye and a thumb and rubber.

Dear Mr. Shaw, It is necessary to give some words to be more disappointed with the beauty of living with the lady. It changes however because the people were very kind and stiff in the air. Every night in the week they are astonished at the recurrence of what would be pleasant to me and I only tell you this as we have been keeping my dear sister from painful clever taxes.

The rest of this letter is lost.

Yesterday was our thirtieth wedding day.

Fanny and I have come here to see my sister. She does not dine with us.

I am grieved to find her so far.

Fanny was delighted with it.

Fanny had been reminding him of this for certain.

Fanny and I took a water together. She is my child.

Black draperies perhaps conceal more than white ones would.

A skirt is hanging.

Nervousness in is on the decrease.

Shoulders are splendid.

We sat at our work.

We are going there to-night.

Have you any idea what time it is.

Yes I think it is about half after eleven.

Fanny and I stayed to supper.

Her manners are very pleasant but she has grown fat and has a redness in her face.

He was not moving his lips and he had some meat and butter.

Harriet was admired for her beauty.

Everybody seemed pleased and I liked it.

We had a visit yesterday from the one who used to admire Isabella so.

He sat here quite a while and took quite a good deal of notice of the little girls especially Harriet. He made her sit on the sofa with him and read a book. He was astonished at hearing her read.

He has a beautiful name and writes our names.

Fanny and I met.

She really is not worth seeing, her example is that she is frightened and humble.

She is the happiest woman in the world.

Fanny and I and the ladies, there were ten men, and only five men. Fanny was dressed in pink and silver.

He looked very much older.

I have not seen it yet.

She is nervous.

Fat with pretty black eyes and a pretty face and I am not in love with the place.

I could not bear to disappoint Fanny.

Fanny and I very pleasantly proposed to skirt the bridge.

We went to see an old friend.

My mother was not very well to-day.

Fanny and I went without stopping.

They were very noisy.

She is thin and almost pretty.

Fanny got home about three.

It snowed all day.

Isabella or a new house.

She wears thin flesh to show her blue veins which are so pretty.

He has had a son and is doing very well.

I believe she and her husband do not care at all for one another.

He is a delightful young man.

Fanny danced.

Isabella seems very well to-day.

Isabella saw her neck.

I am sleepy.

It is much pleasanter and less fatiguing.

The King said, How do you do.

Fanny and I had white hearts trimmed with jet and blue turns and a bundle in every quarter.

Fanny and I had white hats prettily trimmed with blue.

You hold them in your arm until you leave the room.

Several banks and everything seem to be going badly.

There goes that noise.

Fanny looked very well and was dressed.

We did not get home until four.

Fanny and I went with little girls. It is now half past seven.

He has an ugly red nose.

They came to leave me this morning.

She is a dear fat good humored thing.

There is improper behavior.

Fanny and I made a mistake in the day.

We did not discover our mistake until to-morrow.

We were certain to change.

I found it very well.

We came here this morning.

It was a very thin one indeed.

They are a very amiable family.

Fanny is to be one of them.

About five hundred people were present.

They are writing a history of expression. They mean to use choice.

I had a good letter to-day.

I was quite shocked at hearing that a married lady had a morning. She has taken upon herself to contradict it.

It is however a most unpleasant idea.

Susan is her eldest daughter.

He is poor enough.

When it is obscured enough it is very visible. There is a mention of an extraordinary mountain.

I have some hopes however that he will not accept it.

I am sorry to say January is appointed to have some rest.

We left an amiable person.

To be aged sixteen and seventeen, I must say I expected a gayer one.

Mr. Blackwell aged twenty.

To be at nine o'clock in a lit room is to be in a grand scale.

By the sea Fanny picked up shells.

They have given me a very uncomfortable sitting-room.

He is a sincere young man.

They cannot leave a shape.

Fanny danced.

Everybody is so kind and attentive to us that it is quite delightful.

Fanny seems very popular.

I took a long walk with the girls as they did last year and there were many mornings.

I spent the morning with our friends, they also saw the wild beasts.

He is a most delightful young man to express the respect and enjoyment that a biting wind can give in the evening.

Nobody died here.

I dined with the Captain.

I spent a dull day alone.

They took the laurels with the vanquished and they recommenced the getting glad to get back again.

I left on Wednesday and I was glad to be back again.

Fanny and I went to dinner well and we saw Mr. and Mrs. Boyd and also Mr. and Mrs. Henry Blake and two strange persons who amused us. We planted trees.

The rest were obliged to see that there was dancing. Fanny danced with Mr. Sebright and Herman Strange.

In producing a daughter the rest came in the evening.

Fanny and I were not asked, very different from former times.

She is grown fat and plain and thin and old and not I think really beautiful.

It is quite beautiful.

I have seen the little dog and I will not call it beautiful.

A daughter is very pretty.

I have known for many years that it can be stupid and terribly hot, that he can be stupid and terribly hot. I have known for many years that the express is cold and very weak.

It relieved my mind very much.

She gets up late and dozes and says very little.

I have very bad headaches and I don't like to commit to paper that which makes me very unhappy. Yesterday I was not in bed until this morning at eight o'clock.

Fanny danced. She really looked very pretty.

She was asleep the whole time.

I arriving in the garden there was a space where nearly every one standing had a certain arrangement of skirts and hats and nearly always they mentioned something and with the best intention, the very best reason the especial extra sign was the one that showed the proof.

At eighty eight what amendment could be expected.

We had a melancholy dinner.

I am sorry for it.

Lily Worcester is dead and she did it by her own imprudence in creating a great sensation.

She was pretty and fashionable and nevertheless she will soon console herself and her family.

She spent the remainder of the day at home. She has left two daughters, she does not dance of course in black gloves.

It is astonishing how little sensation can be created and how much more is thought of it.

It is crowded to excess and I am at half past ten to find it a hot day.

Whatever you want my blessed baby.

Many anticipate riots.

It is a fine hot day.

As her mother wishes for her I could not refuse to let her go.

Fanny went at night.

Fanny came away before supper.

The bullets are very bad.

She is a deeply injured woman.

Fanny and I are alone the weather is fine and hot.

We read aloud to each other in the evening.

He was so anxious for several visitors and three daughters to stay in the house.

It is dull here.

I am really fond of them.

I should be glad to get home.

A letter which announces that he is going to be married to the youngest daughter temporarily makes them very rich and I trust they will be very happy.

Any one who came here were very happy and much in love with each other.

To bring a little girl two years old she brought a little girl two years old.

She calls her Susan and nothing else.

To-day as usual ended in rain.

In this very time thirty three years ago in the very hat that we saw to-night we went to see ice-bergs the place we went to see to-night, our second day.

My sister is miserable.

It is astonishing to me that she is like my sister.

To speak with tears and kindness and to eat is what happened.

She was thirty years old and she does not pursue it. To speak with tears and kindness I believe he has left her everything. To speak with tears and kindness to speak with tears and kindness.

He is sixty eight, I am fifty four, she is fourteen, he is twenty three and twenty seven, she is thirteen.

She is thirteen.

Fanny was asked by a great many to dance.

Fanny does not dance any more.

We think we are introduced to a very nice young man who is a brother.

The weather is very hot.

The house is very pretty and the place is very nice.

Oranges and lilies.

They did not come for my cane to put a rose on it a gold rose.

I took a long walk.

On the whole she had a very good time.

Aunt Pauline meant to say that my sister was the one who

was married and she was sure to mention it some time. My sister
was the one who was married.

I have an inflamed eye.

I am determined to leave to-morrow and to set out with Nelly
and Frank and Robert.

Ninety is ninety.

Affectionate and kind.

Affectionate and kind.

I enjoy nothing and can move without help.

Aged ninety-two.

The less safety the better, the more curls the better, the more
powder the better, the more eggs the better.

The more eggs the better, the more seldom the better, the
more hurry the better.

Kindness and circumstance and shaved off his beard.

POSSESSIVE CASE

1915

Letters and willows and chimney churches plaster electricity and cabins and later balloons and hops and pages and effective say automatic clean or if a handsome pear able to bear that.

Lit, turn you back.

The plumber.

This is an excuse.

Question.

A blanket is extraordinary.

A card a playing card.

A minute a regular importance.

I'm afraid not.

Elaborate.

Importance and power to change circumstances which might make elegant energetic pleats and boys and upper rarely left him.

I never saw any one so nervous in my life.

Nothing happened between herself and wife. She was very sweet very conscious very slow and unalarmed.

She got it from an actress who fell into mourning.

A plaid cape with two capes.

A splendid effort to establish a little bed.

To be born to be settled to have linen to change flowers to have immortal white ones with green leaves to undertake nourishment, to leave out careless pillows and to never change never change every other day excessively and shortly, no wonder there is a dedication, not more than head and tail pieces and illustration not handily and monotonously.

I saw a picture in a scene showing a single mare and never was there a pearl present never was there a pearl present.

Reasonable, to show a chin, to show a chin.

To show a chin.

To show a chin.

Place a man away away.

Now comes a letter.

Please remember that I shall rest pleased with the expression of haste and pleasure and likeness.

It is too wonderful.

If chestnuts are red if chestnuts are red and hawthornes are below they are certainly not blooming. I said I would show them to you next summer and now they are where there is a whole disappointment. Please baby please etcetera.

A consecrated cross I bear.

Four hundred two hundred twenty fifteen.

A bell in a corner.

Curly princes.

I never saw it I never saw it after, I measured a sister, I shall please, I never can saw everything, I need a stripe.

I am able to do a great deal of good.

I should be able to do a great deal of good.

Cora is such an amusing fool.

In the wide spaces where fertile soil is so short.

Poor old Hermann can't stand it either.

Lizzie's worst sister can't equal any one of the friend's daughters.

Try as hard they can't get a hundred and fifty.

It's pretty good though.

All that ability and courage and no distinction, they are there beside.

I am quite touched with Romeike.

She is sensitive to hills and noises.

I am sensitive to smells.

She keeps pretty young the younger Dane.

Do not carry too much.

Not much too much.

Harriet thought you ought to do it then.

What a pause.

No.

Have you ever died in France.

She is a broken and defenseless country.

It isn't a fact at all.

You have taken it all away.

Regency daughter.

Do you want a little plain cake.

Tomorrow you'll have to say it to me.

The roses smell good in here just the same.

She knows the difference between black and red.

Those are the expensive ones.
They are not sensitive to unpleasantness they have water.
She is sensitive to cousins too.
She has nothing to do at a moment's notice.
Shall I get you your apple now.
Bring me a new fig.
Samples are more necessary than ever.
That is not the way to lament.
You needn't have everything taken out. You will never tell your sweet sad story better than that.
Gardens mustn't frighten baby.
They always are a funny pair.
The other one has no character, this little one has.
I should suggest frightening.
Chances of whether.
I always thought it rather sweet of Adolph on the contrary.
This is the time to pray.
An exact leaf and a relieving hold enough.
It was very fanciful of a city to do it.
I see a thin lady asleep.
There is a charming story of how they made her dance with grown officers.
Now you said that.
We must always remember the difference.
Now you said that.
Where did we get it.
Brentanos or Galignanis.
Cheeses.
Babies before time and hurry everywhere.
Now come oh.
Heavy heavy hangs over a bed what will white colors change it.
Purple wool makes cotton.
Shall.
Sample.
Put a chest very similar.
If you put a thing in a place what is the question.
The understand is that a white paper is in the eyes and this changes not to dazzling not to dizzying. It passes the morning.

In the evening there can be a whole piece of furniture which
makes a bank.

It is terribly mixing.

Don't worry dearest it can be opened very easily.

Your eyes are not wide apart, you are tall and well-built.

Anxious Churches.

Fuss it fuss it faucet.

It is not necessary to know the home life of the average trav-
eler tourist and holiday maker, the widest horse is the one that
curves.

What is a dog show.

No doubt all trout.

Period.

Just sole.

It was so unreal.

In go our heads.

Will you serve yourself first to-day to please me.

Isn't it a reflection on us.

Banks and government loans are the only thing they invest
their money in.

What is she hollering her head off for.

What are they doing talking it all over.

Yesterday and the day before reproductions.

Yesterday and the day before rich men's cats.

They box a box.

They box.

A box.

They are very pretty.

Colored it and put it out in the hall.

She has a sensitive imagination.

Cunning.

Even in Venice she could let it run out.

Nantucket.

I will find out how you sign it.

I can find a little piece of paper there.

Rapid speaking is old.

I'd answer it anyway.

That's what I was telling you about.

I suspect the second man.
You take it and read it to me slowly.
Pot of vanilla forty acres for ink.
I see it before you is an animated reference.
He is older than you and has a baby.
Oh do you know sandy sandy color.
A belief in mexican bell leaf.
An elastic has a beaming effect on a gum tree wither languishes.
To believe a son so dead.
Shell fishes.
Sell fishes.
Little houses or little houses.
Best center.
Now to copy coiled backs.
He didn't like me so he hurt me and he said I was a fool to brush him to brush him with what.
Its an argument its a call its a kind of an apartment, I don't know whether it is cheap. I paid a hundred and fifty. I guess I didn't.
He's a wonder.
He went and instead he worried a window.
He just went about it.
Plans were a case.
A whole time to mention.
A whole time he went in.
He went in any extra cases were neat.
Any extra cases were neat.
I can't leave that way.
That's the way to do it.
Alright.
What effect the setting sun has I must wait till evening to decide.
She says she says the most extraordinary things of that kind.
The ten ten thirty.
I have to do some thing that I own.
There is no use of speaking of day-light.
Part of the Holly died.

Excuse me.

Excuse me Minnie.

Asparagus can grow anywhere.

They've painted them awfully prettily.

What are you doing it with now, a spoon.

What are you doing it with now, a knife and spoon.

What are you doing it with now, a spoon.

A knife and spoon.

Cherries.

It cooked about five minutes.

I don't know what those are.

I adore the new room, I can't. I just adore the new room, credit, hammer race return.

What are you catching.

I adore the new room I can't. I just adore the new room.

A line in wood.

Asbestos.

I have to arrange them not exactly alphabetically. I think they did.

I have to arrange them not exactly alphabetically.

I think they did.

Don't sweeten the coffee and oranges.

Don't sweeten them.

This is my religious cauliflower from the look of it.

Bring those right in that are there.

By accident.

William behind Cora.

She is that.

I'll have them carried right up. Oh no no. This is the other side. Isn't this too funny.

I'll have them carried right up oh no no. This is the other side. Isn't this too funny.

It took Herbert a long time to find out about postal cards.

Yes indeed, very interesting if you are interested in wonderful things which are a delight.

Now I have some idea.

Why don't you take a chair out of doors here. I don't want to.

This one goes upstairs.

These other two go upstairs.

This goes upstairs.

I guess there's an awful lot of ugly stuff in September.

This is a pretty thing.

That's pretty.

That is.

A peculiar left hand.

That's a poppy I don't know what that is.

Somebody has knocked my gooseberries off.

Is that an amusing bell that bell extra.

They smell much more overpowering.

Helen might sell chocolate.

To-night is a very pretty bird and that's not much of a test.

She thinks this one will.

I think she is right. I think she will too.

And now she sends them to her all the time.

I talk to some one else too.

A little towel like this only a clean one.

Perhaps I do it dreadfully.

The table that's glued.

That one.

Not for selling it here.

Will you take a look and see if the geranium is in the water I want it to be.

I am not dwelling on it.

Charming and patient and perfect never forget it.

Perhaps I do eat dreadfully.

I couldn't have one now.

All white don't snatch from me.

I've lost the little book.

I know what I want.

Here it is.

That is what they meant anyway.

He's not as good a genius but he puts dogs in. He puts them in the catalogue and then there is a choice between a little way and the rest. He's not as good a genius.

Oh do you think so.

Do you esteem me.

I curl little Fanny.

How do you do. Frost.

Just the same.

How do you do.

Frost.

They never got themselves into that milliner's shop.

It might just come.

You want to give more notice than that.

It's the wood not the marguerite that counts, it's the wood that counts.

It might just come that Eva was told to.

A particular telegram.

Gradually you find out where it is.

Get his name and his address before he goes.

I don't know why to change black and grey bath robes.

It's a little plain.

Now this is what we've decided we've decided to put wood and plaster wood and plaster between.

Any way a gold top is the top. It is not gold. It is painted with marble and little pieces of red and a way to let it drop is to have a globe. This globe was bought to cover what was not altogether a wish, that is not a wise wish, that is to say it was dolly.

Any bath tub is waxen.

We have changed six potatoes.

In general.

I can remember six or seven miles.

Saying after rain, the cold weather is without noise though it can be combined.

There are two or three months once in two years when a house is painted without feathers and within is no cushion. This has seldom an occupation. It is always ready for the next day.

I think I remember losing some pins and afterwards remembering where they were lost.

There is a curve in a neck.

She was sorry to be forced to say that she would not take it anyway, she said they were terrified. It was not a surprise to see them all and they came to say that nothing more was expected.

The reason that two of them are white is that eight days was not expected. The reason that two of them are white is that it is a resolution.

We live in a house which is certainly not mentioned any-where.

Dark blue or purple silk, dark blue, dark blue color.

Dark blue pink silk and the evening and later I had the misfortune to lose my father.

We I mean my mother and myself moved to a pretty but painted stair-way where there was cloth enough to pretend to forget.

To have a very uncomfortable life means to wear red turned up with green and gold. This is not allusion to the things she gave and the ornaments in green and gold and blue satin which were indicated on paper, this is a conspicuous thing and she was always a dull woman and spoke slowly.

She was not kind and good-natured and you could tell her that a poor man had died.

I had a little sister and she saw it in that place and there was more beside.

The next morning we were up very early.

Any one looked very well but thinner.

A black body and pink clothes and pink feathers, not a black body and pink clothes and pink feathers.

Having a small table and setting it makes it possible to do without shoes and stockings and pins. The only account given was that it disappeared quickly if it was left carelessly.

It will happen again. They did have a baby. Her hat was in front. She did settle further. She had no understanding. She chose a fan. See bells and oak lace. It was put too tender. Little joining. Sullen place. Extreme insight. She said she was glad to come. So sunny. A circumstance to make a clock go. Who loves clocks. I do. I love clocks. I have one, I have seen twenty. I have two and will have more. I can never remember that it has changed that gas is replaced by electricity. Oh not at all Sunday. What might appear in response is it was not sufficiently expressed. The whole family is out beside.

I wanted a little company but I don't have to have it you see. One doesn't rent rooms to people whose hospitality they have accepted.

The pleasantest thing in the world.

Interesting events are particularly interesting to us.

To be a very short woman and to explain a case becomes the fashion for any one. I think I made the ankle thinner and after some years I succeeded. It is perfectly natural to have a bad movement in walking. A brown color with a strong smell turns quite light and they are wasted the brown color and the turning quite light. We did not talk too much we stopped when we saw dogs, we stopped again. I do not know that he is extremely sheltered. He says it is curious that lambs have more ways of not knowing it afterward. They were called buttons. There can be the same windows which are broken and I very much regret that I am not a little disappointed. If so I should not feel that there has been any hastiness in spending all that money. This is to decline many symptoms of unquietness, and horses are not good ones. It is singular that the more observing two things such as they are are that bathing is nearly at the water's edge. It is the funniest and most violent bluish pink. It is kind and excited. Very cool things are convenient I assure you. Nothing can be more easy than more hesitation. In my opinion I was very much delighted. Part of the probability is that it will not come to any thing. I have thought a great deal about these matters.

We arrived here to-day. I asked her to let me see him and she was so in the habit of ascertaining all the joinings that had been necessary for the establishing of more places that it was necessary neither for me nor for those leaving to satisfy a larger precaution and we did so. It is a very quiet thing to have lots of distress and the care of opening the door is one such which we were forced to remove with pieces and paper. A piece of paper is worth five friends shaking hands with us. This was ascertained by an exchange. I am just returning. We were present and looked exceedingly red and alarmed.

There seem to be more husbands and husbands and wives and necessarily they are increased they have increased the family of their unhappy brother. We mean to return Wednesday. I do know what to think. To marry for love and to be very handsome and very clever and to be deterred by no difficulties and to give her attention to dogs suffering with wounded soldiers is not discovered until some years after it is mentioned. In some things she is a leaf in the wind.

An immense man was a person said to have been admired by her. He was seen by the last, calm gay sweet tempered interesting letter of thanks.

What can aged take. They take what there is for eyes. They neglect the only shabby and weak serpent who sees edges which have fire clay. It makes taking tonsils out easy. It is too bad.

Cool pretty. Neglect length and the time to make changes is measured by the fear that the fifteenth of July is more morganatic.

Come Come Come.

I saw a dog which resembled a lamb so much that it was the same as china. I decided to ask an Englishman what was the age of it. He told me about it and then I called it what it would be, it was the same as bitten. I decided to wait until I had been to London. I could see the ones there and return with one in the cabin. This would be necessary if I were to be pleased. We decided to say nothing.

I've just done it.

It's getting warmer isn't it.

I do not eat dreadfully. You said something else and I can't remember what it was.

It's a pretty place though. Besides look let me just have it again. You didn't give it back to me. That's enough. I'll keep it for a little while. I am ready speak to me.

Yes I saw it I have to put down every word you say. Speak to me. There look at it. Do you know what those peaches look like but identical. We don't have to look and look and look. What do you want. He's trying to pretend he's a tailor that is that he certainly does. Yes very. I don't want you to use it. Here here. That will end that. I thought you said the electrician would. Do you think it's pretty. I am so sleepy nobody knows how sleepy I am. It's remarkable and the gloves are dirty. It all goes up I said. I am tired and not hungry. I have five that's all and now I am going to sleep. It's fatiguing. I might say I was out to-day. You're a successful one you are. Not a crown. If the lady was sitting up and had a hat and asked what time is it over there there would be sleeping with packs and packs of cutlery. It was a chance.

In reviving a glove in gently reviving a glove in resuscitating a flying machine in lastly resuscitating a flying mentioning and mentioning honorable distances, in mentioning honorable distances and this not in a spirit to decide whether the country is prettier or the city is paler in hoping for this and much James gave us a dog. He was Colonel Fox and he not perfectly and he blamed bread. Cunning. Likely. Breezes. Chambermaid that is delivery. A murderer is gone in the boat. He steals the nearest bay and moistens the lake, he does measure. Redness. This is not so. Dwell spread and gloom.

A very pretty chair.

At present.

He said he was a cloth and he said he would go and he muttered, he muttered again. He always muttered. Look here this is a matter of business, a simple matter of business just asking. I want to know that there is plenty of likelihood well any way you put it plenty of likelihood of imitation, an imitation. Look here I don't want it to go, I don't want it just to go. At present a climax any way a baby, please to consider that swell swelling is portable just portable and in any way necessary. The tired life that is just the same occasion, the same occasion and plenty of wonder. Mrs. Renny has plenty of accidents, she has plenty of accidents.

There there beef.

You are quite mistaken in supposing that we are all in confusion here. There is plenty of chopping. Everything appears to go on just as quietly and merrily as if nothing had happened. It is a complete shame. It is a way long and there is a fire burning and any way that keys are made are in the same way furnished. At present seventy places have fire at once, before that there were quantities quite nervous. It is perfectly certain that a great number were seen a few days ago.

Tell my father that I resemble him. Just this way anybody, everybody can make the mistake of grappling with the chair.

We had a high chair and at first the baby cried. Now she doesn't make any fuss at all. She just satisfies it.

I say they went.

The only silky face I saw was that of a woman who sat alone and said she had let her hair grow beside.

The intermixture of admission and the act of lamenting is the most uncommon thing in the world. Latterly there are seven. A person I knew was then returning what I did see. I wish to see the three and twenty more and then to see that he could not conceal his tears. I tore my shirt sleeve on the chair.

I believe he intended to have only adding Julia.

He was very fond of fish.

He was leaning and he saw water.

Delicious.

This is a wedding day. What do you do how do you do. I don't like to read. Nervous. Any way they went for long. I hear her saying she was perfect. She was angry with the furniture. We aren't.

We weren't.

No matter not quite able to season all the, not able.

Knocking, knocking before.

He showed impatience. Eyes were of different size. Eyes are of different size. If he wanted not to give it in tin if he wanted it in wood, if he wanted in glue necessarily, if he saw paper, anyway there was sticking and the last time there was silk brocade mentioned in every way. And you my dear lady I scarcely know whether you have not ascertained not too especially that a sentence so deliberately pronounced while I thought I can inform you of the pleasure selected by some others. This is between five walls because something is changed. A vein is a vein and surrounded, surrounded by leaning upon others and a little fire which scarcely seems the same as the three others. This is pure morning and evening conversation.

On the last day of June my September month was the one that was to be chosen and then well then I yielded to solicitation.

But what is this dear Miss Langley these that give you their name and selection. Is it a promised visit and do you claim to be generous and willing. Do you have more affectionate remembrance when you say you will not draw again. Once more be good to and remember that to be forgetful means that you have asked to be happy and very well.

No wonder there is a change no wonder an announcement of an exhibition makes the change use the word and then a little pointedly you mention that you have not ventured to announce another. This I mean to enquire into and you will come, I know.

I spent the whole evening giving much pleasure in a promised visit and neglected to arrange that there would be a distribution of roses. Roses and wall paper make bathing easy. I never neglected to wear ear rings. This marks the site. My absence has heaped geraniums in the house and yesterday when there was a willing carpenter we made a door. We hoped to wait more often and we did select better iron, better iron than was cheaper. Suppose six gloves wash, isn't it very keen and clever and inattentive to not do that which when we have not much of it to trouble us saves the promise nor the complaint. We enjoy complaining. We tell them that we will have it as we ordered and now we will have it as we want it. I cannot laugh as loudly as I ought to do. I do let the chair fall. I do push the table back.

You are right we intend to spend the summer in good health and spirits.

This is a button. The clock which has decided, a decided. Tortoise shell.

That's no good. I learned out of the house.

Pray God I love my baby. Pray God I love but she. You were fond of talking.

He struck water.

He struck water.

Lemon lemon credit.

Five thousand five thousand nineteen and twenty, nineteen and twenty, four thousand.

Water he blamed stone water, he blamed stone.

He blamed water, he blamed Ernestine. He blamed Ernestine and water.

Water.

Careless of a carpenter, careless of much, beside the glass and it has glass besides, be sides, placing of iron, a line on blue paper, white not white but white on blue paper.

Mr. Beffa, it is natural for man to indulge in the illusions of hope. It is natural to realise the help there is and to alter the time to take. It is natural and bold to hesitate and learn.

It is not a perfect coffee. That is an ingredient.

Red curtains keep out the light when they are painting the shutters.

A step on the stair. Asleep on the chair, oh the wicked hammer.

Your brother-in-law is still mad.

Pages.

They get smaller down there. He has to do it better than that. Now Bobby don't complain any more.

Be careful they don't drop anything on you.

I understand perfectly what she means.

Hope in the center hope where they must. Careful reason. Mary made tea. The ladies were asked to sit down. It is not approachable. We had a very magnificent dinner. Breakfast and the weather was so bad we returned Tuesday. Then we said trembling that cold meat were of different sorts.

Mary made tea. The ladies were asked to sit down. It is not approachable. We had a very magnificent dinner. Breakfast and the weather was so bad we returned Tuesday. Then we said trembling that cold meat were of different sorts.

Mary made tea. The ladies were asked to sit down.

Sunday evening when the house was full love to all.

I am available at a moment's notice. I went to the opening yesterday. I saw that they had not hurried by going past. Many of them. Many of them. To be in the reduced state of individual fortunes and population makes every possible exertion to encourage when I will have the pleasure of seeing you. It is always funny the remarks I have been able to make in these extraordinary times. So funny. How did he hear it, how did he hear it how did he hear it. He produced his certificate and I forgot to ask I forgot to ask if his son succeeded in leaving every Wednesday and if he particularly pleased four posts.

Where can I get that in any other country. If I could do any good I am not sure that I would not have attempted it.

To say what.

Only three little girls.

A second son about twelve years old. He was as young a one. It was very very hot.

Three little girls did not leave the room until one. They laughed.

Last Friday at five o'clock I was between both, the eldest and the youngest so my grandmother spoke and told me to take her arm and however she forgot it. He forgot it. Afterwards there were three whose names I do not recollect. They are both very nice girls and so he did.

There were four. Surprise perhaps your surprise perhaps I have declined, perhaps I am kind, perhaps my disposition is naturally cheerful, perhaps a frame would be a mistake, perhaps it is a support under these impressions perhaps it is a suggestion and a spark perhaps I distinguish a husband, perhaps awful and impressive scenes are a disappointment to the dear good mind which is too unhinged to say more. Both are very surprising. To forget them and let them to be begin stating that I am sharing immense plumes of ostrich feathers. It is very pleasant and we were home about three o'clock.

I thought you'd be pleased with it.

They spotted the gloves that were drying. They come so unexpectedly at you with their green painting. Green paint is bright brighter than cement.

The machine doesn't work well. Say it in English. You are such a bad letterwriter.

The tenor won't use his voice. He will use his breath. He is even and then his brother spoke to him and gave him a stone. That was all ready.

The circle page, why do you eat, why have they eaten, stamps are stored and two five and to one and two sucks, two sucking, it is nice work. It is nice work pleasantly presently and then there are peculiar stuffs which are replaced. We were disappointed. That isn't what you call a good transition then.

No I won't hang your things up. Yes I will hang your things

up. My idea of rose is that it is as fine as an artificial one and then surpasses it. This was before they were at dinner. Planning a cream made her choose apricots.

Did the smoke always come out on this side.

This begins with a very careful description and it ends with an exchange between being helped and more letters.

You flatter me my obliging friend. I am almost thankful to the liveliness of your interesting restraint and also the belief in the frivolity of miscellaneous discourse. You smell roses very well and literally and you have a cherished dog and you are dear to me and it is best that that which might have been dull and heavy continues to remain relinquished. It might be better that all the failure cannot be so perfectly significant and that affections are in general prepared prepared to call long drawings. There are no insignificancies in selecting pale distresses and even still there is cause to be offended.

Yet all is not as I wish. I wish to remember more certainly that the world's estimation results results in certain restless baking and a sentence so deliberately pronounced has likenesses. I must not give cheerfully their names and titles.

Roger James is dead. He received many gifts and some were given to his wife now a widow and the arrangements have all been made that by the existence of more the rest are sold. Suppose it could be done that an offer which was made was not released by a part being not discharged. This did not happen yesterday. It was a baby's idea.

Discharged. To be discharged does not mean obedience.

She was not at home at night. When a hall-way is ornamented there is no use in registering more letters than are reasonable. No no one thinks so.

I'll use soap and have something for you in the morning. Bring me a fig and apple please.

I thought it was going to be an apple again.

It makes me so nervous.

You'll ask her around.

Water pipes.

Hot water-pipes change in putting feet where they were.

Fortunately this actual shirring was marbled all through with plaid color. Fortunately this actual marveling was arranged by teeth.

Ornamental wish.

Fish fussing.

Thrust in her foot was asleep.

Do sleep nicely and don't wake up till ten. It is settled by way of the sixth. I do not look like the same girl. This is one of them.

Speech fading ink color yellow. How will it wear.

Plans of green trees, this made greens.

He came often delighted.

Mustn't exchange glances.

Madame Guyon is neglected and passing carefully. She expected to reply to an exclamation and she was accredited because of powder. They mistook her suddenly. Oh dear.

We mustn't forget Mary Helen Bobbie. We'd like to see it wouldn't we.

Let us talk about composition. Composition is not called in place of quantity. Composition is there when all the little and the big bowls are painted white and neglected for colored roses. They are not neglected. They are never neglected. They are handsomely attached to reading pages surrounded with black cloth. More than that. More than that. To begin with a land mirror, to begin with a discussion. The one with blue and circles, the one with blue and circles and oil and measure, measuring not motion.

Bending is the same as walking, it makes cows, old cows and black goats which were beautiful. Now we know that cows are cows.

We are splendid and yellow all yellow where it is.

I want to see one of them burn. It would have been cheaper to come by train. I am going up at any rate to try.

As Miss wishes. If you wish. She was over eighty years old when she was writing the thing. Did I interrupt you at lunch time just then. She has the same interest in massing pleasant facts.

History development and cultivation of roses, would you expect it to be roses.

Wasps.

Do you see how I put it. That might be learning mightn't it.

William J. Jenny, a lady's experiences in eighteen eighty three.
  You don't want that lady's book.
  Our friends the Rivett Carnacs have gone somewhere again.
  Who is Ernest Lamb.
  I make remarks.
  I didn't know then I was going to not make up my mind to.
There was that honest denial. It's very good though just the same.
I can change it. Last grass. Doctor Claribel is coming to-night.
Will you keep still. Shut up. I will dress right away. Neatly. A
revolving life is a sad sad life a revolving life to mention. I think
she has a history and you too Miss Polly.
  How do they spell their name.
  What's it say about us.
  Teasing isn't sweet.
  We'd tell her we couldn't do it.
  His wife and sister inside. He was on the outside.
  Whenever you want to speak you know just speak. I don't
congratulate myself.
  Everybody's manners if you like Harriet.
  It would make him more beautiful than anybody else. I didn't
say that. They named children after their own children who had
died. They did not use nicknames. The confusion was enormous.
There was the father and two sons.
  I did it purposely.
  Is it cold for you I mean.
  To cover the sin.
  Isn't it a pretty name.
  I know an awful lot.
  They're square and her feet aren't square of course.
  About an inch and completely vacant.
  Hare soup and roast duck and green peas and celery and
cheese and raspberry tarts.
  Well come nearer I'll say some this afternoon for you.
  That's what I wanted.
  He said he collided.
  I was sad that is I was angry I was not pleased at the neglect
of little bilious pearls. I hoped for draperies, hoped for draperies.
  If when they are soled and chattering is inherited and spoiled

internally spoiled and childlike childlike possessed, no not knot again. Amiable stepping.

Inspired by Claribel's portrait.

What's the use of portraiture, to tranquilise your mind.

That gives esteem too much importance.

No chocolates till to-morrow.

I visited your post a telegraph. I did not search a long I did not search along respect and attention, I feel not dissatisfied and there are times when soberly agreeable people are daughters. These with myself go to amusement.

Not quite so pleasant as an experienced heart building when a connection has become necessary between a house which is not separated and a room which is needed. The bath is near and some people during the last winter had both their sons.

I have smiled gravely and in practising a train of ideas have been so engrossed with neglect and attention that I may not devote friends to the welfare of another. This made me buy two pets. I will think that there could be no occasion for such small value and letters have not appeared to suggest correspondence, they neglected to mention relations. I passed two weeks in my own house and you will admit that I did not discourage advice. The coals can fall they can realise scolding it is also that place which I first saw as an object ever too prone to be propelled. This has been gravity itself.

No gold fishes are unlucky, red fishes are unlucky.

Reasonable.

He had a time he had a ton.

Brother.

That's exaggerated melancholy.

He is serious and last like, he went to work and he was troubled and if he wasn't troubled he would leave town, he would stay away, he would complain, he does complain.

Listen.

I like little pinks.

He has offered the Austrians.

Although I am yours affectionately I gather that I give my best love and believe me I am much obliged to you.

It is not necessary that I cannot tell you, I cannot tell you and you can say God bless you and being born you are better. Better than the end of the week.

I hope you will call upon me.

I said the same I said that I didn't care whether there was paper or oil-cloth or a stair carpet, I said the same I said that if I said I saw here I shall be sorry to lose the poor Americans. They are mentioned in the letter and even when absent they are it cannot be urged that they are improper. It does hours a great deal of harm. God bless you and believe him that he is very uneasy.

What did I say I said that it was too bad that he was tall, I said he looked as if he was more lame than he had been and that he would mention that he was grander. I said that I could change to Thursday. Then I said that same thing. Then another thing. It was not mentioned and I caused the reply to show that in any case a little beard does cause the hair to fall out. She said that the cat had forgotten and she preferred dogs and that she did not go out enough to choose a library. This was all said by me and then there was a description of a leaf which had not been noticed. It was not replaced.

Can a couch have springs.

All the time that he sat he said he was thirsty that was because it had happened that a little basket it wasn't a basket had been taken and not for shoes, the shoes were to be resumed.

Classes.

A whole basketful of snails. The idea had been to have a whole basketful of snails.

Will you sit by a fire.

And now she gave him Jessie.

I made that.

Almost.

Do you think polite french people if they think that a man is not going to bring something that is promised would they make their sentence saying that he was to bring it so that it would not state that he would forget if he did not bring it. Do you think they would be anxious to be careless.

Is it right.

What do you think.

What do you think, I think color pleases.

If you want to meet Neville Cook give him a card.

There.

No I won't eat to-night.

Emotion and consolation and winter patience and realising, realisation.

No there is no use in talking line, line is achieved it is drawn and not thusly sacrificed by length. Oh to please us.

Oh to please us.

I was tired to be frightened. I was tired to be frightened.

He was a principle to me.

To speak of the baby, she was by nearly to the stairs and if there was a waste anyway there would be there was a waste. That's what happened.

He does explain plaque of chance. A pleading wing.

That's it.

She was right, she was right when she went she slept badly she slept very well, she ate an apple she hid the pin she was right, she would settle it, she was right.

Now I know why.

He said it liked better than all that and he said all that was in the changing hen, he said he saw and all the laps were there binding a weather study together by.

Was that right.

He said. He said.

No wonder they laugh at me I am so loved.

He doesn't look like Woodrow Wilson.

I am going up.

Down.

Its better than lard.

You feel for him.

I wonder if any one who ever told me anything told me that.

I am going to stay in bed all day.

I regret the recollected papers.

It will be pursued by water a little water which is not wetter by smell. She says I am thin and beautiful this year. I am employing the Scotch dialect to which I am not accustomed. In building a vestibule I have come to the satisfaction that in elegance and intention there is immediate delay. He said a pretty will. Perhaps it will do good. He saw that there was cement. He saw the cement and he suffered he suffered reasonably.

Let us arrange about the workingman. We must know what we think. It is necessary to know what I think. I think splendidly.

There there read that he is shameless that he is polite. Read the letter.

I saw Gibson go on a dressing table. He was not dancing. What is dancing. It is this it is the contrast of materials and this means that wool and after all does one not include gold thread and silk and stitching it readily. It is not annoying.

Cousin in peace.

Cousin and niece, persons, leaders, letters, announcement, standing up certainly.

Dear Madam.

It will give me great pleasure to invite him and to neglect nothing in anticipating an arrangement and in really mentioning the sound of a broken visit.

Three red books, they are not the same, one is larger, the other is not larger, and the one that has been mentioned is not satisfactory that is to say a certain part of it which is the part that is heavily worded is not sociable and completely selected makes no change. It is so stern. He is so stern, and this is not mentioned by delay, and who has a little wall paper, who has a little wall paper.

I looked all through the samples and I was tired and there was a thunder-storm and there were trays and I wanted an umbrella stand and I did not say so, I said I would think about it and I would ask the price of a black and white rug and then I decided that it would be grey and that I wanted it white and black and then I did not leave out the only piece of white glass, not white glass natural glass and then it was too late, six o'clock was too late.

No. No No No No, not again, again, sheltered pumps, he wouldn't swim, he wouldn't swim, cup, cups, cups life, cups life supper.

We just chat.

He caught her lame and he told her slightly. He was wealthy.

He was pleased with indicating a rose wood dressing table. They are not used now.

In summer.

I am going to visit gently.

The hammer.

One result alas of the arrested visit to the place is materialising in an earnest appeal to stay certainly. Certainly what.

I gather pencils in a place and I seize knives and I open doors and I ask a carpenter to close that is to diminish wooden places. I really cannot be selfish.

We have decided to use cheaper matches in the kitchen.

Cheaper matches for the kitchen.

Would she mind finishing a dress. I don't think she would mind if she was finishing a dress. If she finished the beginning. In any way. Indeed there is. Indeed anyway.

We saw a house. It was like a ground. It had sashes and a large hall and it was so pleasant. We did not want it.

We wanted a glass curtain. We wanted to see where we went in and we saw birds and fishes and we did say that about flowers.

I don't like it.

I hope that there will be convenient ways of having it taken away.

I expect that it would have been polite.

Oh so.

Waves and waves and waves.

It was last month.

She cooks prettily.

Able to state examples.

Able to state circumstances.

Able to state, went away.

A regular a regular fire ajar.

He is the very best worker.

And now gentlemen let us have peace let us be earnest let us realise that there is to be music, let us gather more roses and let us guess which comes when it is announced. Which is it. Is it stockings, is it leather, is it good for bags, is there a door open. Answer everything and decline to be deceived, do not disagree if there is need to repeat say the same thing. This is the way to begin the clock striking.

Do not ask about six o'clock. Do not purchase a home. Do not be pleasant and then have to decide when there is to be a fire. Don't interfere, don't leave the room. Don't dismiss a servant. Have a place for a correct message. She came.

Very close.

I heard to-day that the next day next day. Was to be. I invented a man.

He was so sweet.

Singing a pin seldom a pin save it for a mysterious sun-shine. I cannot.

Helen was told to.

I am not perfectly acquainted.

I enjoyed this. I enjoyed that.

That pronounced.

Call it a lamb call it an unpronounceable residence call it peacefully, call it with stretches call it with withered seldom all butter joy. Call it any way to be preserved and near. Obey it in leisure and earn and earn nevertheless gentleman.

Strange. It is strange. Is it.

I wonder why next next is.

Is it is it not a person.

Is it because of present answers. Is there no ready cake.

I meant to be wishing.

And would you.

I can see the medal I can see why he did not mention it, I can see why he did please to keep away and to let little pieces float and in the last moment there was a little girl and she acted in amazement.

I can easily see how nobody can be tall. It is arranged with faces by faces.

It is sentimental.

All but a chat.

I hope to paint I hope to be painted I hope that he will paint. I love her I suffer.

Irrigating peas enveloping clouds arranging studies divesting furnaces recounting ounces originating plans burning trays, a nuisance. When were there amiable winter nellies. I know there isn't. Do say many do come to a fitting some day I will be so pleased.

She is deaf to all.

You don't often say things three times.

Able to state reluctance.

I do not repeat boxes.

And he had such a sad face.

I would rather than a blue cape.

Let us.

If he said instantaneous.

He saw it.

He saw it.

It was a sandwich and in it came slenderly, it was a sandwich and it in came Amy Linker. It was a match box and in it came red matches with yellow ends. I don't like big boxes.

Bestir.

You know six can't come.

Jane came Jane came Jane came Jane came. He said it was printed.

I wish to say I wish to stay that she used to be behind the open window and she was leaping she was leaping out widely and she made a kind of cup so that you could drink sugar without chocolate. Every morning they said that and besides she measured six inches.

It was a surprise to know that I knew her and I said it, I said that day and why should little apple cores be laid all over the table and forks and everything.

Tender message.

He was invited to sit a day. If we had known that Wednesday was Thursday. If you shave a beard where it is then how can you expect white how can you not expect white hair.

I did I shall do I shall restrain and leave light and meet Mrs. Eisner. I shall meet Mrs. Eisner and another.

Pudding pudding.

To come back to speech. Indolence, special heights always to bless, white sponges and little capes, it was so dear to me.

She wore a low cut dress and gloves all evening.

Say something more.

They possess grace or beauty and in most instances are under-sized.

Its never an exclamation it is only to cover.

Where.

By potatoes.

Ladle please.

Go bust.

The way they know how to ring a bell believe me. How can she remember.

She doesn't remember in other words.

This is to prove the fitting and consequently permanent one.

Gertrude's greetings to you.

It was most amusing.

A little place and it's quite bare in spite of keeping up certain trains.

It happened to us.

We went many many years ago and one of them married on account of stage fright.

My careful darning of stockings sometimes I am reminded of the bath tubs and hot water but let it imagine I will look up the quite extraordinary way they have of how kind of every one always is to me.

A boiler attached to a hot water faucet any hour of the day is generally this use of them, there is a great deal caused by repairs and painting.

It does seem as if next week eight hours however seems to agree with me.

That's what surprised me.

I see.

I remember do you know I remember being surprised.

Do you know I like it I was getting to be important and I liked.

Do you know, I liked it.

Recently I met everybody I saw them all and I declare I met everybody.

I met a man, he acted queerly, I saw how it was, I spent some money. I didn't mean to guess.

Everywhere can be to-morrow.

A cat sat.

Please wipe away.

She didn't seem to mind it she didn't say it she didn't say she didn't seem to mind.

Please save the brush.

I looked and was pleased I looked and was pleased I looked and was pleased.

Walking in the electric light and turning off the light and looking at the electric light and leaving the electric light I stay upstairs. I do not like to change shoes. I do not like to change shoes for what. I do like the roses. She bought them with olives.

I didn't think that I could explain sentences. I did think I could explain sentences. I didn't think I could make references. I didn't think I could leave out recurrences. I didn't think that I was brilliant.

I did answer places plenty of places where there was warm weather naturally hot and I did go home that is to say I did not believe in points not more points.

Mr. McBryde.

It is natural to indulge in the illusions of hope. We are apt to shut our eyes to that siren until she allures us to our death. Is it that we are among the number of those who see not and who hear not the best that leads us to salvation shall we be among the number of those who having ears hear not and having eyes see not the things that lead us to salvation.

It is strange that a little dance is prepared.

She did get herself big earrings.

Last.

All day.

Last all day.

I may be careless about wearing my clothes the first time.

That isn't what we want at all.

I am surprised that you don't know which.

Eight seven eight pages.

That would be a natural joke to change it to wouldn't it.

I have very little doubt that it will excite considerable attention and lead many persons into a wholesome train of thought.

Isn't there anything that pleases you in it.

I always think that something else would have been so much better.

Now I wish to be quiet and easy and respectful.

Daniel should take his comforts away.

It shouldn't be.

Irving thereupon thought but did not take the advice of Sir Walter Scott.

Yes of course green is tender.

Do you think that's it.

Why does he say that he is not going to go.

I am pleased.

We went to dinner and saw a dog and we lent him to a man, we sat with them and they said they would and they had beside them then that thing that they were mentioning. This is what gave me the idea.

It will make a very charming sitting room.

With nothing around my neck do you mean.

Just to air this out a little bit.

I think it was very sweet I don't know what it was I think it was very sweet that Constance had a maid of honor's house.

Ousted.

I don't think you need to read the introduction.

Any little apple.

Do you mind.

I don't care for it.

There is something you get frequently.

Do you mind.

A whiff of plaster.

I don't care for it.

You were inquisitive and gracious.

You wouldn't expect her to go out of her way to hunt it up from just having seen a review.

Excellent exclamation in resenting contradiction with niceness.

They both said he was a robber.

Did he say we shouldn't have made a fire yet.

The room is so beautiful now.

I know why the knife handles are cloudy she rubs them on the thing after she has washed them to clean them and she holds them hard in her hand.

I guess that's it alright.

She has no little pleasures.

You ask if she was mad with such alarm. You don't ask if we were mad.

You don't ask if I was mad.

Was she mad.

Force myself yes force myself yes.

Do you think you could get a better one.

What would we do with a better one.

Turn a little at the top.

Sewing it really sewing it.

Carlock wants a centimeter or two of extra plaster.

She'll leave us before then.

I'll decide what I'll decide soon.

Do you remember when Juno invented a kind of handwriting.

That's right you shouldn't have.

Let sleeping dogs lie down.

For a gentle quiet person to sit down on it.

She said it was too thin I said it held my weight.

Is she disappointed.

We refused grandma that is to say she asked it.

Please consider conscientiousness.

I knew it.

He's awful.

I am afraid it hasn't done you any good.

I am indifferent.

Do you.

I learn that tremendous rectification places a coarse towel in shares. He does make money out of heels. He follows into before them. He neglects circles. He does not he does not he does not sneeze. Let us encircle let us encircle graciously. I am so pleased with cloth.

I've got one upstairs, I must tell them before six o'clock to be delivered to-morrow.

That's what I didn't like about getting an expensive one.

Have we clean sheets to-night.

Yes it's Tuesday.

I am eating a piece of cracker.

Ginger snap in the cool of the evening.

It doesn't seem a very difficult thing to put up.

How do they do it.

I am going to have a bath to-morrow.

Mary Rose is in a cow.

Lessons.

Not a selfish play.

Look here the trouble with Mary Rose is just this she is individual she looks like a fox terrier. She is terribly heavy and it is an occasion.

Mercy on us.

I don't care if the rose colored line is straight.

I do care if the rose colored line is straight.

My sister said that they knew you.

She read it straight and she read it late and she read it in debate yesterday.

I think that it would not be desirable for me to have pictures by scholars instead of by masters.

The other is all finished except the neck.

Please catch it catch it water.

You old idiot shut up.

Why is nervousness please.

Please why.

Bury the great tomato, keep the strawberries, eat the cake with paper, leave the meat, measure out the milk, arrange for the radishes regulate the little bags of fried slices and with all prepare the rain and the sun and the roses, not the roses because of the little dog, the little dog ate one. He shuddered. It was a priest that is to say they were sisters and she frowned she did not frown by mistake she moved the chair. He came in to ask if he might smile and this was received by all of them so that he was a false lilac very likely. I cannot do it. The Campbells are coming.

One two three one two three one two three one two three I never talk.

I discovered remarkably.

He kissed her hand and he kissed her hand and he kissed her hand and he bowed and she bowed with her head and he said I am indifferent and she said narrow and he said for us there is no difference and she said I cannot say that the thing is longer than it was I can only say that there are dark spaces and he said oil mounts it mounts more than oil.

I wish I could honestly say that I am hopeful of the hotel, I wish I could say that the sun fatigues my eyes I wish I could honestly say that it is distressing I wish I could honestly say that there is an upstairs and a downstairs I wish I could remember numbers.

If you want to clamber and sing with delight you want to have grey hair turning white and then lose a watch and then find a memorandum and then have multitudes of red curtains and then in an agreeable moment go to London. What is it darling. Nothing dearie.

You won't look at larkspur and you ask strange questions.

Feathers.

Ostrich feathers.

Please don't.

Do you want your slippers I'll get them for you.

Easily.

It was sweet to make Jenny detest tea.

Oughtn't you to mention all the examples.

Please eat lunch.

I am disappointed Saturday.

No.

We said we were extremely patient.

We asked Daniel not to mix, he put in white, we asked Henry not to leave he learned to eat we did not ask Nettie to be polite we asked Michael to rest often we asked it by delaying the pointing we met with a pipe for the hot water we asked William to please see a nail we asked him to observe closely we asked him to detain the ceiling we asked him to arrange being ready we asked him to follow any molding. Then there was a likely politic soberness, it was ever doubtful when there was beside hay in the house. Oh cannot you say perfect. Cannot you please. I please. Can you please walk. Can you please walk behind. Come at once. Chamber music. Dr. Claribel invited us. I don't want to put in any reference to the best way to relieve actual and premeditated and perhaps debatable want I wish only to refer to the fact that in every way that there can be reliance there is naturally meaning and clearly there was change, there had been polished glass there had been unpolished glass that is granulated glass and it was a surprise when the change took place and they all came Sunday. Workman. To see a difference between workman and brooms and vacuum cleaning that is to say sparrows makes one incline to purchase revolving currants, strawberries are finished that is to say they come high and we were lucky to preserve them we preserved raspberries, we did not preserve gooseberries, we will when we find that the glasses have the right shallowness and depth and width and feet, and this has been not ordered one could not say that they have been ordered one could not say ordered one can say that they have been asked that they have been suggested that a model has been given that they have been appointed that the expectation has not only been denied but it has been even suggested that the model should be lost and not copied. Oh why cannot one be restless. Suppose a little lead falls off and there is a hammer there and then there is an explanation. Hardly any one can be so careful. Hardly any one is more resolved. Hardly any one.

Dear old Mildred dear old she. She is sweet for liberty. It is delightful of her to be fifty-three.

The box is turned away to say wavering painstaking eyelashes. She did have it bitten. Poor dear puppy. It is not a puppy, it is a dog it has hanging not from it.

I know the name of a place in a car. I cease to care for a piece of a car I cease to please cutting I never shade a dog. I make a place to leave steps I make an arrangement and I mind the best tea. I like it strong I do not neglect to eat, I refuse I don't know why. I spend the summer cheerfully I shall be back again I shall not please myself more. I see praises.

Do come. Do do come.

I am coming, I hope I am coming. What a lovely place. I do wish I had been hot. I do like it so much. I do see what you mean.

There I can't make it rice. It was eggs, it was peas.

It excites me.

May I have your permission not to mention it beside that. Yes certainly.

Do you fatten it. Do you fasten it. How splendid.

Which when I told her.

Two were as much delighted with my dancing as if I were their own daughter.

Earnestness.

Are you in earnest. These were my younger sister.

Five little bananas.

Bathe Mary.

I bring it to her and she was sure she knew when she did know when Miss S. said so.

Our little sausage looks like a mutton. Its name is mutton or button.

Come Claribel come to tea come often pointing out places and coats.

That was a knife and fork.

The mingling ages checks chimes and a hair washing not four thought and he said there was never a deposit shall he cluster not the tie.

Why close place.

A chicken roasting and a gave stove pose. Rose leaning turn, I didn't think it would do it. I didn't know it was that shape. Always. Incredible, sound. Not a spot. She had a ring. I respect you Frederick.

I see I have a trained eye I do microscopic work.

You are here to tell them what I tell you to tell them.

The other silver adds to the weight on the top.

During the day I covered up this red don't you know

She says Fred believes they're all honest.

Do you like it. (Yes I do.)

Put down do you like it.

That I always said wasn't.

I am proud that I said it distinctly.

I have been planning it several minutes.

A station where there is she says he is honest.

If there are bills and there are stretches and there is a scarf and there is return a young man waiting says that he will talk together and there is a use in saying instantly.

She said it is a trouble to me to do all this.

I began adding I tried to arrange to spend the afternoon seeing pictures and I spent all of it in correcting mistakes. I have noticed it and it is so.

No I know.

To begin the same form and measure a no I didn't. That was why I asked her and she said he had given her that which he had and she had that which he did not breathe and always hesitating not that. Isn't it wonderful how I never said I said it.

Three f[e]athers.

He had a turn to have it. He was not ancient fishes. Red fishes bring misfortune.

I don't marry.

I can a column.

No use in dressing in delving. That is not it vacation.

To have scarlet fever or fall from a precipice to have to have astonishment kept him silent. She had a good set of teeth. to recommend her. I thought it proper that he had.

To preserve a fortune for seven children caused much telling. I saw tears starting according to his ideas that I should go where I pleased.

My daughters should write to me. I should not like to mention my mother's surprise at my extreme tranquillity.

One above the other and the edges meeting and the hooks sticking out and I only felt really that it was contempt.

I asked him suddenly what was his opinion of me.

I told him that I was a most lovely person.

My brother or both filled the newspapers.

She listened with sympathy to sorrows.

Oil on the surface of water rose like oil on the surface of the water.

I may say respect.

Only, Forty-three.

No.

She was dressed in grey.

I sailed with my child and a very beautiful horse.

She was a sensible and determined woman having previously decided to change her name and having announced her politeness not obligingly.

I blushed with anger and surprise she thought with anger only.

She herself gave a situation to an only person and to forget the charms of my society.

You are running away an hour a day almost to me.

The service which was choral was conducted by the Reverend Francis McClellan.

He thought it would be a good idea to make them of wood. Go on. He saw two pieces of Spanish wood and my sister said that those two were very good ones. Of course it makes ventilation or you forget that.

It is a beautiful thing it is a wonderful thing. Now we are going to have the same thing every day.

Darkness.

One day there was a sun. I got up early that morning and I heard that there was a threat a threat of what a threat of not pushing electricity. Then I decided to leave and to see what there was present. Two little carved wood which were column and then Miss Mars. She looked so beseeching and beside that she was rosy. Not rosy enough to swim. She was not meant to swim. A saddle blanket was hung in the window. Beside that there were two shawls.

In a white wall there are nails of the nails there are pins and pins have excellent blue safe stretches. What is a weight. It is a splendid Scotch lead tube.

When I came to arrange the pictures I found that I made an arrangement which necessitated my leaving a whole row two whole rows not leaving three whole rows I left three whole rows. Somebody smiled.

A hot day means it.

Who planted geraniums.

I'll put the Silbermann check in the top drawer here.

Nice must pins.

Can our beautiful hats be put there.

Excuse me.

If I try this thing on and if I don't I don't see how I am going to do it now.

You want to be very because I am going to. You are not sneezing yet are you.

Papers of clocks.

He uses a lot of names.

As Harriet would say they love it.

Is flesh advisable.

Who planted geraniums.

I held his hand and called him Harry.

A wonderful time goes with it if I have two three five six seven eight nine eleven thirteen eighteen seventeen things to do.

A woman eighty three saved a boy from drowning.

I am sure it can't be lost. I will. It doesn't signify.

If I wanted to complain I would say that I asked to have it thick and it was thin. I asked to have it thick.

Did she mention the hose.

The nomenclature likes one but doesn't keep it going.

Please leave me. You mean she can't remember.

Leave off snow.

Where is the mantle piece.

I am sure I didn't.

Notably that.

One should leave out papers.

Never bless her I love her little golden heart.

Wire door. Self contained mats. Coats of oak. Noisy weights. Copper canes. Lean on them. I happen to be rather fond of Grace in a way.

Sleep late to state river beds.

I can't imagine where.

Stephen Ink. I was convinced that I wanted him and we wrote and they said yes. They had one and he was older and he would leave out a sentence. It was a Remington sentence.

She reminds me of the queen of Chinatown in the state and moreover I was not expecting it.

One might so easily not.

Extraordinary pansies.

Something to put some flowers in any jug not a glass something that's small.

With injury to their persons at that time.

Clare ate.

Camilla.

Camilla Brewster.

The nice one with the good hat.

Gertrude says the ladies are more wonderful than the roses.

doesn't mind the rain as it gives her a chance to catch up her correspondence.

In honor of the movement.

Row seas.

Yes.

Yes.

I'm going to bring a book can't I.

Cold heavy furred.

Yes yes.

Who is a raving beauty and my delight.

A weeder a wire a well sung clinger a representation of Henry the eighth.

Didn't you know it was the sun.

John Stanley.

She was she was wiping her face. She needed toothings.

Not a word.

I have become wedding.

I don't speak it I don't speak it.

The difference isn't enough to talk about it.

Please drive slowly through Ely.

All cock.

We've entirely lost the tremendous little round figures.

You'll allow for the sun.

Up goods train.

Very very very very.

If you wake up get dressed.

You're your grandmother's daughter.
Any colored queen.
Do not.
Very colored queen.
Patches of miserable release.
All the courses are fine.
She does mean charming.
Not good.
Good Stabling.
Letting spice.
Harriet Wright.
They're the sheep.
They are not so special as the ones with the black heads are
they.
Able to stand splendidly.
It is.
Beware of wet tar.
Faster.
Do you always make notes in churches.
Paula Hope.
I love you Nellie Nelly is your name.
Hope Paula.
There is a house that was burned down.
Have you had a delightful drive.
What that apparently.
You subtracted it and told me.
Tired of green peas.
Paula is just ready.
Suggestions for thanksgiving and prayer.
Things I don't see.
Choir and congregation outing.
Framers of the circumscribed silver pot.
You make a mistake which is a serious mistake to make.
You spread the change and you do outwardly essentially
reason because of it. Let me explain here. To be utterly soundless
is an emergency.
Shall she explain styling coarse print.
Erasmus Herbert Erasmus Herbert Erasmus Herbert.

Oh can you do I can hesitate. Oh I can do I can suffering. Radical sobriety.

Neat scenes. Oh how can you be pearly.

Pouncing strains.

What I find and I mean to raise special reasonable recollections what I ought to refer to is when there has been not a deal of pleasure not a selected prison. This is all my shame. I must ask you not to mention my mother.

Oh Paula Paula.

She came in while I was asleep.

Did she come in while I was asleep.

This is most interesting.

Rich and married Griffiths.

I had a good time but I'd never want to come again.

There are some things a girl can't do.

Is she doing morris dancing no its only gloves.

With red roses in a side car.

It would be.

It's the ugliest town we've seen yet.

My father is a martyr and is unkind to me.

If you have more pounds than I have it doesn't matter they don't belong to you.

Let us extravagantly misuse destiny.

How did she happen to know Brummer.

I used to say that I saw placed to purchase I used to say that it was a pleasure to manage matters, I used to say that I particularly desired better progress I used to say that I would change purses.

Then came the period when they liked London better. This was the reason that they talked about. They did talk.

It was an exceedingly great pleasure to pass any one and in a safe way there was hesitation.

Suppose Jack and Jack went up the hill would it make any difference in translation would it not show that there was a universal and that is a good thought had there not been admirable violence. This is so perfectly referred to.

A very unjust affair.

It was not often that she went upstairs.

In spite of many things to do here the rest and quiet of the country and garden have done us a world of good.

They look so astonishingly unlike so special and individual with no attempt at being anything but just what they happen to be. Very good that. He showed us all about the pictures he did like. It has been too interesting for words. As you will remember we came here Saturday afternoon. She has a very curious story. She was the youngest child and only daughter of a family so that late in life but still many years ago she married for money. Yesterday we had a long day in charming small towns. She plays Herrick for our amusement. She is amusing but uninteresting I think. Meeting him and hearing from him at the same time was a coincidence. A loving Alice. But as there are words which are impolite in themselves just as words and actions are impolite she forbore to indulge in them. Everybody who is cured rests a great deal. We all want to be happy. I suppose and we do what we think will make us so. Do you think Aunt Maggie will like going. She has her garden there hasn't she. I didn't mean to tell you I meant just to say that I thought I had better go away. He was delighted to find what he was looking for. I think it would be a good thing if some old woman would tell a story. We always do I think instinctively individualise somehow.

It's more important to write to Mike first. Do you want me to write now.

Oh have you.

Friday street Friday street Friday street Friday street Friday street Friday street Friday street.

You think her eyes go in.

I think I like this.

I think great window street would be nicer.

Put this away darling.

Pleasant Bertie's own brother.

Seven Walpole street until last Thursday.

That does take away a little bit. You know it does say in down stairs.

Claire's making me do it there is a secret in some vain way.

Exotic nursey or exotic nursery.

Angel remains of a Brooklyn bridge.

Flannel Flannel.

There is a pleasure in a sound secret. There is humming in asphalt. There is restraint in searching. There is bold chalk meadows in actual places. There is spools of splendid relation. What is I see the safety of all the working classes.

What is a book. A book is easily set and not lightly and not beyond not further than most apples not a cherry tart. I don't want to believe father. I ask them not to come back again without having been to theatre.

Why do I live in Knightsbridge. Because I have never heard any metal music that I seize. Because I see it clearly. Because I start to-morrow. Because I remain pressed. Because I color busses. Because I come soon.

I'll make up three by myself. The first is that I respect muster. The rest is that I mention the purchase of yellow pansies. The other is that it is a restless boil.

That's against it if it's a restless boil dear love.

I mean to be balked.

Isn't it funny isn't it funny.

I'll be alone in January.

He's almost spiritual.

You don't like not to.

Will you please give me some small paper.

She believed herself to be french.

Pencils turn in the center.

If you push why you push pettishly.

He said he was so received by one who being a regular corrector of learning and pleasure makes misery stop dotting.

She said she was not sorry.

Poor little aged restitution.

He was glad that he had been able to receive loyally, it mattered that there was peace, it was horribly extraordinary that resources should be left to be located it was by going it was by being gone it was by gone.

I am disappointed.

I recognise it because I do admire him so much.

Bride cake roast ice cream leaves goats splendid noon to-day for soaked every day by day for the peculiar and not for in all or sunday.

Not a success I say not a success.

I say special recollections and feathers and left tall hats and when I tell you where to go what do you keep running around for. When I told you where to go. This is a success this is though a success. She walked up and down and had a movement. She wrote letters to her father. She mended some silk stockings. She went out and asked them to think about it. She pushed her eye that way. She was prepared to receive letters. She arranged her scissors and she did not ask that more china should be be bought. She asked for addresses.

She was not pleased when I asked her to show it to me so that I could use it in doing what I was doing. She said it was on her mind.

If your meaning is that you would go if it said that some train was convenient if your meaning was that and if there was no mention then of verbs would you feel that there came to be not anything ridiculous of course that hadn't been used.

Mr. Kennerly, it is natural to resume and therein express that while two distinct sisters have pleased have been pleased to release us from a train that it was to be expected that the time would be mentioned. It is said to be finish. My baby will be disappointed.

Did you say yes.

Cherish it as a gift from you to mamma. Cherish it is the right thing.

And now to me that's enough you think.

Just like my baby she was about fifty, two years old.

When her mother dies she quotes in the first letter she writes that her mother dressed her up I fancy and all.

She was very sensible in her judgment though in a kind of a way.

It would carry anything.

You could care to put into it.

It wouldn't do.

I think I'd like that better.

Not really that better.

I won't bother.

I like a piece of wood with black covering. That makes it so.

That clock must be very nearly right I mean it must be slow. Tell it to me perhaps I might.

I like it waving.

I am ready for a long one.

You just put me out each time. It's enough. One two. These two.

I can't tell you which. Now I don't know.

I know what I wanted out of that thing, soap out of that hand. How many books are you returning Cora.

They certainly ought to.

We'll finish it and then we'll get two new ones and then we'll come back you see.

You don't need to put that down.

I don't like it changed.

Fruit and vegetable department.

She led a happy life with her cousins the Lockwoods and their friends and many merry parties and picnics were enjoyed.

That's like us. Do you think they copied us.

You can't tell about provisions down there.

I forgive you little one.

That doesn't start you worrying does it.

But they are perhaps sweetest of all to a girl who has been led forth by habit and by nature to seek them.

Kindly kindly in the immeasurable majesties of pressure kindly in the intricacies of clearing kindly in the various number of stinging cardboards kindly in measure, leaning makes two armies, they are meaning traits.

She isn't though.

The self absorption which was to become her marked characteristic was noticeable even at his children's party.

No I'd be punctilious.

Gertrude wouldn't like to be the general staff. They won't let that go out.

There's another sentence I can't end but its about the wise this time it's about twice.

I'll write you and let you know if I don't come back, thanks so much.

She has inherited her father's exactness from his science.

I don't want to see pudding.

Just a second.

I said that I thought a walk would do us both good.

I understand extra.

I wished to learn if they were bites.

I was not possibly pleased.

I mentioned furniture.

I took a chance to clear off the chair. I meant to be careful. I nearly approached heat. I was not pained.

Now then.

When leaving a chair and liking a particular standing fire and not kneeling and using heels, when some some day with windows stream into bed, vital cake, vital candy.

A covering. I heard conversation.

It said Wales.

Well when it did and answer and mutton much mutton when it did and ever and alike watches.

They came to wear them ahead.

Not at all.

I am not going to use ten again I am not in the best gratification.

Poor dear waiter germ in waiter.

It's more like a comb for Inky than a crown for Inky. It is a comb for Inky.

So much gentler and just a minute.

Do you see what they are doing with post cards allowed to be sent by the soldiers.

Isn't that wonderful.

The last time I went I gathered yellow hair buttons and now I mean to ask for anything else now I mean to decline white cuff-buttons. I mean not to prefer yellow I mean. I mean.

Are you anxious.

Are you anxious.

So much gentler word just a minute.

On one occasion indeed the dog saved her from drowning

she had not seen the incoming tide and she collected straw hats splendidly.

But whether in morning or evening attire she selected real hair and jewelry, she purposely delayed everything.

She was invariably extremely annoyed.

She was equally accustomed to others at that time.

He was unmarried.

It is diverting.

She is so young and she is very beautiful. Do you think splendidly. I like it so much. I mean to varnish often. I do mean to please mother. I shall spend many days together. I shall part with anything. Extra. Beside pleasing, there is mother. A mother and no pleasure.

They were such honest nice people.

I believe that he going to be of use.

Her voice too was monotonous and I was disappointed.

To your surprise no less than to mine I am still here.

For now there is no one else who can write english.

I don't think men meant to educate me. I don't think certainly I don't think that notwithstanding the practice of more consequences great writers require costlier payments. This serves also to illustrate her own opinion of herself. It is the more correct way to address a woman of eminence. Likeness makes literary culture the vast and versatile knowledge of the color of different lands.

Planning an arrangement of saucers and leaving it firm and friendly and arranging a sandy dressing table and making it tall and mercilessly screening corals mercilessly screening corals ends flatly.

I saw I saw well.

Angry but tall.

To be sent by others.

I must take care of Eric.

Raising and rolling.

Clean.

I miss finding I miss shining.

Look here, splendid is rather recent splendid is rather recent.

What I mean to tell you is that certainly there is a last present

when serving is by fifteen and marriages are a little wet. I don't
sing. I cannot sing. I have a restless color.

What you like.

A piece of line.

With startling audacity he has in many cases called them by
their real names.

It is very terrible.

A rose is a marguerite is a poppy what's the matter with you.

You should go to the left do you always forget.

Oh don't confuse me.

Collect.

That's very nice.

Shan't you swim.

No eye glasses.

I had one.

Thunder.

Yes I am afraid so.

Perhaps the old ones revived in walking.

Yes I must confess to a great deal of perspiration.

Is that alright.

Candy is cheaper than cake.

I have greatly weakened my head and my memory.

I must admit that her method has been admirable.

I was about four and a half years old.

I was ready to be kind to him and crying bitterly this made me
remove this impression from my mind that did not please me at all
and I remind little pictures and washing a little glass that there
is an observation.

I confess I am frightened.

She was often unkind to me and she could never get on with
my grandmother who was very sensible and rather a slender old
lady and very likely gentle and sensible so that they may know.
I cannot help wishing others.

They gave this stupid advice.

She did not look alarmed.

As my grandmother loved me very dearly I hardly left her.

A year day by day.

She joked with him about the tender things he said to her.

As he was a very honest man he had not extraordinary force when he smiled.

Your mother is here.

Nonsense.

Your mother is here might I believe that.

Ever since the half of yesterday I passed that way. It is really singular.

Doesn't matter.

I can shoot I can shoot very skillfully.

I like to sit where it is.

I like to sit.

When an utter blister seizes in between then cloth is a kind of waywardness.

Not bold.

Then this is internal.

Say it he said and she said it.

I'm not normal.

After apologising for what he had done and the sorrow he felt to see my grandmother in that state he retired.

He approached my grandmother to tell her of her danger and he the poor man was so touched that he said very little.

Finally she was promised what she wanted.

I confess however that I was trembling and I meant to reassure mother, I did grieve on the eve of her departure and I mechanically set about going farther.

It will be a living picture of ingratitude.

I was trembling because my mother had never loved me and I circled about and I made a promise and I did lessen birds I showed the whole perturbation and believe me.

I don't mind settling pleasures, I really don't ask anything better. I do please and I am enchanted by news.

She was.

She was hurried.

She hurried.

One book two taken two taken together.

I am pleased to hear you relieve me please relieve me.

I am delighted with that.

You know you mustn't.

Please mention me.

I am delighted with that.

You know you mustn't.

Please mention me.

Where he usually spent the winter amusing himself.

My mother was enchanted with the news she was regulated by that she she entreated her to allow her to come and she meant to mention it beside and nearly and by way of a different way.

Nothing from her friendship.

Nothing.

It had to be.

He has always wanted to go at present.

Dress to bring back and wash.

Raw apples don't agree with me.

Leading language has gotten to be neglected by some others.

Please promise me to stay and if you do if you will I will not be strange.

I plan a morning and I mean to.

No not that, not that mistake.

No not that mistake.

I am very pleased with myself yesterday.

I have never before lost two umbrellas in one week. I generally cannot.

Not expect I do not expect. I do not expect.

Oh silver.

Not a tall which not at all whatever. Which is painful.

Which is painful.

Clearer even that attaches.

Buy a lot.

I don't mean to be singular. I don't prepare dredges. I don't see why there are oats. I don't plead mustaches. I don't select chairs. I don't reasonably shadow anywhere, I don't place much and where is it in winding where is it beside a plate. Oranges are painful. They are so interior. Not only because I mind, but because I do mind all of it. I do prepare to state that single old plums are eaten together and I am very sensible of the differences.

You are not an american my dear.

SHORT PIECES

LETTERS AND PARCELS AND WOOL

1916

MISS CRUTTWELL

1917

WHY ARE THERE WHITES TO CONSOLE
A History in Three Parts

1922

Dear Sir. Will you tell me if you have English needles. I do not care to wait as the air here is not very pleasant and besides it's dark. Do turn on the light. Thanks so much. I am waiting. I wish I could remember a Palman street. It is a thing that certainly sometime has had tall people in it. The tallest one was very large. He asked the price of linen by meter. Hand made it is 20 dollars a meter. He was satisfied with the answer. I remember a Malloracen. He is thin that is to say his beard is black and not very heavy and he is a little grey. He certainly sells women who work and little girls and there is no wool. Wool is higher. It costs one franc more this summer. I have no hard thoughts about wool. Wool is black.

I wish to tell you about everything. In the first place the women are capable of embroidering. They sit to do this. We are well satisfied and pleased. Do say you know the address of a door maker. It is so important to have carpets. The doors fit so well. Do please close the door. Do be friendly. What is a niece. A niece is fatter and fatter. I am not satisfied with a letter. Not at all. Not what I intended. Not at all what I intended.

I wish to remind Helene that she must be careful of fire. Everybody is careful of fire. Besides that she must knit. She must make stockings with designs. I address this letter to her.

Dear Miss Genevieve. It gives me great pleasure to thank you for the stockings you have so kindly knitted for me. I appreciate very much their resemblance to lace work. I believe that I will have pleasure in wearing them when I am at home. If you desire me to wear them sooner I am willing to please you. I like stockings knitted. It is an art that had it not been for the war would not have come under my attention. I understand that the work of your pupil is more than creditable. It is delicate. Of this I am speaking.

I sign myself
Constantly your advisor
Constance G. Birthday.

It is easy to decide about wool. The thing we asked for

originally was natural wool. This is stiff.

Dear Sir. Have you something strong in the way of thread that can be used to string beads made of some precious stones. Can you recommend to me a material that will not give me uneasiness that will be certain not to have an accident. I would be very grateful if you would send me a sample of such thread or silk.

We do not want silk we want another thread a thread that will be strong that is strong.

Please give me the different sized beads. Please let me look at a little table. Please do not bother me. Please do not bother about my hair. I know just the kind of needles I want. I want french knitting needles. I am so worried about that wish.

Dear Sir. I am enjoying my fire very much. We will need wood again. Please send it not chopped up. We want big pieces and long. We were not delighted. However we have enjoyed our fire. When we leave we will leave our dog. We hope he will have a comfortable home.

Dear Sir. It is getting very late. I am not careful to address you or your brother.

Goodnight.

Sincerely yours

Henry.

Dear Sir. I always say what I think about roses. I also send word that I like my bills sealed. I might call them accounts. I do not wish to send anything back. Thank you for giving me information about a dressmaker. We are enthusiastic and awaiting warmer weather. It is very cold to night.

Sincerely yours

Gerald Moore.

I like these letters. Dear Sir. When I see you I wish to ask do you care to take with you the things I have given you. I hope you do not feel hurt that I have not wanted them. Thank you so much. We will speak of it another time.

Helen.

Dear Mrs. Herbert. We understand that you said fox terrier. You did not mean a bull. We had understood that it was an Eng-

lish bull. It would amuse us very much if it were a fox terrier.
We hope that you can be certain. We hope to see you very soon.

Dear Miss Herbert. You will come with your mother. Yes.
We will hope that your brother is younger. He is isn't he. He
looked younger. We hope that the weather will not detain you.

Letters.

In the beginning we meant to have everything. Now we want
more and more. We have it in the degree in which we address
you. We address you to-day.

Dear Sir. I wish I could write your name correctly. I hope you
are not annoyed with me. You might very easily be. We have
splendid shooting here. We did not use it. We cannot ask you
to join us. We continue to address our letters.

Sincerely yours
Jenny Thompson.

Dear Sir. Will you have a dish. You can let us know and we
will do our best to satisfy you.

Henry and Herman.

Dear Sir. Why do you not send us something. We would
like it. We would be sure to and yet the daily paper on Sunday.
No I thank you.

Mrs. Hendy.

Dear John. We were not pleased with the wood. The wood
on top was olive wood. We are not severe. We say we wish it
heavy. We wish it to be heavy. We are not going to ask you.
Thanks so much. You have been very kind. We are pleased to
hear about you. Answer me again.

Sincerely yours
Henry.

Dear Louise. Would you rather have a handkerchief or some
fruit. We are thinking of sending you something for Christmas.
We have decided not to send you fruit. We think we will send
you some table linen. They embroider it very prettily down
here. We will not decide to-night. I am not sending off this letter
at once.

Yours
Herbert Brook.

Dear Sister. I am happy. I have splendid brothers and plenty
of glass ware. They are never broken. Little pieces come off and
we put it away. Remember me kindly.

May-Belle.

Do you often think of me.

Dear Mrs. Penfield. I do not know how to mention it but I
do not believe you know my name. It is awkward but I have
not a card. As it happened I did not have enough with me and
I have not been able to send for more. I will write my name on
a piece of paper. You will remember to take it.

Sincerely yours
Henrietta Guilbert.

Do not mention leaning.

Dear Chris. You have forgotten to take the furniture polish.
It is needed as the servant is to do the polishing and she has not
the recipe for it and so she can not make it. You will attend to
it. You are very obliging. Alright. It will look like satin. It ought
to. There are many days probably almost a week that she can
give to polishing. Do not forget to buy ribbon.

Always yours
Margaret Dawson.

There is plenty of time to move in. You can mean anything
by that but what is the use of explaining. He will be careful.

Certainly sir.

Dear. Do not let that young man come again.

Yes sir.

Do not let the young man come in. Explain to him that we
are not at home to receive any one.

My dear sir. I expostulate and it does me no good. I receive
gifts and it is not necessary. I refuse them and many people are
courteous. Do you understand that. I do. It means that noises are
not made by the very cautious. I hear noises.

Yes sir.

Dear John. If you were a woman you would be a servant.
You would lie you do lie. You would be a soldier. You could be
a soldier if you would. There is no one in your family. The
mother is very painstaking she changes easily. Do not forget to

be there altogether. I know you are succeeding very well.

Your sister

Lucy.

I wish you all the compliments of the season. How goes it.

Yours

Gwendoline.

Have you heard of imitated handwriting. It can be done in embroidery. Thank you for mentioning that you enjoyed receiving the books and everything. We enjoyed sending everything. We are very happy. We think of you continually. We hope you will write often. We are certain that you enjoy swimming. It is too cold now. Goodnight.

Gwendoline.

Dear Sir. Do not trouble to come on Sunday.

Yesterday was a holiday. It was a day marked by a procession.

Sincerely yours

Henry Klein.

To my sister. I am coming to see that power real power comes from the part of withdrawal. that necessitates choosing an image. My image is in my wording.

So it is.

Dear Sir. Let me go home. I am very comfortable there. I have very valuable goats. I do not care for them but they are a source of income.

So they are.

I regret that we do not supply you with the milk.

I do not like the taste.

Oh yes.

Sincerely yours.

Herbert Grey.

Father and mother we do not address them that way.

Does the son want to marry.

Dear Sir. Do not come again. We are not interested in furniture. We intend to sell ours when we leave.

Sincerely yours and best wishes for the new year.

Henry Arthur.

Yes sir.

My dear friend. We will be glad to come again. We find your servant interesting. She explained to us what you are.

We hope to see you soon. Happy new year but we will surely see you before then.

Wishing to be kindly remembered to Mrs. Dartmoor I remain very sincerely yours.

Gladys Gold.

Do you or do you not dream.

Sir. The next time of our meeting will be arranged for. We have no need to be anxious. Leave me in peace and place your trust in reasonable excesses. Do not be nervous and say to me yes we are together. So we are. Thank you so much.

Yours

Constance.

Yes sir I write in English.

Dear dear friend. I received the package and I have tried to fix my tooth myself. It succeeded very well and now I am not satisfied.

I hope you are and that everything in your home is giving you satisfaction. You know you were not pleased with the electricity. It is really excusable on Christmas eve but not again. We are all agreed to that.

Always

Augustine.

Dear Sir. It is splendid they make so many mistakes. I cannot tell why I am happy but I am and very content. The reason that I am content is that I am so pleased with the winter. I thought it would be colder. It was for a time.

Remain strong and we will continue to be satisfied. No one can tell you how much I appreciate your kind wishes.

Maybelle.

Did she marry him.

Her name was Claire.

How did she spell it.

As I write it.

Does she.

Yes.

Doesn't everybody.

Oh no.

Dear Sir.

Remember me to Hermione.

Always
Arthur.

I cannot express to you the great pleasure there was in reading to you. I often read to you and I find that your interruptions act as a stimulus and the result is that I find it extremely difficult to realise my fatigue. You can understand. Surely it is not necessary to explain it further. You are very careful and so am I. Indeed there can be no greater pleasure than that which we enjoy.

Adelaide.

Dear Lee. I might say when this you see remember me but I do not mean it so. I wish you to forget all impertinence and justification all relief and excitement and I wish you to seem to attach yourself to generalisation. I do not mean by that that I despise generalship or even a finer phase that of calculation but do be easy in your mind connect everything with observation and do be worthy of identification. Do be worthy of it. We seen and then we are supplanted. Do not be terror-stricken.

Thank you.

Yours with realisation
Bertha Cistern.

Do be rich sir.

Yes sir.

Why do you go into that room sir.

Because to-day is Sunday.

Indeed yes to-day is Sunday.

May I have permission to leave.

Yes.

I will go to various places.

I did not hear you.

Dear Sir. When you made a mistake about the initial you did not correct very promptly. I suppose it was due to the holidays. I hope I may have the handkerchief at once.

Yes it's quite ready.

When will you have the other things ready.

My father was to explain that it would be impossible to carry out the order.

But you will do it.

Yes we will do it.

Your father agrees.

Yes he agrees.

Yes.

Very well.

Good afternoon.

Good morning.

Dear Mrs. Herbert. Why will you not come and spend the day with us.

But we will.

Yes indeed.

Good night.

Yes indeed I remember the exact wording.

When this you see remember me.

Or

Let me be lost in the street.

Dear Sir. It is extraordinary that there should be such a difference of opinion about the use of the words on and in. We have often had discussions. After all it is a matter of usage. One can change. One can believe the South Pole to be warm.

Thank you so much.

Yours

Daniel.

Why do you change. We do not change rapidly.

Yes indeed I have been bitten.

When did you meet Mrs. Baker.

We met this morning.

Dear Mrs. Baker. You truly wish to sell your furniture, pottery. You are quite sure you will not regret it. I cannot undertake anything at present that of course you understand nor will I do anything in the matter in the future. I understand that you like arms and ivory and have some examples. They are really the sort of things that are least fitting in a country where arms have a value. To-day there is no temptation to believe in the past. The past is beautiful to us. Is it prominent to-day. We are all pains-taking. We feel that we have failed in returning your visit. Do not be angry with your brother. Say that we have a common language.

Always very sincerely yours
Herbert Baker.

I understand that you are eager to see me.
Yes I am.
Would you like to come Saturday.
I would.
Would you prefer another day.
I don't think so.
Dear Mrs. Gilbert. We are very pleased when you tell us that you do not know that age is impervious to discipline. We are also pleased when you declare that there are hopes that all the time there are hopes of winning. We enjoy feasting and we please ourselves with thunder. Do not stare. Expect our decision. We are indeed critical.

Thank you so much.

Evelyn.

Dear Sir now I have a subject I can answer about a book. It is a large book well illustrated and not dedicated. It is given to me. I have asked them for lunch. Will they notice it what. That I said how do you spell your name. Of course they will have noticed it. It doesn't make any difference. Not to-day. Very well.

Goodnight.
Katherine.

Why is a name Katherine used in visiting. Visiting whom. Visiting the saints. But it isn't. Why of course it is.

Dear friends. We are sorry that you are detained.

Jane.

Yes Mike.
Dear Mike. Did you know that the Marquis of Claremont was arrested for insulting soldiers. Of course you did you must have read it in the papers. Do you remember his name. I cannot recall

the circumstance but Mark tells him that he does and we were sure that you would know all about it. I need not tell you how much we depend on your memory.

Dear Mike say that again and let me see if I can say it. Historical.

Millicent Cranery.

Millicent did not mean historical. She is ambitious.

Dear Myrtle. Why cannot you say what I say. We just chat.

Henry.

A letter to-day.

Dear friends. Come to-day.

Sebastian.

Why do you say a word.

I don't want it so soon.

To-night I have left a note. To-night I have not left a note.

Dear Sir. Will they come again. We were pleased to see them but we do not want to see them again.

Signed
Wellfed.

Dear Sir. It is strange all the time. The women are not strange all the time. Words fail me. Do be careful to hear it. Say I was told to go. Keep away Sunday.

Herbert Gilbert.

I did not know it was a woman.

Did you.

Do not say yes sir.

My dear Eveline. Why did you come at all. Why didn't you decide upon a hotel. You know how very comfortable the hotel by the station is. I don't mean it as a place to live in but a number of people stay there. Do they like it. I think they do.

Yours hurriedly
Ruth Fletcher.

What is the name.

Dear friends. Are you still pleased with me. Would you prefer walking. I have the habit of doing as I like. Not always you say. No not always.

Thanking you so much and beautifully
We are indeed interested
Henrietta Pearl Woods.

Do you remember that name. Yes I do.

Dear Sir. What do you mean by repeating.

I mean that there is an advertisement there are advertisements
that repeat.
Gustave Woods.

The woods the poor man's overcoat.

A new letter.

Can you pronounce it after me.

The woods.

Dear Sir. It would please me if you would let me have the
use of your pen until Sunday. Mine has been broken and can be
fixed. I know you are not using yours.
John Paul.

You do like my interruptions.

Of course I like your interruptions.

Dear Sir. I do use the same words.
Philip.

Who is Philip.

Dear Sir. Come together. You mean mixed up.

No don't anger me. I mean among as if it were a palm.

Oh yes.
Cecilia.

You are robust.

Dear Sir. I wish you would learn swimming.
Henry Somerset.

MISS CRUTTWELL

Because we liked it. We had splendid Egyptians and they did
lose a thousand pounds a year.

I am not going to speak of them again.
Page 2.

Letting a bishop be killed.

All speaking the language.

Page 3.

Accredited to San Sebastian.

Ellen will not go.

Listen to me. We have come here to think and read about China. Some people like glass. We do too. We also like wax candles.

I promise you that it is not a mistake.

Page 4.

She gave birth to a child. Great joy. The one thing I can't understand is recognition. To thank her prettily. I thanked her prettily. We liked the wishing.

Page 5.

A long history of being angry. We were angry with her because she said if he had been twenty years younger. She was accredited to San Sebastian. A great many people like watering places.

Page 6.

Pounds and chapters. Listen to me.

Page 7.

Crying.

Page 8.

Crying, why do you see me.

You can't see me you know.

Page 9.

Laugh again.

PART 2.

Eclipsing by feeling.

Page 1.

Kindness. It is a great kindness. It is a great kindness.

Page 2.

What were brothers. I have no interest in nephews. They are killed.

Page 3.

Deceive me, deceive me and deceive me.

We want to know another.

I have splendid peaches. You mean in paper. In paper and cotton. Yes I see no need of wool and silk. Silk is oriental.

Page 4.

I do not wish to think about friends.

Page 5.
Page 6.

We saw her to-day.

Page 7.

Can you please roses.
Can you sleep at all.

Page 8.

We have seen Madame Marval.

PART 3.

Page one.

Recollections crowd upon us. We are sixty. We have said that we love a soldier. Soldiers grow young.

Page 2.

Madame Marval has seen the home of Cagliostro.

Page 3.

I do not wish to change.

PART 4.

Page 1.

Reserve green.
Plain girls.
I have known her intimate.
With her friends.

Page 2.

This is a success.
Pages.
Lewis a hat.
And clouds.
We are selected with clouds.

Page 3.

I do not exercise feeling.

Do you mean sweetly.
I do mean sweetly instantly.
Can you guess doors.

Page 4.

I do see sweetly.
Leave me crying.
I have no leaf.
A desk.
A desk and moisture.
This is the flower of my leaf.
Shall we see money.
No. Oh yes. I can assure you.

Page 5.

Congratulations. I do not mention wine. White wine is difficult to get. Health is good. Nervousness is strange.

Page 6.

Why have you wished to come again.
Words have meant houses.

Page 7.

Light and sales.

Page 8.

What can I wish. I can live to please and I can refuse succor.
I can see the selling of that word.

PART 5.

Page 1.

Tiny teams.
Glass work.
Green bottles and bread.
Healthy charms.
Saddles.
Splendid little dishes.
I cannot see poison.
Harm in floats.
No harm in floats.
Do you know what I mean to abolish.

Page 2.

I have forgotten the song. You mean her appearance. I have forgotten earrings. Yes. Oh yes.

Page 3.

Little persons are tall. Leave knives to me. You don't understand grass.

Page 4.

Now I have been mistaken. Now I am forgetting. Now I see the reason. Now I don't complain.

This is a disappointment to me.

Page 5.

Forget to see me.

Forget to see me sink.

Forget to see me hover. Forget me for that cover.

This is not a disappointment to me.

Page 6.

Do you see why I wish to have that. I see why you wish to have that.

Page 7.

Do you understand paragraphs. I understand paragraphs.

Page 8.

There are plenty of seamen but this does not interest me. Do you do you learn letters.

Please forgive me.

PART 6.

Page 1.

Recently there has been a circulation of boards. Some mean prophecies, some clothing, some soil and some glory. We believe in all. We have special branches for chaining.

Page 2.

This is a pleasant thing.

Page 3.

Varnishing, do you shine clear.

Page 4.

We do.

Page 5.

Hold pieces.
We hold pieces.

Page 6.

I do describe my mother.

Page 7.

Be happy again.

Page 8.

The pleasure is mine.

PART 7.

Page 1.

This is Saturday.
Religion and butter.

Page 2.

Whistle to be thin.
Can I whistle to be thin.
The whistle that I hear is there.

Page 3.

Remember to-day.

Page 4.

You do not refuse to remember to-day.

Page 4.

Colors are lies.

Page 5.

From the standpoint of white all color is blue. You do not
mean blue. I can fancy that.

Page 6.

From singing.

Page 7.

Can you tell me why you were startled.

Page 8.

Please remember me partly because of the interest in savages
and partly because of wishes.

PART 8.

Page 1.

Delighted.

Will we get anything out of it.

Page 2.

Delighted.

Yes you will.

Page 3.

I am so glad.

Page 4.

So are we.

Page 5.

The last time we sat together was when we were not certain about prophecy.

Page 6.

We are certain now.

Page 7.

Certain in the sense of sure.

Page 8.

I do not like these words.

Page 9.

Neither do I.

Page 10.

We are agreed.

Page 11.

Of course we are.

Beginning.

Because we liked it we asked for frustration. Do you like it. Do you like hope. We like hope. This is not as I understood you.

Page 1.

Little Russians.

Page 2.

An excuse.

Page 3.

Blighting.

Page 4.

Not blighting.

Page 5.

Vienna.

PART 2.

Page 1.

Believe in bleeding.

Page 2.

Do not believe in bleeding.

Page 3

Believe in going.

Page 4.

Not every day.

PART 3.

Page 1.

Leave her to me.

Page 2.

I am going to see the name.

Page 3.

Yes indeed.

PART 4.

Page 1.

There is no real money.

PART 5.

Page 1.

Now we come to this this state of the case.
Many steps and speeches.
Many steps and colors.
Colors are white. I can not say it too often.
You are very pleased with that. Indeed I am.

Page 2.

Little cigars.

PART 6.

Page 1.

When sisters have a dog.
I have a dog.

Page 2.

I was thinking of half sisters.

Page 3.

I am very happily here and prefer colors.
Not national colors.

Page 4.

Come to-day. I come to-day.
I do not say that splendidly.
Oh yes you do.

Page 5.

You have not been coming. No I have not been coming because I was afraid of intruding. Do not believe that. Then I will not.

Page 6.

We were disappointed in our dentist.

Page 7.

No I will not change the name.

Page 8.

Not a child.

PART 7.

Do not speak to me of wishes.
Do not speak to me of fishes.
Do not speak to me restlessly.
Do not speak to me of selections.
Do not speak to me of noises.
Do not speak to me of clearances.
Do not speak to me.

Page 2.

No that does not make them happy.

Forget it.
I do not speak of it fiercely. Not fierce and tender.

Page 3.

Let me see cheerily.

Page 4.

Yes oh yes.

Page 5.

I do not believe in South African rebellion.

Page 6.

Oh yes you do.

Page 8.

I have forgotten them.

Page 9.

Not at all
Not at all
Not at all.

Page 2.

Pilgrim glasses.
To drink
To drink.

Page 3.

I was aware of it.

Page 4.

So was I.

Second half.

Miss Gentle has left for Italy.

Page 1.

England. Oh yes.

Page 2.

A gentle word.
Ripolin.

Page 3.

A common country.
A quiet town.
Registered force.
Life of the trees.

Seen to-day.
Birds to examine.
Days.

Page 4.

A great many things missing.

Page 5.

A great many things missing. We are missing a great many things.

Page 5.

Explain to me what you wish. I wish to have Sundays for instance.

Dear me.
Do you understand.
Yes I see what you mean.
Thank you.
Believe I am not precious.
You are precious.
I don't mean it that way.
Of course you didn't.

Page 6.

Page five and page six.

Page 7.

Do you annoy me.
Spell.
I know windows.
So do I.
In Spain.
We meet then.
There
And
Here.
Do you mean that you were recalled to it by the way.
I do not.
Speak harshly.
And lean.
Do not describe me.

Page 8.

Dear me.

Calico.
Yes calico.
That is not her name for me.
That is not her name for me.
Say it again.
That is not her name.
Does he swim.
Eggs.
Yes eggs.
No to me.
Or for me.
In believing me weddings are preferred.
I will not say so again.

Page 9.

Express the lamp.
That was not a trunk.

PART 2.

Come and swing.
Not in wax.

Page 2.

Sleep do.

Page 3.

Yesterday.
Yesterday be mine.
I have coats.

Page 4.

So have I.

Page 5.

I do not care to see meat.

Page 6.

Do not you.
Do you please me.
Claribel.

Page 7.

I exchange glances.
And letters.

And praises.
And scents.
I exchange sermons
And leaves
And braids
And do not laugh.
I encourage lilacs.
Do you encourage lilacs.
I do not think so.
This is not an expression of opinion.

Page 8.

Let me leave hastily.

Page 9.

Can you wish it.
Leave busts and crimes.
I hate the word.
Italy.
Wednesday
Preparedness.
I like what we chose.
Yes Lily.

Page 10.

Correct me.

Page 11.

I have made a mistake about a book.
And furniture.
Furniture is so beautiful.
And so are moths.
Henrietta does not say so.
How kind of her.

Page 12.

We win wishes.

Page 13.

And not cloths.

Page 14.

Any time to listen.
I have the time.
To be in place.

In parlor clutches.
Oh no Mrs. Thebes.
Can you smile so kindly.

PART 3.

I believe it.
You believe it.
He believes it.
I make it.
So do I.

Page 2.

Page two is pleasant.
Pages are pages.

Page 3.

Come to me cross.

Page 4.

Not like you not to like you. I do not like americans. You
mean in english. Certainly not. Certainly not storms. I have been
afraid of storms. Nor of the heat. I like the heat. In the room. And
not on the grass.

Page 5.

Let me come again.

Page 6.

I mean to say wishes.

PART 4.

Not in merriment.
I do not like the word.
You are quite right.
We were right.
And we were right.

Page 2.

This has nothing to do with names.

Page 3.

Land Rising next time.

Page 4.

Is this land rising.

PART 5.

Please me with not with peaches.
Please me with peaches and water.
Your tastes are so simple.
I love a wife.
Do you confide this to me.
I confide priests to you.
Thank you so much.
We beat the Dutch.
Oh the complaints.
And the years.
And the plays.
And the dogs.
And more please.
And the right leg.
Do not search.
Nor stretch.
Or stretch.
Stretch away.
Stay here.
And in time.
Call me.
I believe you will.

Page 2.

Do you look to see.

Page 3.

Good night feather.

Page 4.

Yes reverberations.
I feel so sweetly.
And you are too.
Thank you for winning.

Page 5.

I hope you will be able to say so.

Page 6.

Indeed.
And in green.

And cut flowers.
To press.

Page 7.

I think there is tenderness in it.

Page 8.

I do not remember the name.

Page 9.

You mean the words.

Page 10.

We all mean the words.

Page 11.

Not Jane.

PART 6.

Of course
Of course haughtily.
We are so thoughtful.

Page 2.

Can you see splinters.
Glass splinters.

Page 3.

Quite well.
In this instance.

Page 4.

What is the name of the system.
I do not ask the question.
Nor do we.
We believe in special pictures.
We do not bow kindly.
This cannot be said to me.
We date it.
Not to-morrow.
Call us together.
And then sing.
Little leaves of Isadora. And we were never sympathetic.

Page 5.

Yes.

To think of it.

Page 6.

The wet establishes the century.

Third half.

Leave me to reason.

Page 2.

And examples.

PART 2.

Many examples are courageous.

Page 2.

I was frightened by him.

PART 3.

Dover.
It is Dover.
That is Dover.
In the middle of the part I cry.

Page 2.

Wishes.
White wishes.
All wishes are curled.
Have you that in mind.

Page 3.

Ninety times out of ten.

Page 4.

Can you be here this winter.

Page 5.

In the middle of sticking glasses.
Sticking glasses together.
This does not express them.
We used a word.
Cows.
Regular cows.

Sugar.
All sugar.
And water.
We have not reflected.

>Page 6.

Were we surprised.

>Page 7.

We were surprised at their size.

PART 4.

Plans in row.
This is not her language.

>Page 2.

In uttering swim.
These are not her words.

>Page 3.

Very likely not.

PART 5.

Does the moonlight make any difference to you.

>Page 2.

Magnetically speaking.

>Page 3.

Established masterpieces.

>Page 4.

And desks.

PART 5.

Does she sleep.

>Page 2.

Does she hear.

PART 6.

Do you mind missing water.

Page 2.
You do not understand.
Page 3.
A conference.
And an obligation.
Page 4.
Do you know the best hammer.
Page 5.
We are old.

PART 7.

She is willing to talk candles.
Page 2.
Can you not save them.
The thing
To me.
The name for a wedding.
We will never mention that word.
Page 3.
Please keep Miss Cruttwell.
Page 4.
That's the way the candles say.
Page 5.
The king of the kingdom.
Page 6.
We do not like Frank.

PART 8.

This is a boy to-day.
Page 2.
How can she be such a dull little person.
You didn't ask me that.
Page 3.
I am missing you.
Page 4.
Do not say more than that.
Page 5.
Yesterday.

Page 6.

Yesterday I went away.

Fourth half.

PART 1.

When I am sure of my wishes.
I am sure of my wishes.

Page 2.

When I am called upon to make a ring.
You have never made a ring.

Page 3.

Can you plan for me.
What would you plan.

Page 4.

I do not like anguish.

Page 5.

All of it is taught.
I see what you mean by that.
I explain what are prophecies.
We all feel that.
Can you cloud me.
I can color you.
So can I be severe.
Never to me.
I have heard you say so to me.
And I am very well pleased.

Page 6.

Let us make a part.

PART 2.

Do not worry.

Page 2.

Where are you.

Page 3.

Why do you not come back.

Page 4.
We are glad to see you.
                                    Page 5.
Explain war.

PART 2.

I hope you will not be pleased.
I do not mean this.
You know me too well to think I do.
Fly by a night.
                                    Page 2.
Set in bunches.
                                    Page 3.
Why do you sit.
Here.
Because of the window.
Yes.
                                    Page 4.
I cannot be frightened to-day.
                                    Page 5.
Capable of having two wicks in a candle.
She is not capable of having two wicks in a candle.
I can do this and cannot do this and cannot be deceived.
I can be deceived.
                                    Page 6.
Can you question exercises.
I do not believe in receding.
                                    Page 6.
Receding in breeding.
This is not the name in question.
                                    Page 7.
What can you do in sorrow.
What can you do joyfully.
What can you do in printing.
                                    Page 8.
Have a feather this summer.
Not I.

PART 4.

Capital art capital art reading.
Harriet Susan Lynch.
Plenty of time to miss Harriet.
Yes I can see furnaces.
Furnaces that heat
This is not known.

Page 2.

Collecting princesses not collecting address not collecting
princesses.

Page 3.

I do wish you would come.

PART 4.

We do not make a mistake.

Page 2.

Say that you are prepared for winter.

Page 3.

We do not want to see you.

PART 5.

Fresh water salt water salt water see.

Page 2.

And can you excuse them.

Page 3.

I can by wishing.

Page 4.

Now what do you wish.

Page 5.

I do not wish anything away.

Page 6.

I can make that clear.

Page 7.

So can we.

Page 8.

And see.

Page 9.

Do you hear me.

Page 10.

Of course I do.

PART 6.

What is the next part of part 6.
The next part is very pleasant.
I cannot expect that.
And worry.

Page 2.

Part of it is old.

Page 3.

Fasten it altogether.

PART 6.

Now comes the time when I have a luncheon. I also examine
the party. You do not know what this means, this means a play. I
do not write a play. You are complimented.

Page 2.

Can you feel that you please me.

Page 3.

Can you recognise land.
In approaching.

PART 7.

Give many instances.

Page 2.

I cannot think about feasts.

Page 3.

Neither can you about bread.

Page 4.

No indeed.

Page 5.

Butter charms me.

Page 6.

So does water.

Page 7.

And sugar.

Page 8.

I think about sugar.

Page 9.

Can you plan.

Page 10.

We can all plan.

Page 11.

And feel very much aware of hearing.

Page 12.

We can all read quickly.

Page 13.

And nothing matters.

Page 14.

You mean nothing matters to them when they are here.

Page 15.

Or there.

Page 16.

And that is exactly thought.
And I feel this and I feel no friendliness.

Page 17.

Do not believe all.

Page 18.

I do believe what is necessary.
Yes you do and you are in the right.

Page 19.

A great many exclamations.
We told each other that.
And we were disappointed.

Page 20.

Not with the advance.

Page 21.

Why should they think of sweetening.

PART 8.

When I have made a peculiar gesture and I have been careful to mention my relation to the desisting caress then I change and I ask for a sketch.

This is that joy.

Page 2.

What did you say about women.

Were you angry.

Do you mind.

Can you feel a discrimination.

Can you be harsh.

Page 3.

I can see a quick intellect and I do not use the word.

We are all so full of charm.

This is no disaster.

PART 8.

Why cannot you say you suffer.

Because it is not very necessary.

Then you believe in the necessary.

So do we when we say we have no wishes.

I do not say that when there is an end to the war.

In this we think.

I do not care for despair.

Neither do I for deceiving.

Neither do I for hope and Hindenburg.

I said it Hindenburg would leave.

Leave us

Forever

And we will be pleased that we have won.

Yes Dover.

And the sea.

And the kind of flowers that are necessary in the winter when there is butter.

Of course there is sugar.

PART 9.

Do I know the name.
Do I know the name.
Do I know the name.
Do I know the name.
Do I know the name.

PART 10.

I think I have finished.

WHY ARE THERE WHITES
TO CONSOLE

A HISTORY IN THREE PARTS

Clutch is a new word, clutch. Now remember what I said I
said I was talking to you.

Occasional plenty is fairly well expressed. She said she knew
it.

Serving in turn return to serving. I am sure that they will
not like it. And now speak.

Let us begin with their not singing. I wonder about song.

And now to remember their not meeting.

Did he claim did he claim. I said when she said restoration I
said I wanted the rest without the oration.

Did he claim them, did he claim that the third man was on
horseback and rode down too far. Did he feel that about women
and children. He felt it to be living quietly and peacefully. Nor
did he remember statuary. How do you remember. How do you
remember. This is an introduction.

Splendidly foreseen.

Now inaugurate

A satisfactory dialogue and monologue.

Do be civil to her. Do be civil to him and to her.

This is to be related to the beginning of their celebrating

what was to be accomplished. They were entirely different in their way.

Bewildering what do you mean bewildering is a word that carries no weight. I have practically sold my house.

We describe the conquest english and french english and a missionary. A missionary stays a week and the english and french come to-morrow. The missionary stays a week and the english and the french have come and are leaving to-morrow.

Gradually we know that they are examples of confession I confess to an interest in a trepidation. And so do I and so I speak of it.

They are introduced and we commence their extra edition.

Extradite extra edition.

Above above me.

Did Rose say that she meant to diffuse to diffuse hope and reluctantly retain kindness. Did Rose say did Rose say anyway you pray. Did Rose say anyway I pray to-day, did Rose say that anyway she would slowly betray, what her bowl. I know what I mean by reeking. And now eyes and arise. And in the way of separation ties.

In this way American glory in this way I say American glory does not fade away. In this way I say in this way span it I span it in this way I say in this way I plan it. How can you call her. Not, No, To Know, No, To Know, To Know, No.

Not to know.

I know that Janet and Rose, I know that Janet and Rose I know that Janet and Rose I know that Janet and Rose arise.

PART I.

Ministering.

To minister they minister I minister, a minister. A minister is plural. A great many songs are plural so are bells churches and admissions.

Now to kindly bow.

She said and she was saying come do not come do not come to rename me come do not come do come and do they come and are they carefully coming are they coming. In this way they do not recognise birds.

Now they have been told what I mean to be told that they have received eighty trees.

We do not color photographs.

When I was young I suddenly decided not to smother grass with water or oil with water not to smother oil with water or water with water. I decided not to smother oil or grass or water or any other addresses. Then the thought came would I wish and I did not wish I did not wish to recollect stepping stones to joy. I had an article presented which I felt would be the one to have fasten as an apron. Do please me with an opera apron and do marry me to gray. How often have I been delicious. How often. I do not know.

She does not say I am not returning to her, she does not say that pigeons coo. She does not admire butter-cups and yellow pansies she does not credit her own volume with voices no indeed she doesn't she establishes rows of presents. Come to stay away. Come to stay anyway.

In the past present future and arranged to come I say it with the same descent. I say it with the same good nature that characterises men of the great waters. Waters art gallery. Dismiss all thought of eloquence. Critical eloquence. How do you spell critical eloquence.

A conversation between whites.

Now to send for mustering.

Did she send.

Did she send.

Did she send

Did she send.

Whites and whites.

Why were there whites to condole to console. Why were there whites to console to condole. Why were there whites to condole to console to console to condole. Why were there whites to console to condole to condole to console. Why were there whites to condole to console to condole to console to condole. Why were there whites to console to condole. Why were there whites to condole. Why were there whites to console. Why were there whites to condole. Why were there whites to console.

If you would gather if you would rather if you had rather if you did gather, if she did not gather together a hat and now hats have not a feather if you would rather.

Conversation please.

Conversation to please.

Conversation.

They do not converse.

Conversation and please.

They do please.

If you please, every one repeats more than they said. They said each one of them said two of them said they said that they were not separated by more than a mother. Leave us to women.

Now then a regular story.

PART 2.

Janet said that she had been stung again and again by a bee and that she never neglected attending to the sting.

Rose said that she wore them and read. She said she wore them red and that was the meaning of bewildering. Who were more bewildering than bewildered and they were not bewildered then. Do not mention them altogether them.

Janet said she walked suddenly everywhere and sat here and there and sat there and she said she sat here and she walked here and there and she stood there. She did not stand everywhere. What did she say.

Rose said I said I said it anyway I said it in any way. I said it and I said I did not select the place to stay to stay away. What did you say. I did select a place that would stay. Did you select a place where they would stay did you elect to stay away. I did not select a day. No indeed.

Janet. What did you say.

Rose. What did you say, Janet.

Janet. I said I was interested in the season in their seasons in those seasons. I said I was interested in those seasons which are of more interest to them. Seasons which are of more interest are the seasons which do or do not which are or are not of interest to them.

Rose. Spell a rose.

Janet. Say how do you do passively. We pass to play.

Rose. Why do you find where do you find when do you find how do you find how have you found where have you found why have you found when have you found which have you found.

Janet. And reading apart we recently announced the winning of the harmless sample of that free example. Is there another free example. I don't interest myself in that free example.

Now attaching everything together.

Who is intended to be the one who is to indicate that one.

They indicate that one and I indicate one and they indicate one and the past we do not remember butter balls or sandwiches or velvet. Truly you don't. Indeed I don't.

PART 2 AND A QUARTER.

Two and a quarter who has bought her. Who has taught her. Who has caught her.

Who had caught her. Who had taught her. Who had bought her. Who had fought her.

Two and a quarter.

If they said they feel them. If they said they feel them and they feel if they said they feel them, who pauses.

Do you know what pauses do you know where they are do you know why they do come to prepare for themselves there where they recognise their share. They share it to-day. What can they not suggest as delay. They stay.

Two and a quarter.

To begin there was a memory of daisies. A memory of daisies did you say. There was a memory of daisies as you say. Was there a memory of poppies as you say. Was there a memory of poppies as you say. Was there a memory of poppies and daisies as you say.

I can guess and dress.

I can guess distress.

I can guess and press.

I can guess and guess.

I guess yes I guess.

I guess distress press dress distress I guess I dress I press I confess. I do not express all of my longings.

Longing any way.

Not too loose and too long.

Not longing any way.

Two make two and four make four and four make four and we enumerate.

To come back to purposes.

Purposes, a narrative.

Color.

Coat

Careless

Countess

Climate

Cut

Climb

and

Care.

Purposes. A narrative.

She knew

She knew too.

Purposes. A narrative.

She came to see

She came to see me.

Purposes. A narrative.

How can a narrative relate hairs to heads and Elizabeth to Elizabethans. How can it. How can it relate coats to hats and shoes to homes shrubs and houses. How can a narrative relate heights to shawls, ribbons to carpets and rest to cups. How can a narrative relate inches to inches and birds to veils and voices to carpets. How can a narrative relate Friday to Friday and plains to plains and saving to saving. How can a narrative relate pillows to pillows and white to white and buttons to buttons. How can a narrative relate sacks to sacks and ease to ease and meeting to meeting. How can a narrative relate recent attention.

I will trade you.

What will you trade me for.

Trade is made trades are made.

How can a narrative ratify a reason.

Pardon me. A narrative.

I was easily interested in knitting and in volumes I measured curtains and clouds and I was thoughtful when there was no necessity for shadows. I very easily meant to be a girl and I scarcely measured why I was colored. How were you colored.

We do so easily like days.

When I was free to tremble I almost suddenly mentioned napkins. Napkins are used at table by hosts guests and servants. I almost suddenly thought out places for cups. Cups may be religious. Do you remember that out of all the whole wide world they chose me. Choose me and say that you can call a colonel a general if he advances further. They plainly culminated. In this and in that capacity in my capacity and in their capacity I do not refuse recognition.

I am not one who pardons lengthily.

Pardon me. A narrative.

Seemingly they do not seem to see that I have decided to paint trees. Let us learn to paint trees. Let us learn to paint trees. He was interested. She was interested. They were interested. How were they interested. They were interested in their answers. And how was I interested I was interested in their answers. I was interested in my answers. And how was she interested. She was interested in my answers. She was interested in their answers. And how was he interested. He was interested in her answers. He was interested in their answers. He was interested in his answers and he was interested in my answers.

PURPOSES. A NARRATIVE.
SUB-TITLE QUAYS.

I can indicate ways of relieving the pressure caused by excess of silence. Can you indeed.

Now we point the way. I wish to tell you all about fooling. He fools me nicely and I am not a fool and I am not a fool and I am not a fool. A foal is a child of a horse is a child of horses. The way we can cling to humbling, they humbled men women and children by listening. They never spoke a mumbling word. They sang clearly, they spoke reluctantly, they followed alarmingly and they refused immediately. They never were open to criticism nourishment or interruption. They were not clamorous. Neither were they clamorous. Neither were they clamorous nor violated. Nor were they regionalist. To be a religionalist is often not necessary. Timmy how do you.

Agreement, a narrative.

I can plan can I plan, can I plan it.

To agree let me freshen it up.

Now place me where I am.

To agree let me be collected by it. I recollect having known my father and my mother.

I can plan can I plan can I plan it.

I can agree to the morning sun.

And where do you place.

I don't place you anywhere at all I let you alone.

I agree to recall all that I remember I agree to recall all that I can remember.

I can plan it can I plan it.

I agree that the water may seem to be fresh.

I agree you agree you do agree I agree do you agree with me. Where do you place me.

I can plan I planned it, I had a hand in it I planned it, I plan it do you undertake to mean to have me plan it. I plan it. I had a hand in planning it. I plan it. Don't you plan it.

I agree that you do see, do you see me do you see that you do see me. Where do you see me. Do you see that that is where you do see me. Do you see that you do see to seeing me. Do you plan it Janet.

Come back. A narrative.

To spend my time in the morning. When do you spend your time. To spend my time in the morning.

I have no more hesitation.

To spend my time in the morning.

Do you prepare that in that way.

To spend my time in the morning.

Come on.

There are more there are plenty more there are more than twenty more of them.

I agree to finish.

I plan it, can I plan it.

I agree to be what there is to see. I agree to see what there is to see. I agree. I agree I do agree.

PART 2 AND A HALF.

Startling reiteration.

I never startle.

Don't you startle when you hear that some one is there. Don't you startle when a chair is there. Don't you startle when you appear. Don't you appear. Don't you follow when you come in here. Don't you as you are there don't you come over here. Don't you come in here.

She answered I am able to read and to measure. And how do they measure. They measure solids with solids and liquids with liquids and pets with pets. In this way addition is easy. We add all of it.

PART 2 AND TWO THIRDS.

When they came they saw. When they came they saw and do not expect them to come and see do not expect them to come and to have have seen do not expect them to mean that they have come and seen. They came and saw.

We do not feel that when this you see you will look at that tree.

A great many people tire of more than two thirds and then immediately carry them and see them and believe them and conceive them. No one is famous for erudition.

Does he remind you of some one.

Yes of course.

PART 2.

When Saturdays come apart from you when Saturdays come and we part too when Saturdays come and we have some way to go you say so and I say so. When Saturday comes and does she say all day and every day we undertake to stay.

This is the same at the beginning. Why do you carry Harry at the beginning. Why do you carry Carrie in the beginning. Why do you carry what you do carry in the beginning. Why do you carry that in the beginning. What do you carry in the beginning.

PART 3.

Closely to a narrative, we look closely at a narrative and we narrate what we saw. We narrate what we see. We narrate what we see and we see to this.

Rose and Janet.
Expose and plan it.
Repose and fan it.
Disclose and began it.
Rose and Janet.

PART 3.

A reputation for more.

Anybody can care to come and see me.

Anybody can feel that the day is not kept away.

Anybody can say that they wish that we had all of those wishes.

Anybody can reason with themselves and repeat that they know that they can know more.

Anybody can furnish to themselves and for themselves and anybody can be satisfactorily periodical.

I know exactly what I mean by a periodical.

I suggest to them and they have suggested to them exactly what I mean by periodical. I mean by periodical a periodical and all of us can say yes.

PART 3.

No account would be one where, on no account would there not be one who was one who won and was winning. Won and was winning. Was winning and won.

One and won. She won.

This introduces the chapter which is the one which addresses one to the other and expresses, do we know about caresses. We know what echoes say.

We know what echoes are, and we know what addition is and we also know about additions and lettering and little noises. We also know how we accompanied in place of Adams. Now to question categorically.

Did she see her.

Did they repeat that.

Did she attach them.

Did they fasten this.

Did they color that.

Did they decide this.

Did they fasten that.

Did they attach that.

Did they repeat that.

Did they gather this.

Did they trouble that.

Did they gather that.

Did they replace theirs.

Did they replace that.

Did they find that.

Did they separate that.

Did they determine this

Did they double that.

Did they find this

Did they separate this

Did they determine that.

Did they double this

Did they receive that.

Categorical questions are answered by these answers.

They meant to reply.

PART 3.

Prepare to mistake means. Can this be said of Ned. Prepare to mistake means prepare a mistake. Let us see clearly. Let us clearly see that mistake means mistake. Let us clearly see that to prepare a mistake means to prepare to mistake, to prepare to mistake, to prepare a mistake. A mistake means to prepare a mistake.

Come together again.

When.

Come together then, then come together.

I do see how infidels talk. They talk with the language of dishes and daylight.

And what do you say to attachments. Attachments are made everywhere by the turn of a stair. And pleasant faces are desperate. Do please plead.

And now cover the strange stairway.

I feel that I have nearly said that bushes growing are bushes growing and they are green and they are only red when we feel like reversing. Reversibly speaking. Can you collect reversibly speaking. I did once.

I should not have concluded to attend to theirs.

PART 3.

I agree to part part three.

PART 3.

A mile a day. In this way and in that way. When I say a mile a day I mean in this way and in that way. When I say a mile a day I mean it in this way and in that way.

One way one went in that way one went a mile a day in that way.

There are two of them. The one went a mile a day in that way. That one went a mile a day in that way.

There are two of them.

One went a mile a day one went a mile a day in that way.

In going a mile a day in that way how many days are there to while away.

One went a mile a day in that way. In that way a mile a day is not prepared a mile away.

One went a mile a day in that way.

PART 3.

A pause comes when the center is sung, a pause comes when the center is rung. A pause comes at the resemblance to the decline to fall. Is dragging stationed there. If we move do we go. If they are apart do they go away together. If they are a part do they go away together. I said that a pause is made by separate estates. Are estates separated from one another necessarily. If we speak of estates do we mean adjoining. Now listen to me sing. I sing. Now listen to me. I fancy that I listen to you.

A character celebrated for the space of sentences. Sentences are not always spoken.

PART 3.

Not successful.

PART 3.

What do they say when they speak to me.
When this you see remember me.
What do they say when they speak to me.

PART 3.

Illustrate and Introduce.
Conversation and days.
In their praise.
Observe their ways.
In their praise.
I see to seeing.
Yes.
I see to seeing to them.
Yes.
Now for thought.
I walk you walk they walk we walk. I walk we walk you walk they walk.
I walk they walk you walk we walk.
I walk we walk. I walk they walk I walk we walk they walk you walk.

You walk I walk they walk we walk.
We walk
They walk
You walk
We walk.
We walk you walk they walk I walk.
And now for their thought.
And now for their thought. They thought.
I felt I dwelt in marble halls with gold and pearls beside. I felt that I dwelt in lovely halls with lovely color on lovely walls and loving words beside. I felt that I dwelt in lovely walls. I felt that I dwelt inside.

I felt that I dwelt I felt that I dwelt upon velvet and felt I felt that I dwelt that I felt I felt that I dwelt upon what I felt beside.

And you did.
To please me you did.
To please yourself you did.
I felt that I dwelt in marble halls and that I was gifted beside.
Nicely
Very nicely.

In the distance they disturbed themselves to please me. They kept their distance.

They managed to express to redress to impress and they moved about.

How astonished we are to know how they moved about. And did they finish this.

How astonished I was when I was intended to be bold. Bold do you say, walking do you say, flourishing do you say, darting do you say, attended do you say, settled do you say appointed do you say. She was astonished to know that it was to be so.

And then in that irresistible way, who walks waits wonders and remains irresistibly. Who wonders walks remains waits irresistibly. When are colors concealed. When they have been predicted. I predict that you do not intend to stay away.

And so do I.
In this way we remember little ways.
And now how are hours known as a passage.
I feel that in this instance I do declare that there are to be in

there that there are to be knots of colors. Now do you reconcile flowers with water. You understand an error and an elevation and a proceeding and necessary tastes. If I taste I feel no such anger. And if I taste do I carry a letter farther. Let me think of a and b and c. Let me think of a condition of arousing. I do not arouse the most quiet. No indeed. I miss it.

Now to replace not lace there is no lace to replace.

Now to replace.

Come and call me Janet.

Yes.

Come and call me Janet.

Yes.

When I see flowers I admire flowers.

When I see flowers I plan flowers. When I see flowers I prepare flowers. When I see flowers I recall flowers. When I see flowers. How pleasant are flowers.

How favorable are flowers to flowers.

How far are there flowers.

You see this is what interests me. I am interested in returning in returning I am interested in returning.

When I marry I say seven times seven make forty nine.

And when I address you or them when I address myself to you or to them I feel that there is not any more distance than has been described.

This does not discourage me nor should it discourage. It should encourage I encourage you and you need not prepare to go away.

Alright.

Now let us earnestly compare hair.

This has not been done.

This has been done.

You do understand preparation and money and biography.

Now let us begin as if it were to begin.

There happened to be fastened by the Credit Lyonnais more attachments than those simply in France. There is America North and South America, Europe Egypt and Algeria.

Very well.

After that there is Terre Haute and all of the Mississippi.

In this way we do arithmetic together.

Fifty fifty.

That makes a quarter a day. And all of it has no origin.

No one knows the original. It is attached printed and placed and unions have nothing to do with it.

Guess again.

I did not guess that it could be you.

You guessed that two are less than you two.

I never believe that houses are cold.

A continuation.

They never disappear.

Do they never disappear.

How are you ever to crave cake.

How are you ever to disappear hear.

How are you to disappear.

How are you to disappear.

I do ask you how are you and how are you to disappear.

I ask you and I ask you how are you to disappear here.

I have not asked you how do you do how do you disappear here.

I have not asked you.

I have asked you how do you disappear.

PART 4.

To part to depart to prepare a part, to care to cart away all ones belongings all day, to start to have a heart to prepare a part to part to start to care to part to depart. No not in this union is there no strength. No. When Rose does not say no, when Rose does not go, when Rose has a pretty gold head, what do you say to go ahead, when Rose it has been said when Rose when I arose and when you arose, arise, do not decide do not decide what is settled do not decide, do not decide. Beside why do you not decide. Why do you not decide beside.

Beside.

I know how many are left when every one has gone away, I know exactly.

You do not understand preparation.

I feel that a home is enough.

And where do I go when I go away. Do you ask me to color everything in that white way.

Of course I will not stay away. Of course I will not go away. Of course I mean to color more white in that way. Of course I do.

Does moving make miles more. How many more miles are there before there are the miles that we said furnished the landscape.

Did you ever hear me say I wished it for water and not water and winter and not winter. Did you ever hear me say that beauty is not beauty and that I do not fulfill fully. What do you fulfill. I fulfill my wishes and their wishes.

In this way we have separated moisture.

And in the eyes.

Who has eyes.

And in the eyes.

Their eyes.

And in their eyes.

To be in their eyes.

To be in the eyes.

To be in eyes.

She he and it and they said.

Led.

Eyes do not lead.

Eyes do not lead.

Her eyes have been fastened ahead.

And why can you convince me.

I cannot say all there is to say.

LAST PART.

Fattening slowly.

Who corrects whom.

A room.

A room is not noisy.

A room has no dimensions if one comes in too soon.

And in this way they apparently led the way.
I cannot tell you how fond we are of Janet.

There are no whites to console.
There are no whites to console.
There are no whites to console to console.
There are no whites to console.
She said to say we move in that way we remove in that way
we remove ourselves anyway.
Can we connect two.
Can we connect two and two.
Depend on me.
I depend upon you to do what there is to do.
And serving.
And deserving.
And accept my salutation. I salute you and I say I am not
displeased I am not pleased, I am not pleased I am not displeased I
am not I am not able to regain frontiers. In this way a particle of
the way has the necessary attendance and they stay and what do
they mean by confidence. To have confidence means that
importance their importance the importance of it is not denied.
And she was not forgotten.
Did you spend it.
And did you spend it.
Did you send it.
And did you send it.
Did you send it.
And did we send it.
We feel that it is our gift.
We feel that it is our gift.
Now the thing I would like to know is this how do you
change prepare to change and not prepare for a change. You do
not prepare.
You do not prepare and here and there.
Do you resemble here and there.
Do you resemble them here.
Do you resemble them here.

This is not merely in addition.

Why won't they.

I am doing finer and finer things all the time.

Why are there no whites to console.

She stole.

When one speaks of that, when one speaks of that where is that where is it.

When one speaks of that when one does speak of that.

She said she had the fame.

It is well that there is a flame. And blame and the same. We feel that it is our gift.

In this way we call.

I call.

You call.

You call and I call, I call to them, you call to them, they call.

All call.

Why are there no whites to console.

To condole and to console. Who knows the difference.

She was a white rose and she was a pioneer. Can a pioneer see here.

She was a white rose and she was a pioneer and they went there with a chair. This is indicated by the fact. The facts are these they please they do not say we are to stay, to please ourselves we do we do go from door to door, from the door of one room to the room, from door to door and before, before this they gave this as an instance. Instead of marrying, she was married again, instead of marrying it was understood. We understand that she chose. We understand because we choose we do not choose to have you here. Here and there, here and there yet. Do you underlet it yet. Not yet.

In this way the study of the theatre is the theatre and the study of sculpture is sculpture. And the study, they study so that they come to share what. We do not say they share. We spare this and apart from them.

To conclude.

First food.

Second stewed.

Third brood.

To conclude.

First. She needed the sea.

Second. She needed to be away from the sea.

Third. She could not be a treasure whether there was any intention whether there was or was not any intention whether she intended to be.

No one knows more of that dish. Bouillabaisse. This is made of two kinds of fish which are opposed in character, one of them being large and the other small one strong and the other very well the other was very well put in there. Then there is saffron and preparation. And what did you hear them say. I heard them say that they had had it three times.

Let me tell you how to raise dogs cats rabbits pigeons and prayers. By concluding to amass, by concluding to regret, by concluding.

And then come and delay. How can France by pants, and feathers feathered. Ingredients. How can you spare me. And how can you praise me. I praise you to the skies.

How does she praise me. She praises me to the skies.

Skies and skies. Have you skies. Have you mentioned skies. Have you meant skies. Do you mean skies. She praises me to the skies.

Have you seen how he was born. Yes indeed.

And have you seen where they blow glass.

Yes indeed.

And have you seen where they make thermometers.

Yes indeed.

I can separate myself from this thought.

I thought.

I thought that you had thought about it. You thought I had decided about it.

I did not pretend dreams. No indeed not as to singing. No indeed not as to singing. I did not pretend that I had perfect dreams. Not as to plants, no not as to plants. And there was this excuse. Near by there was a home for the aged. Never forget the Romans. They did.

What are they doing constantly.

What are they constantly doing.

Miss Janet Scudder is an example of the intention to realise that there is no road to ruin. She understands wreaths and wrath and wishes and she understands claims and counts and calls. She also understands puns and learning and reliance. And she also undertakes messages and sermons and resolutions. And she smiles and she mentions dolls and she undertakes fairs. When you undertake fairs how often have they mentioned that fairs are not pairs. They said this of New England and why do you feel exactly that and what do you feel this exactly. When you feel that you breathe breathe fairly you fairly breathe and you need you do not need to go farther. After all if the water says so can you come back. Can you come back and forth. Can you come back and forth and when you can hear a crowd you can hear that a crowd you can hear that of a crowd. Not to crowd.

On the contrary Rose why mention why suppose why do you suppose why do you not suppose how can you suppose where do you disclose what do you disclose what have you disclosed, why have you disclosed and as to repose when do you expose repose how does one expose repose where does one repose and expose repose and why do you share why do you share your hair. My hair your hair, you share I share we share you share they share we share we share hair, and they care do they care when they care do they wear what they wear do they care why they care do they marry do they carry, do they do they do they do they mean to realise markets and money, do they, do they mean to be funny do they mean to be funny and do they measure there what do they measure and where. Many many tickle you for sin. So can religions miscarry.

DIDN'T NELLY AND LILLY LOVE YOU

1922

How sweetly we are fed.
Credit me that ingratitude is instinctive.
Credit me understanding the repetition of religion.
How sweetly we are winsome.
Credit me with origin of crediting and editing and obliging
building so that we can see the same tree.
The same as the tree.

Part one.

He prepared in that way.
What did he say.
He said didn't Nelly and Lilly love you.
May we describe the dream.
We are sending the wine and bringing the poem.
Now guess stress.
Distress guess.
Florence in Italy.
Florence in the United States and Italy.
California in France.
California in France and America.
Now you know why occasionally very occasionally they
never parted.
Hear them speak.
They speak.
Fierce and tender I send her.
Didn't Nelly and Lilly love you.
She was beset.
Climb it.
Climate.
When he arose.
Was it a rose it was a rose, was it a rose he arose and he said
I know where it has led, it has led to changing a heel. We were
on a hill and he was very still, he settled to come and tell whether,
would he could he did he or should he, and would he, she wound
around the town. She wound around the town and he was
nervous. Can we ever. Can we ever, can we ever recognise the
spot.

As I have said it is an instinct, ingratitude, recognising the spot, loving her dearly, asking her to do it again and breaking her coral chain is an instinct. Didn't Nelly and Lilly love you.

Once upon a time when Poland had a capital and Washington was the capital of the United States there was born in Allegheny in the state of Pennsylvania the seventh child of a father and a mother. The father had many a brother, the mother was as a mother what would be reasonably certain to necessitate kindling not only religion but traveling. And so they traveled to what was then a capital kingdom which had in it no relation to eliminate any education unaccompanied by intoxication.

Two years old.

Three years old certainly and not weather beaten nor anxious nor reliant nor attending. He attended to the breathing. She came swinging her breathing as she came registering that as a separate suggestion.

In San Francisco in the state of California representative antagonism had not any meaning.

She came not to corrupt impeding but just to tower. How can we have a tower there. We haven't. We have extending.

I extend to you.

And do you too.

Thank you. I was there.

This was received ánd then there was not a separation but a resultant registration. I register that it was I caused it to be registered that there was a birth and a reception. I received and she I received can you see how a word could have the third part first. Two syllables. She and as for me, I said she can see, and she can see. I can see. I can see.

A division.

I was told it was cold, it was cold I was told.

Tolled for me, the whistle on the steamer, and we went by train the whistle on the steamer whistled and we went by train. She went north to Seattle and she went by train and in Seattle there is a great deal of rain. And I I went back to the petted section of France Austria and arithmetic and I always forgot the languages which are related to their view.

Can you color trees green and violets blue and I love you and salt water too. Can you color trees green and violets too and all for you.

It is the custom when there is imitation to speak the language that resembles green. It is the custom when there is tangling to color the silks the color of roses and green. It is the custom when the country is willing to leave the coloring in green and ver- milion. I often wonder about pink and about rose and about green. We knew what we felt. We felt felt. Austria made felt and I felt that the ruler, do not despise a colored ruler, I felt that no one was any cruder.

How can you control weddings. When all is said one is wedded to bed. She came and saw and seeing cried I am your bride. And I said. I understand the language. Don't Nelly and Lilly love you. Didn't Nelly and Lilly love you.

It is a coincidence, he has studied the connection between a coincidence and extermination. It was a coincidence that he moved there and that she stayed there and that they were and that he came to be there and she came not to be fair, she was darker than another, how can a sky be pale and how can a lily be so common that it makes a hedge. I do know that she never met him there and that he never knew and that she never knew, and that his father and his mother, and that her mother and her father and her brother, that neither the one nor the other one, ever regret contradiction. We never met. No we never have met. No we did not meet and was it so sweet, and was it so sweet, indeed was it sweet at all. When you don't love wind or colder weather was it sweet at all. Was it at all sweet. I feel nearly as well as ever. Better. Yes very much better. Now actually what happened was this. She was born in California and he was born in Alle- gheny, Pennsylvania. She was born and raised there but was well aware and why should she not be well aware that to declare that in the distance to declare where in the distance, she went there, when she was littler than a twin, because after all ingrati- tude is a twin, didn't Nelly and Lilly love you, she went there when she was younger than allowing for that reason. She was seven years old. There we are. She was not at home. How are you all at home.

He was at home. Where was he at home. He was at home in

his home. Thank you again and again for everything and also for the earring. They have not met that is to say, receive her. He received her. He had received. And now how radiantly do witnesses see sunshine. How radiantly do they like remarks and fencing. When you think of visiting do you really think of meeting with pleasure. I do not meet you because you are present.

I love her with an a because I say that she is not afraid. How can I tell you of the meeting. How can I tell you that she wrote, that I did not write, that we quote, I quote every body. What do I quote. She quotes this. Don't Nelly and Lilly love you. And I remember that I did say it and I deny it and I say I said. Not so quickly and I really said, What did you really say. I really said what was in my head. I am afraid that I said. Didn't Nelly and Lilly love you. What kind of circumstance was it when I said what she said that I said. It was very well said. Didn't Nelly and Lilly love you.

The circumstances were that we were talking of the relative heat of the countries which we inhabit. I inhabit a warm country. And so do I. And I inhabit a country in which the heat is so great that probably you would not care to walk about in the heat of the day. That is quite true. And you. As for me I do prefer and now I say I did prefer such heat. And now I say we will come this way. Follow me suddenly. And where do we permit ourselves to declare our fond affection. Here. And we say. I passionately may, May I say, I passionately may say, can you obey. Remember the position. Remember the attention that you pay to what I say. I cannot thrust you away. He was perfectly sure that he could endure what he would say. What did he say that day. She said, anyway I can sway with the circles in that way. We have never mentioned circles yet.

Care for me. I care for you in every possible way. Didn't Nelly and Lilly love you.

By columns, I figure by columns.

Did you hear that in the right way.

We mentioned that we had intended to meet brother by brother and brother by brother. This meant no defeat for us or for another. This meant that our future would be for ourselves alone. And so we proceeded. And on the next day I gave the list away, the list of the second day. Do please give the list of the second day. Winding and discrimination and as sister and I do not know when frivolity is acceptable as success and gold, no one knows that gold was to be sold and gold was to have been held. I hold what I have to have held.

And now the real reason why when she wrote she never mentioned me.

Godiva revisited or an excellent retaliation.

She called him a pope and she never inquired just in which way I was inspired. Didn't Nelly and Lilly love you. I addressed this question when I wondered about arms and tears. And was I ever ridiculous. I am afraid I could merit chastity. Can cedars deceive, can cedars deceive as they deceive.

I never deceive cyclamen. And why not when they are radiant. I said, this way in this way or for this anyway or because of this in their way I said can you say, I said had you said what we had said we could resume. The way to resume is to resume. Did the question ever cause confusion. No indeed her mind is clear. Cover in that place they cover in that place they cover the cyclamen in that place. Cyclamen categorically expresses reddening and re-reddening. In this way brown and coral in this way a deep voice and a credit to me. Are you a credit to me. Cause me to stir. I stir the decision. I decide to win my bride. She is my bride and more beside.

I have ceased to apply ages to ages.

And now reason about lettering.

The letter which announced her birth also announced that the forest that in the spring they had not made the excursion because he had reason to mean arranging everything. Can you be what, can you be very hot in April, the end of April the thirtieth of April for instance. Can you become heated motion by tradition by voluntary rushing. And then carry me there and reason for me. I reason for her. I have a reason for her. From then on cauliflowers cauliflowers can have mauve coloring. In warm climates where they are long and not green. Come to me for baths.

Indians are not stout nor do they shout red indians where

there are windows. She remembered the obstruction. I didn't sadly. And now where can carelessness be intentional. In that month.

Loving birthday wishes to my husband.

All that is fairest brightest and best. On this your birthday dear Husband be your guest.

Birthday greetings to my dear wife.

My darling wife may all that's good in life be yours to-day and lasting happiness be yours that shall not pass away. And as the years roll around all gladness may you find and every hour be brighter than the one you leave behind.

When they kindly met and were not meeting as it were where they had representatives when they kindly met they met to be asked will you come and see me.

She came late I state that she came late and I said what was it that I said I said I am not accustomed to wait.

We were so wifely.

She has any quantity of energy and a great deal to do.

When she came late she did not wait and I did not wait and indeed why wait. I love you. Didn't Nelly and Lilly love you.

How can I handle feathers, accompaniments, stations, astrakhan furs, arms and doves, and bitter winter. The winter is not bitter when it blows. And we know we were raised in a temperate climate. Climate and the affections, you know climate and the affections. Why can she in April have a Spanish shawl. Why can she have a Spanish shawl at all. Because I gave it to her.

We went away day before yesterday and she followed later. Who were we. She and I say we. When we went away she followed later and I met her. Did you get here. No I met her and she had lost her key. She found it again immediately. Then we were not together, we were not together whether we were there or whether we went there we went there together.

Do you remember whether we were evidently anxious to be together. Were we evidently anxious to know that a description had been left to identify why we cry.

How can I ever thank you, do you think I can ever thank, really thank and then thank.

Do you think that you are going to be true. Truly you somehow managed to impress us all. Where can we credit an Italian. Italian Italian who says Florence is Italian. Who says California is France. Who says they can hesitate to glance away. You did stay. And then didn't Nelly and Lilly love you.

Do you wish to be there at all. Didn't Nelly and Lilly love you.

Do you wish to be there at all. Mutter to me.

We came to pass there in time and she said moon-light is warmer in the summer. And I said I can explain nearly all lizards and their constipation. Lizards do not go away they stay. Real lizards do not go away they stay. Real lizards I mean colored green and living on the wall and when they make a mistake they fall. How do you very, how do you very nearly do what you do mean to do. How do you very nearly do, how do you do. We never were blaming Amelia or Eugenia nor Maddalena nor even Harriet, Carrie, Estelle Jane nor Sarah. Didn't they have hours in which to pray. What do you say, didn't they have hours in which to pray. Where did they stay. Did we stay any way. How can I mix summer with winter, this summer with this winter and this winter with that winter and that summer and that summer and this winter. And then we had a terrace there. How do you care how do you come to care here and there. Here and there I said here and there I said here and there.

Can you decline history. I have this word here, the history of a tear. He David often asked and did she make you cry. Try. This was at home this was at home she was at home, she was to be at home.

Can I remember the house where I was born. Can I remember the day that she mentioned to me. I said to her you always please me and she said to me I do not reply I expect to reply by and by and I said do you know that he said by and by is easily said and I said I certainly said I can share that and that and that. And she said, what. And I said I can share that and that and that. And she said you can share that and that and that. I said let me [be] beginning again with the neglected addresses. The first address was the one in which I addressed you as having come to this city. I said to you, how do you do. I also said do you like French bread. After that we knew that no one was present when we were able to say that we had intended to stay away. This is one way of demoralising their comfort. How comfortable is Isadora. Isadora, how comfortable is Isadora. We knew how to quote. We knew that songs are religious, we knew that quarters are one fourth of the whole and we knew that Nelly and Lilly, didn't Nelly and Lilly love you, we knew that warm and cold that warm and cold and temperate climate and the affections we knew the history of places. I place you.

Continue.

We continue as above.

We cannot consider it as at all likely that Creoles are difficult to placate. How many kinds of Creoles are there, there are Scotch Creoles, Portuguese and French and she was neither Scotch, Portuguese nor French. She was not a Creole. The wonder of it was not that she was not a Creole. The wonder of it was not that I permitted that I did permit, I did not permit, the wonder of it was not national neither was it religious neither was it personal neither was it an excrescence. The wonder of it was that I have never been willing to remember that there could be any other, any other door or doors any other chair or chairs any other and they had asked and this door does it lead to the street or does it lead to another door. Is there another door there. We felt that we dwelt in marble halls and that we had no other plans. And in Italy and in Italy they do paint marble. And in Italy they do paint in the manner of marble. Florence is in Italy and California in France. Now do not startle suddenly do not startle them suddenly.

We can meet, we can meet, we can meet them on the street. We can meet also we can also meet merrily very merrily when we are not certain of distances. The distance from there to there, all the distance from there to there. Rounder and rounder where is he around her.

I fancy, I fancy that the history of his recollection is clear. I fancy that he has been that he has often been told that it clearly that it very clearly is as the history of his recollection is, clear. He said I can spare you an occasion in which together we will meet as they meet them.

The history or histories of a birth place and traveling.

Do you remember just why you said is it to this I have been led. I have not been led away, let us say I have been led in this way. Why say what you do say. Let me tell you the history of fire works. Saint John is the patron saint of a city not named after him. They celebrate the day of his martyrdom by celebrations. We never repent, we turn our backs away we say can we say, Caesars can we say do as I say. Caesars do not turn away but stay. I put the Caesars to bed and this is what I said, I want you to do instead, instead of what, said the Caesars, instead of not doing it and this is what I said. But as I was saying the celebrating did not cease, it was necessary that I should walk and what did she say, let us wait for the day to come and I said marines and navies and she said, does no one wait there. And I said yes, and she said yes and I said oh yes. How can you collect all the advantages there are when there are a great many advantages.

We will not mention what was said when she said that she questioned me as to what I had said. I said I knew and she said you know and we said, no we are not to go. And now how about the vow. I know now that restitution and you can not declare reparation a restitution nor restitution a reparation, you can declare that you are there. There you are.

Pardon me did you say that she was born when she was born. Certainly I said something. Collect me, collect for me. Collect for me, in the same way as you recollect clearly.

The history of this is that there are that there are weddings which are placed by royalty as they are placed and weddings which are in their place by the autumn summer winter spring and February. February and April say February and April. How do you do.

Colored ribbons of notes.

No one can say of them that they decided to be wide. No one can say of them that they decided beside. No one can say of them that they decided that the bride, can they exercise their pride. A bride beside, can you say that a wedded existence can have precedence. I precede you. And now for the story.

Once upon a time there was a little boy. It was requested that he be a beauty and all that. Thank you so much.

If a railroad train is moving and another train is moving and both of them are in the station waiting why do we not have the same phenomena in a motor car. This shows us to be a receiver of flattering. She does not flatter me.

She came readily. She was weaned but before that, how very expectedly signs did not fail. Quail. Do you quail before me. I didn't.

Erect and right, and Mexico is no toy. No one knows how a toy is made.

Once more I refer to the meaning of birth and blessing. Dilatory do date what you ate and drank. The third. The first the third the first. Now do you refer to dates or ages.

Leave me to be, what, I do not leave you.

Readily made readily made, why is it readily made.

To aid, to aid to aid and an aid. She is an aid to all whom she aids. She aids me and I am sure that she has aided Lilly and Nelly.

Aid and added, to aid to be added. I am sure that she has been added to me. She has not said, mountains. Mountains exist as wholes.

Now please tell me about fishes.

Fishes, stones, shot and pebbles and not shells are dangerous to the teeth.

If fishes were wishes the ocean would be all of our desire. But they are not. We wish for land and sea and for a birthday and for cows and flowers. Our wishes have been expressed. We may say that the history of Didn't Nelly and Lilly love you is the history of wishes guessed expressed and gratified. Didn't Nelly and Lilly love you.

It happened once upon a time that there was easily marriage and a marriage relation. Can you witness a marriage. In the marriage when all the exchange is resolved upon is a marriage where cleaning can be done and ought to be done and where a bountiful providence enriches the music boxes. In relieving music there is no jealousy and yet how could twenty years after more than twenty years after be resolute. They resolved to shove. I can guess what is the price of water and more than water. Why do you mention just what was resolved. I resolve to recognise you and I do. And I resolve to read the rest of it to you. Do you please me. Oh so much.

I have resolved not to say that I agreed to their saying what I had said. And was it denied. Not at my side.

Now we will mention the wedding. If you please. Will the bride acquiesce. She could say yes and I could write many to find such a pleasant opportunity.

And now I will tell of charm. What is charm. The Americans and the Spaniards have it, and the elegance of radiography, all smile when they think that they have the world beneath them. What is the difference between under and beneath. Teeth. Teeth remain firm. Teeth remain firm. Pet me tenderly and save me from alarm. I have no sense of a pastime. Our pastime is to measure beds rather to measure beds.

Can you be fairly necessary to me. Didn't Nelly and Lilly love you. Tell me what you said.

Now I had best fasten it to the door.

Let me remember that I can not pretend to have bettered the answer. You had better give an answer. And I said can you remember that I said, I was not resolutely led. And be wise here, remember how can you have played. I remember asking you this thing, can you have played.

I remember your mentioning hours of practicing. I remember your embellishing my illustrations and I also remember coercion. Coercion and cohesion.

Have I refused to beguile. A reason for all this comes to this as an opening. I did not say didn't Nelly and Lilly love you all day. I said I have been very happy to-day. We mean to read clauses and clauses and phrases and phrases and books and books and writing and reading. We mean to smear the water over the rabbits and inundate the dry earth. The earth is not so dry. In that case we mean to say we began and we began. Come to me to the satisfaction of the garden. The public garden. We stay at home and decide that publicity is our pride. Come and stay. Hear me. Do you hear me. Come and stay. Do you hear me.

Now I wish to tell what she resembles I wish to tell this very well.

She resembles at the same time everything I have mentioned. In the historical sense there is nearly every satisfaction and and in this particular we are not deceived. I know my history.

A historical novel is one which enriches all who bore colors and stones and fires. To be fierce and tender to be warm and established, to have celebrations and to lean closely all these establish a past a present and a future. The history of establishment is a history of bliss.

Now in fighting history we find acknowledgements. I acknowledge that you are often precious.

When they began to assist when he began to assist when she began to assist, when he and she began to assist they began to assist them. He began to assist when there was mention of cleanliness and a fountain. And she, she was measured and measured. How sweetly the vowel the already eased country and city, the flooded merchants and almost all the trains established communication. I do not mention others than those that were concerned in mingling in elaborately mingling their addresses. Count on me. Oh yes and what do I see, I see public bathing places and a division. She and a servant came between, she and I never hesitated before that door, she and I cry. We did not know then that we were crying loudly. And please do not hurry to me. It took all that time and when we arranged for the time well in a manner of speaking we arranged very well for the time. We arranged that at that time that doors and then again summer we arranged at that time that suspicions were not poignant nor were objects placed. We plan what we plan. And what we planned. We smile at the bay.

There was no water there was no water there there was no water there there was no water there.

Didn't Nelly and Lilly love you and they were mentioned together. They were not in that respect remarkable and yet how did you know their name. Their name was not the same.

Didn't Nelly and Lilly love you. The occasion was radish, a radish, a red dish, in the sun, tears in the sun do not cool the cheek. Tears in the sun do not run do not run away, do not run away to be the same anyway. And now close it to close the heat out. Close it to close the heat out.

I have promised that I will not mention my iniquities. I take great pleasure in promising.

The splendid example the splendid example here the splendid

example, to be here, the splendid example in order to be here, in order that there is to be here that the example is to be here, in order that there is to be here the example in order that the splendid example is to be here, in order that the splendid example is to be here in order that it is to be here it is necessary to admit coercion. Did he kick and scream in the stream and did she dare, did she dare to respond. I respond you respond, he responds and he says yes there is a splendid example.

I find some words very annoying. Annoying is easily met. I annoy him yet. She annoys him yet. I feel that that moment is past. Now indeed there is no speed. Now indeed currents and wild horses. We have forgotten horses. Didn't Nelly and Lilly love you.

She meddled with this she meddled with this then. He did not ascertain what the wedding meant to him. He said I miss I do not miss, I do not miss, he said I do not mistake you, he said I am not mistaken, and he said I am not patiently waiting and he said hearing and everything and he said how can you mean to be beside, and he said, besides and he said I am beside myself and he said I can do as I said and he said I do do what there is to do and he said do you say that you wish to please me and he said by that time I have said that he believes that he himself has read something of a composition and he said how willing I am to wish no invention and he said I do not say dwell and spreading and he said I will find you an hour glass and she said thank you for that intention. He said that the advantage was that he had a great many ways of marking what he saw and he said I lean to you and she said I am satisfied with repetition.

How can you make weddings a wedding. How can you make of weddings a wedding.

How can you make of operas a single piece of phonetic writing. They made many reasons for individual reorganisation.

Then came the exact day. Didn't Nelly and Lilly love you.

I can tell you all about tenderness.

Now listen to me carefully.

History can rush along. And what do we do.

We agree you agree I agree and I agree. You agree we agree and I agree. I agree. You agree we agree I agree.

Now then compare glass and a violin. Compare glass and a violin.

This makes us suddenly know that I told you so.

We find that there was really no need of men and women. Sisters. What are sisters, and sisters and brothers. What are sisters and brothers. We found piles of linen and silver and a credit to men and women. And when we happily settled. And when we happily settled the south. We do not go north to go South, nor do we go to the center repeatedly. We go and we stay and we purchase we may purchase the things that are meant to be suddenly seen.

How can every day suit a queen. And how can decisions meddle easily with all the wall being divided into three parts. I can tell how you mean to say this. I can tell how you mean to say this.

First we gather together. Then we correct couples and after that we arrange medals. More often we tower.

In the meantime we make famous that which is meant to be called readable. About this we have a difference of opinion. Some select a cord and others wood and both together make a fire. We have changed our stove to a chimney and our metal to silver our pink to grey and monkeys and our yellow to assistance. Then when we were all ready we said which. And I said I wish to stay and she said I stay and they said how can you delay and we said it is better to be settled than not and we said go away and he said I can easily go on that day. We we were there we we were there we we were there and we are to be called, we are to be called the resident reader. Then come to see me. We have never changed the wording of that word. Come to see us here.

When we were able to contract we contracted for a door to a door. Thank you that was a success. And then there is every reason to be pleased with actualities. When I arouse myself I say, I did not say it in that way. And in the same ready way they say and in the same ready way they do say.

I do not repeat a title. I feel that I have thought that. Thoughts are revealed by evidence of nationality. And when this access is in process and when this process is praiseworthy, how many praises do you hear. I hear you praise me and I say thanks for yesterday and to-day. And to-morrow we do not doubt. Then clearly you see what I have never objected to and you. Can you believe my word. Arrangement, we arrange in the best way for the beginning.

It is very peculiar it is very strange that authors are visited. It it very peculiar that collections are visited. It is very strange that everybody is visited. It is very peculiar that in front of them and more often than that that in front of them they do not believe in repetition. I repeat that nearly everything is eaten cooked. Except salad. And she is very fond of that. Nearly everything has been mentioned excepting irresistible onslaught. And why do they hesitate to say that he was unnecessary yesterday and to-day. He knew when he was occasionally repeating. He knew when he was occasionally repeating this he knew when he was occasionally repeating that. Didn't Nelly and Lilly love you. We haven't seen Nelly since then. Didn't Nelly and Lilly love you. We haven't seen Lilly since then.

And now to withstand history. History has this meaning, it covers them and it uncovers them and it uncovers them and it covers them. Let me tell the history of letter paper.

We were easily deceived by our intention of illustrating a rose by a rose. We were not easily deceived. We did not deceive them nor did they deceive us nor did we deceive them. We were not betrayed nor were we unreasonable. We did indeed know that history had this meaning. We did know that happiness and remarkable happiness we did know that remarkably happiness we did know that they outdistanced double impressions. We also did know that we had not undertaken sheets and initials and also illustrations unnecessarily. We surmised that we were equally to be measured by the rose and by the table. Upon the table and upon the table we replaced no one. We added increased coloration and we added white and vermilion. Not really she said and we said, he said and we said that a rose had just this signification. How nearly we were not certain that this did happen then. By this I mean that I can not recollect the historical present yet. I cannot regret this lack of concentration nor indeed can we be represented as uncertain yet. She knows and I know where these things grow and we know what we mean to bestow. I mean to bestow and I do bestow, how do you bestow, I bestow almost all the dates. I date it to-day. To-day is the day.

I reflect that you reflect about me. I reflect what you reflect about me. I reflect about the conditions of matrimony.

If you were used to this, if you were at all used to this then what would you miss. He said I think of the standard of bliss. Standard has two meanings it can be a banner or an estimate. Standard has in this sense two meanings, I mean to express a wish.

I wish that I were seen to be in the meantime what was annexed. Reflect for me. Tell me that around about that around and about, tell me that around and about that I around and about. Satisfy me sentimentally, and now for a fetish. When I thrill along, when I drill along, soldiers drill to their song I sing of the prohibition of what of reflection. I reflect together.

I see you and you see me I reflect you and you reflect me when this you see repeat for me what I repeat when I repeat pleasantly. I repeat what I have said. What have I said.

I have mentioned that a part of reflections is the history of reflections. Let me tell you further. For instance if it had not been that there was a continuing would loving be indulged in and would there be calculation. I calculate in threes and fours and I in twenties and I in ones and twos and I in the third dimension. I calculate that a horn a motor horn I calculate that a horn is necessary to this end and now I speak above all noise.

Remember me to you.

I reflect upon the causes that there are for recognition, I recognise older ages and I recognise pillows and I recognise finishers. I also recognise curtains and weddings and I also recognise complicated wishes. What do you wish me to do.

This is the history of reflections.

It was very singular that there has never been ready the recoil from capital. A capital is a principal city and capital is possession and capital is to be very well pleased.

In this sense rapidity is certain to be measured. I rapidly measure the older addresses and he wonders do they rebuild operas. Operas are encouraged and so are beds of roses.

In the history of reflection we have ultimately and beginning we begin intimately in considering the history of reflections I have this as my authority. Almost all the changes are stereoscopic and all the emblems are multiplied. I multiply for you.

Now then press this for me.

And teach me a whim.

Let us color letters.

The history of reflections is measured by radical symbolism. And why do I astonish abruptly. Send me sentences. I send them the sentences they read in their start. We start apart.

Color me heartily and hear me specifically. And how did he know that I was enamored. Please do not finish this temporarily and why do you not say, history is this, history with us is this, the history of reflections is this. This is the history.

I mix I mix I mix what do I mix. I do not mix a bird and a bettle nor a second enough. I mix in the necessities of papers. I hear her turning leaves. And then I look up and I say how sweetly camellias may how sweetly camellias may. And now for the organisation.

The history of reflections.

I attend to them. When you see all of them being used and when you invite them when you do invite them to feel them let me relate. Do you see that you state that you translate. I translate. Naturally, I naturally relate.

The milk of religion is this, cream and orange and citron. The milk of religion is this, come to their close union. Believe my engagement.

I feel that I refer to that reflection.

I cannot organise oil.

In wondering in very nearly wondering. In very nearly wondering whether there is deliberation. She says. Yes. There is deliberation.

In wondering about rendering that there and in there. How can you practically follow me.

When this you see remember me.

By closing mountains to mounting and winning water wealthily how you utter more than they said. They said yes, I wish, come to me, say what you have said, do not be remarkable, have the suggestion made, freely be sensitive, see the occasion narrowed. Now let me tell this to her.

You know exactly what I have said what I have prayed and what I am. You know exactly for what I wish. I wish that the fish are fishes. And that a cow is a cow. I wish this and I say when in this way I pray, I pray you to do as I do. I do do as you do. In this way you reflect me. I reflect you.

When you hear me speaking creditably. When you hear me speaking creditably you find it to have the value of their stage. Now I have said I mean to be favorable.

How rarely incubation neglects thoughts.

In this way I think the same. They do not reflect birthdays. Call me too easily.

I can manage I can manage that.

I can manage to have the rest said. I say you can conceive. I say can you conceive why I stay. I say can you conceive of an invitation to-day. In this way reflections take their place.

I reflect about Abraham and about how that name came to be famous. Also how it happened sentences came to make a blessing. I bless you for all of this.

I merely do not see why he wished to remain unintelligible. Do you see why he wished to remain unintelligible. Do you understand why syllables separated in such a way that around them there was audacity. Believe me.

I cannot tie a knot in wool.

For this reason and for this reason alone I have no opposition, I have no one in opposition. For this reason and for this reason, for this reason and for this reason I do not call subjects subjects. Have they no choice, do they not choose citizens. And what can you please, how can you please where can you please. You know very well that I do remain to please. And now let me not feel that I have not said that this has lead to their frustration. I do not indelibly deter them. He said that there was that trace. Who traces them for them. I can be hourly faithful. And I do see what I have said what I have said.

I wish to remember this presently. I mention it here because I feel that it will impress. I wish to mention the practicability of housing a cow. In this way cities prosper and Caesars render that which Caesars owe. I do not say this to intimidate Caesars nor do I implore I sweetly caress and impress. Caesars do not reflect they do so well show by the daily activity how useful how tender and how strong and how a Caesar will do no wrong.

Mark me I am expressed.

Thank you very much for your kind attention.

He understands this, I understand that, I understand this, he understands this and he understands that. And then excellent dwindling.

Come to me Francis and friends.

I have developed their relative retention. Do not apply selection to respect. Respect the carpet and the floor and the door and the rest of the pleasure. I please myself too.

Come to me too.

Come to me too to-day.

Come to me and tell me what did you do yesterday.

I cannot very well elaborate the earnestness of categories. And color too.

Pardon me when I say he is not selfish.

I blend the glass and the goose. They usually do this for pleasure.

Pleasure is not partaken of because of annoyance nor houses nor is it really a saddler. We have almost forgotten a saddler.

We really admire more savings than ever. And do arouse me. Follow me fairly often. Follow me fairly separately. This is not their reflection nor indeed their relation. They relate themselves to bestowal. Please seize with ease.

An orthodox wedding is an orthodox wedding.

When you have the principal witness decorated, I cannot end there where double where they double together. Where they doubly caress. Caress tenderness. And now accustom me to counseling. I counsel you to listen and to remember that more than one that more than one that more than one. How can you furnish accentuation. Do believe me when you hear me. And now roses for camellias. Did he believe me. Prepare to emerge. I urge you. And you ought to know that willingly that you say as willingly as I am willing I need this splendid suggestion. Explain ribbons to those who wear ribbons. I do not ordinarily infer that there is more favor more in their favor that there is more in their favor. I do not ordinarily mean all this as their spectacle. To be spectacular. How do you mean. To be started in a wire. Why wire.

Eighty nine and ninety. And no less. How curious the handsome is as handsome does. How curiously it sounds.

I have always had a great many responsibilities. I am responsible for this.

Are you responsible for the shilling.

I have always had a great many responsibilities and I am responsible for everything.

And I am very willing to understand strength and resolution. I am very resolute and I admit that the selection of it has been a great pleasure to me. I have selected willing. Are you willing to remember that a cousin is in relation has relation to resemblance and restoration. I restore this to you. When you are through are you a Jew.

Don't explain restlessness.

And now save me for this.

I am earnest and prepared and there is no one to say how are you able to keep it a subject.

She has been told to be gay.

And now I reflect hurriedly and necessarily.

I reflect hurriedly and necessarily and I accustom I occasionally accustom I am accustomed to rest and rising. And in the meantime she says, she has explained that credible witnesses do say that they have decided as to relative climates.

We have often wondered why they relate this of climate. Climate and the affections. How often have I said they quote that. Climate and the affections and interruptions and can you recollect marriage. Of course you can't certainly you can't. Certainly you can not.

I have wondered about engrossing civil ceremony. Have you.

And what does nobility do.

And what does royalty do.

And what do they do.

In this way I cleverly arouse and really rally them. I can not complain in ecstasy. I said what word would best suit the expression of my appreciation. And she suggested, exquisite. I said

I considered daisy more decorative and she and I said we will say that. I'll say it.

Consider the rapidly growing water-fall. I can remember the word cascade and the word carrousel. For merry-go-round.

I have come to increasing isolated reflections by very simply asserting that at all that they come at all, that they easily come and that it is necessary that they come at all. I furnish them this in that case. I have reference to the extent of the use of that single instance.

Climate and the affections. I have often been quoted as quoting that.

Plan a repetition a general repetition a general of rivers.

We have said that we thoroughly understand that a city in order to have distinction must replace seas by rivers. Seas by rivers. We have thoroughly understood that we need houses when and where we wanted them and that we have repeatedly the pleasure of refusing. How can you be playful and precious. And how can you be so actually reached that even foreigners are famous.

We have come to come there.

And now reach this for me and hand it to me.

Thank you.

And now eagerly satisfy me.

And now pray say yes.

And now consider how unnecessary it has been.

And now tell me again what you have told me.

There there, I say, there there.

There there, an excellent pair.

I stand firmly and I say, rapidly I say he rapidly makes deference necessary.

I defer to you.

And you.

And you.

She and he, he and she, they decide it this way. They have a thousand chances in this.

Now then repeat quietly what you have said. I have said that I do not believe that I do not believe that we reflect more than they say that we reflect. I say that indeed we reflect popularity as well as authority as well as master-pieces and joy. We reflect about this, we decide alternately. We alternate between hiding and precision. Which is the more precise.

This is nice.

Which is the more precise.

How soon will you be fair.

If you are not fair to me what care I how fair you be.

This is very nice.

You understand that I undertake to perpetuate what I state.

I state this and I stare.

At a waist-line.

Can you believe that colors and colors that there are colors called to be presently called established.

And now smile at me determinedly.

I determine myself that this is not a fancy that very really and presently I will establish rows and rows of roses.

A rose is a rose is a rose is a rose.

Satisfy all the dates.

We find that dates are more delicious.

Now then call me again.

In a minute.

And now we find that a bath after breakfast.

That a bath after our breakfast. That you must breakfast. That there must be relation in religion and in civil ceremony, that all ceremony is civil. As for us we often reflect as to whether suddenness is religious or civil or perhaps both.

I think it is not at all present in absence. Because really if they were present and they were they anticipated what. Each other. I anticipate you.

Thank you for that.

Thank you more and more and merrily.

I thank you pleasantly courageously and courteously.

And now no insistence. I do not insist.

Let us converse respectfully.

I respect this in you. And you mean to allow the Atlantic to allow an Atlantic very nearly the Atlantic we have determined to press this to press them.

Come and call.

I call for you freshly.

Respond with ease.

I want to tell you about the trees. I have been very well satisfied and I do not mind displeasing them.

He says that he knows all of the directions that he takes. He says that he knows that accidents are found all around. He also says that he cannot diminish water and all of that is not ready. Are you ready.

We reflect about hurry. I hurry to you. And you hurry. You are in a hurry. I am in a hurry too. I have an extra reason for saying come again.

Now then fresh and refresh. You refresh them for me. I refresh them and you say fish is fresh. It always is. It always is. I say can you supply me to-day and I say and I say yes.

I say yes and he says yes and they say yes and we say I guess yes. I say I guess yes.

I say I guess yes and we say yes and you say do you see any connection between yes and yesterday. I will repeat this. Do you see any connection between yes and yesterday.

I congratulate you. Upon what. Upon what she is and upon what he is. I congratulate you upon what he is and upon what she is.

I congratulate you upon meaning to be crowned. I am to be carefully crowned. I am to be carefully kept there. He kept him right there. I am going to be carefully kept right there.

Now say to me. I have always had a great many responsibilities. Now say to me I am prepared to be prepared. Now say to me do you wish me to do this. Now say to me and what do you say. Now say to me, certain reasons are your reasons. And now say to me what did you say. You say this to me and we decide together not one before the other. Again and again. Again and again and again. I was not dreadfully embarrassed. I wasn't either. Nor was I at all troubled. Neither was I. Nor did I bother you. No you did not do that. And how often have I said, that you said you did not organise charity. You did not you do organise charity. I am charitable. I am charitable, I am genuinely charitable. And the instance. Consider the instance, consider transport in this instance.

Do not find it selfish. I think of her. I prefer to think of her.
I am being led I am being led I am being gently led to bed.
I am being led I am being led I am being gently led.
This is not nervousness.

I find that they return that they do return. I find that they do
return, I find that they do return. He says that it is the fault of
the sand. Is it.

And now respected wife let me speak. I wish to say that every
day that Katherine barometer to-day. I wish to say every day,
that daisy does stay. I have always had a great many responsibilities, in pointing out reparations does she in pointing out reparations I have earned what I have earned.

Let me know what comes first. Let me know about her restraint. Have I as much real real occasion to enliven me.

Now then again. Now then and again. Now then and again
and then now then again.

I have every realisation.

There was a way of assisting him, there was a way of insisting
for him there was a way of persisting with him there was a way
of recording an arbitrary collision. And he said how is the
driving there and she said. Stop him. Alright.

I love my love and she loves me, I can reflect and so can she.
She can be responsible for me and I can see this responsibility.

I often decline praise.

He murmured about excess.

They murmured about excess not about excess of tenderness.
They murmured about excess I exceed the limit.

I have been carefully careful.

Mister and Mrs. Picasso, and their boy. I made a joke. Mr. and
Mrs. ourselves and we make it they, they make it say that we
make it pay.

Yes indeed we do, yes indeed we do.

I return the line and they incline to reproduce the twine. In
this way we say that the hand leads the way. This is a description
of Mr. Man Ray.

Have you been at all interfered with.

Have you been at all interfered with. The meaning of this
is have you been at all interfered with.

When you have seen the result of reflection, and reflection does result in this, when you have seen the result of reflection, reflection does result in this.

Have you seen the result of secondary merriment. Second to none he said, she said, they have said second to none.

Under the circumstances under these circumstances under the circumstances marry me again.

I am a husband who is very very good I have a character that covers me like a hood and must be understood which it is by my wife whom I love with all my life and who makes it understood that she isn't made of wood and that my character which covers me like a hood is very well understood by my wife.

There was a chance that Mr. and Mrs. Peale did know that they were telegraphing after telephoning and telephoning in order to know why they were so reasonably sure that they stood to win. I like that phrase we can assume that we have won. I like that phrase.

How talented every one who kisses is. They kissed the current and they kissed there.

How shall we win an ordinary apostrophe.

How can you remain extraordinarily permanent.

I have always been fond of permanent.

Chauvinism a part c'est trop tard.

Do not regulate window ribbons.

Now I will tell all about her success at the salon.

She exhibited a picture which was painted. It was a small picture graceful and undistinguished delicate and pretentious and with it there went a condition. The condition was this, authors must not be readers. All their astonishment was be fair, be very fair. And why did they resolve to accept and to accept. Why did they resolve to accept and to accept. Why did they resolve to accept and to accept. Why did they resolve to accept and to accept.

Come again and waver.

I do resolve that merchants who sell water, and water is so dear to me, I am resolved that merchants who sell more water than candles merchants who sell more water than candles have this interest for me.

I interest myself generally in them. And for them not at all for them not at all for them.

How suddenly we scented the weather. How suddenly. Now reflect. I do reflect. I fasten it firmly.

What was it signed. It was signed for you.

Now then.

Again and again.

What did you say.

She knew what to do.

How do you do.

It was very easily arranged that they should encourage exactly where and when they had represented them. Where and why do you say you mean this.

I do very fairly, he is very fairly, they very fairly understand me.

They very fairly understand me and I do authorise them to address it.

Address it address it.

Address it.

He is very merry.

She is very merry.

Do not neglect a tooth, do not neglect a tooth, do not neglect a tooth, do not neglect positive poison, do not neglect ingredients and do not neglect do not nearly neglect to say that.

Not this evening.

What did she say.

And now once more get into the rhapsody, others rhapsodise, we are accustomed to think of it as Christian, others rhapsodise.

Now and the moon.

I was so astonished at the alteration he made in the glove, she wanted it to catch, what, you know, she wanted it to match.

I can breathe easily to-day and I say, and I say to you I did not mean, I did not mean to deprive you of responsibility. I have always had a great deal of responsibility. I did not mean I did not mean I did not mean to detain you by questioning this and by careful market. Now then say it, careful market. I did not mean to detain you by a careful summary. Careful, carefully, he carried that to the Indian. One little Indian two little Indian three little Indian boys, four little five little six little seven little eight little Indian boys. To an American an Indian means a red-skin not an inhabitant of the Indies, east or west.

A wife hangs on her husband that is what Shakespeare says a loving wife hangs on her husband that is what she does.

I have heard almost all the announcements they have made.

I have indeed wondered if a chinese skirt and a chinese dog and a chinese letter and a chinese cross, he is rarely cross, I have often wondered if it is representative.

And now happily we are said to be in the eye and in the mind an artist. My husband says of me that I have the eye but not the hand of an artist. My husband says of me that he thinks remarkably.

I have been so often interpolated.

My brother says that I should not interest myself in what, you would be astonished, you would be astonished.

I answer we know the interest we take.

And now may we say that we have been interested.

May we say that a pleasure has been a pleasure.

May we say come pleasantly.

May we say that we have always had a great many responsibilities and now we do not consider it this.

I plan and I have a plan.

I plan that the weather will be such that it will be a pleasure to use a fan.

I have been agreeably able to color it adequately.

And now there was no hurry.

There was no hurry now.

There is no hurry.

I have planned for their care.

I care for them.

I do care.

Do you see them often.

Do you remember how we decided that indeed if he came we would have it said that there would be no admittance. Do you remember that we decided that we had entertained him as frequently as we would and that now when he came we would have him told that we would not receive him. Do you remember that.

She always calls after you and says grumblingly one might say she always adds violently but you do not fear I do not fear, I do not fear and she may hear, I do not fear that he may hear.

Hear hear.

This in a way is the custom.

The custom is that they see to that as a custom. Their custom is to remain advantageous. I do not freely recollect speaking. So have continents.

Did you hear what she said, they are going to have summer time in April in New York city and Chicago. Listen to her and you will hear her. They are going to have summer time in April in New York city and Chicago.

I have been moved to tears.

And were there eggs which were supplanted by flour and flour by milk and milk by wrestling.

I know about wrestling. And how about Sofia, Sofia differs from the girl because she has the letter the extra letter and I know what I see when I hear. I do not hear them at all.

You were pleased not to hear them. I was very pleased not to hear them.

I know that there is no flattery in this. I know that there isn't.

Now then let us tell this to one another.

Do you remember how often we bought cake. Do you remember how often we bought venison. Do you remember how often we bought what we needed.

I feel that none of it is in it in the same way. What did you say. I said that I was certain that I had not put it in in the same way.

What did you say.

I said yes and the name of an acquaintance.

I said yes and the name of the acquaintance.

And now able to state what I know.

I mean that I was sitting there in the chair and that when there what do I mean, what do I really mean. What do you mean.

What do you mean.

I come to realise that responsibilities are used in this way. I am useful. Yes I am useful. And decorative. Yes and decorative. Yes and decorative. And acceptable. Yes and acceptable. And announced. Yes I am announced. Whom shall I announce. You might just as well announce what you feel which is faith in Caesars. All of them say yes. And I say yes.

Now then as to appetite. We have a very good appetite.

He remembers that to quote. What did he quote. He quoted the quota. Lindo. Why is Lindo a quantity. Why is Lindo a quantity of that of which it is composed. Lindo a quantity. Lindo Webb. A quantity of which it is composed. I gently feel of it. This makes it the other way. What did you say. I said I did there first, first in the sense of before, in the sense of before this. That before this.

The canon of Italy the canon of Italy makes the noise and we say, they say she says we say that he says unfortunately he unfortunately says all that he says this is our criticism of that. Meet it but do not greet it. Meet it as the best way to meet him. He is around the sound. He is the declaration of the canon. The canon the Italian canon, the canon of Italy is not debasing. Do believe in honey, they do not they believe in oil. I say and we say and she, she is right. She has been right and she is right and she will be right and fitfully when I say to him, I say to him I beg your pardon. This distresses me and makes me ashamed and I say never to-day. Never at all to-day.

I mean to be human nature's daily food. I mean to be.

And now explain exactly what you mean by prunes and figs and apples and why you have plenty of confidence. Why have you plenty of confidence. Because wishes are horses and beggars do ride. This is equally true of asparagus. We see.

Responsibilities.

Sonatinas are all there and they are not to be followed by prayer there they are to be followed by the songs as sung, she ought not to be living there. I know that result. I know that result. A sonatina followed by another is plenty good enough, I feel no musical estrangement.

It is the same story and now I will say it like this, a window in the roof is the what is it, and it often makes the rising around, the rising of the conclusion.

Oh shut up.

Have you been educated by the brother of a sailor. I'd hate to be put to music.

I think that all of this is very unpleasant and not very affable. Do you not feel that way about it. I do.

Now come to think of it all for there are the three men and there is the one man and when she sings there you are and when she sings, she is the one who has the remarkable opportunity. She has that as inauguration just as has the president.

They think of babies of work of resignation and of black-smithing. They do occasionally repeat that they remember salt.

He has had so much to eat. He has so much to eat. And this makes him reasonable and repetitional. She is not imprisoned by gestures. She is not at all imprisoned by gestures. She is not at all imprisoned by gestures.

That is just the same that is just the same as that.

He leans gleefully.

Don't forget it and don't forget that it is not a mother but a father. She says it is not a mother but a father. She says it is not a mother but a father. She says it is not a mother but a father. She says that it is not a mother but it is a father.

She knows everything but the third, third what, but the third congratulation.

Do remember me for this I do not want to be persistent. I do not want to have them sing. A sonatina will be followed by another.

Thank you.

Do you do you indeed.

He said I will tell you this to move you.

Recall, do you recall this at all. I recall that I said that when I was not equal to myself I would attend to the others and I am doing it. I said that when I was very nearly explained I would not measure by soldiers. Soldiers how do you mean soldiers how do you mean by soldiers. I said I would not measure them for that.

Where are they.

Why are they filling the room up with wood-work. Did you say wood-work. Are you sure that you meant what you said.

The first one wasn't good but the second one was very nice.

She says she said, early to bed. And she did not say that it was easily done, nor was there any rain. In Spain there is no rain. When this you see remember me.

There is no rain in Spain.

When this you see remember me.

And now I adhere to what I have said. I have said that I can offer no opinion.

Do not blame him fully.

And now to distinguish this one from that one.

Do not repeat it as formerly. I am more than ever attached to myself.

Early yes early with it and have you spoken of the barometer.

We have four knees.

Cut into their little tall shelters is what the municipality has decided to do.

We know how to blame them.

Mike would say force them to engage builders, and do not force anybody to exchange cotton for a collar. Do not face hats. How did you think of that.

Now then carry a gun. A gun carriage. That made you laugh.

Let me repeat the text the context. A gun carriage we do not think of a carriage because to-day. What is to-day.

Do not forget what it will cost, do not forget that she is not to be crossed, do not forget that words are clear to her, very clear indeed. Do you indeed love me.

He considers he considers you to be perfect.

And what do you consider me. I consider you to be aware of that.

We want to see the Robinson tree and there were more trees there than there had been.

What is sweating, that's what I like, says Mike.

The Lieutenant Colonel was found dead with a bullet in the back of his head and his handkerchief in his hand.

I gather from what I saw at the door that you wanted me to come in before.

I can erase, I can place I can face I can face and erase I can erase and place I can face and place. I can place and face I can face and place and erase. I can erase that and place this and face that. I can place and I can erase I can erase and I can place this. I can place that and erase this. I can erase this and face this and I can place this.

SHORTER PIECES

AS FINE AS MELANCTHA

1922

EQUALLY SO

1923

How can causes be strange. This is a history of a moment.
Monumental valley.

He was unknown and they were known and she was there
and she was there and she was there and she alone was not there
and she was splendidly attired and Demuth knew her. I feel very
well.

All of this reason. I remember the excellent references that
were needed by her brother. And I too I remember very well
how old she was when she knew my mother. And I too I remember brother George. And which one do you remember. I remember Nellie and John and Olive Greene. I often spell a letter. How
amusing.

A conversation between Russell Ward and Rudyard Rhodes.
And how do you feel about a change of name. I cannot change a
name. And what is your opinion of the value of recognition by
any government of an individual. I am convinced that I hope to
be satisfied by meeting again and again with no serious obstacle.
And in this way I can recall a memorandum already submitted.
And what is your feeling about religion. I feel the value of
religion. All religion. Not at all. It is fundamentally opposed to
my feeling to consider as considerable more than two forms of
religious belief. Thank you so much. And which are the two
to which you refer. Believe me do believe me when I tell you
that I insist that I consider it only possible to consider seriously
two forms of religious belief. And when do we forgive procras-
tination. We feel certain that success will crown our efforts.

In many conversations there is an intimate expression of the
exaltation caused by a change in procedure. We always proceed
to know the violence with which we are produced. We neglect
no expression of vindication. In reasoning clearly we reason sincerely. We answer briefly we astonish no one.

We are now speaking of conversations of a conversation between civilians between a civilian and another civilian. They
often mention an armistice and an earnest hope for a speedy

reunion. How easily we reunite. We resemble those who reunite.

Repudiate decoration.

Clearly.

Repudiate decoration clearly.

He said the reason of this repudiation is that it is a useless elaboration. What do you mean. I mean that it has been noticed again and again that abundance that in abundance that the need of abundance that there is therein a need of abundance and in this need it is a necessity that there is stock taking. If there is such necessity can we critically abandon individualism. One cannot critically abandon individualism. One cannot critically realise men and women and so and so we hesitate about decorating, about decorating house and garden. So sweetly do we pile, more than pile a change in return to the heroine who is reasonable and who has an architectural following. Smile for me.

He and she both replied. In a minute.

We have no trains to-day. We have no voices reasonably. We have a story of wealth and revision. Not a revision of wealth we do not know where the derivation of his abundant emancipation. He has always been emancipated from dreams and sharpness. How can he smile. He does not say. Do I love the flowers and the selection and also the windows. How pleasantly they imagine realism. How pleasantly they imagine pluralism and how pleasantly they ignite the return of their fortune. We imagined that they had a fortune. He has a fortune. Certainly riches are very willing. They are very willing to be thrilling. They are very willing.

This would not be the same that he had been having. Simonson, Simonson said that he was often late in going to bed.

All conversation has a wretched union. Some person some one is some one's bird. How do birds mutter. I mutter too.

Do you see how to connect baskets. Do you see just how to connect baskets.

He was induced to wish. He was induced to wish for me.

Star light star bright I wish I may I wish I might have the wish I wish to-night.

How can I describe Melanctha. Melanctha was an extraordinary was extraordinarily was ordinarily received as a climax to welcoming. I welcome you back.

I welcome you back and I welcome you.

Famous for the big idea, she is as they say famous for the big idea.

A conversation between brothers.

Secret diplomacy but they can be taller they are not very tall they can be as tall one as the other only actually the one is taller, not perceptibly and they contradict one another not aggressively and they tire one another never relentlessly and they urge one another never reflectively. One reads Voltaire and the other, the awakening of a sister in a brother of a brother in another.

They have no cause to pray they have not any cause for prayer.

Prayer and hair, we feel it in regarding inheritance, if they learn French with a greek accent what will be the consequence. Easily eradicated. And if they continue indolent. Change of situation. And if there are many men. If there are many men and women older than they will that affect them unfavorably. We have seen to it, that food that food, that food fed to them that the food fed to them is abundant. We have seen to it that they need not annoy one another. We have seen to it that they correspond with their mother. We have seen to it that they are properly provided for. We have seen to it that my own means of elaboration do not in any way augment their privation. How can they be deprived of Negroes. Please black my boots. Please black the surface of the earth. Please. I remember very well when it was fashionable to own a black and tan. A dog of a certain race. And now. Please remember me to Susanne. She is his second life. And no one reads him reads to him to-night. No one reads to him any more to-day. He was surprised when he was questioned about his presence, and yet one may say surprise is not exhilarating. He himself is recollecting not only this but that. Smile for me please. Smile for Emil and Susanne and George and Marion. Smile for them.

He went away let us say because he could not stay. This I

gather to mean that he was seen to be sent away, he had an illness
let us say and the other one went away although he might stay.
He did not have an illness any way and he did say that he was
not going away, the other went away for an indefinite stay.

Receive me, I refuse the sun. He refuses to remain in the sun.
The sun does not refuse to stay and so descriptions remain of an
unusual season.

Conversation.

I have hoped to see you often. I had hoped to have the
privilege of making your house my home. I had hoped to remain
here permanently. I had meant to make good my footing with
you. I had indeed hoped to remain indefinitely in this city.

Indeed had you.

I had hoped to find it permissible to explain to every one
everything and further than that to write it. I had indeed hoped
not for that alone but for myself. Indeed we refused you from
the being. I was not certain of it, I knew that you were not
favorably impressed but after all am not I a person of importance.
I am accustomed so to consider myself. And we have considered
you so but we do not want to have you in our home.

So nearly have we explained ourselves.

And now for Thayer, and now there. How can I be there and
not here. How can I be here and there. And everywhere. Everywhere follows naturally after here and there.

Introduce me to that, I introduce myself. No that is not correct you did not even present yourself. You were brought. So I
was. You were not invited you were brought. I bring myself
altogether. I altogether bring myself.

And who is famous. Who is famous for the big idea.

Please pass the cock, please pass the bread. Please pass me
and say, I love chicken every day. And pray what have you to
do with it you are not a member of the family.

Conversation.

In meeting one another we say may I come to see you and
then she is shy. She it was who said may I come to see you, and
we, we are always delighted.

I begin, oh yes I begin. She does not avow marvelous, she

does not marvelously join England.

And how is Dolly, Dolly is dead to me. Dolly is not wishing for a wedding. Dolly is Dorothy.

Oh how can you say hens are speckled, and cats are frequently wooed, and never wed, no one is wed. I weed and weed. And a heavy voice. And a heavy voice. And the same intonation. And the same intonation and the same emphasis and the same flowers. And not more nearly related. Not any more nearly related.

Begin this as a story.

Splendidly he mentioned the climate and the garden and his success and his familiar circle. He was not splendid alone he meant to breathe and his voice larger than his voice and his voice and when a red color is white like thickness what can we celebrate. We can celebrate that sound.

It is a very extraordinary incident. He was not molded not not mellowed not chosen not voiced. He was not many fingered and why deny why deny the strength the bulk and the tone and the insouciance, he was not merrily timid, he was not merrily Mary. No indeed sounds to me no indeed sounds to me in volume. How can you be so radiantly far. No, far away to-day. Not far away to-day.

An incident in the life of Harden.

He came to his own wedding and he was not surprised at the misunderstanding. He understood every one and every one was doubtful. How could he relish the trust of others. He had come he had suddenly come away from them, they were infinitely respectful and he himself was unaccustomed to odium. How fairly we strive to pacify.

In the meantime winning who won the Wednesday, in the meantime hatred is expressed in winning. I won a way. I won a third of the choices. I won an unusual form of riding. Why do you term grey hair as blended. He was not blended with another of his age. I was more than astonished to hear him recover himself. How can you be read.

The incident was this. He found himself suddenly vacating a place which he had been occupying. He intended reasonably intended to return and he informed the majority of them that in all probability he would return later. He then left and he requested a cable answer. She was unable to gratify, not unable not unwilling not unquestioning, and thoroughly expressive, how selected are the means how well selected are the means for willing the return of money for kissing, for kissing, for scents and for thunder. Deprive me of nothing and care for the sea. Deprive me of nothing and come and care for the sea.

In the meanwhile there was a difference in religion. Can you be religious for me and can you a teacher of religion replace me, can you deny that it is for you to choose how many religions are precious. How many religions are there that are precious. Deceive no one by yourself. In this way the incident came about. He came again and was very willing to be very willing to say yes Dorothy has gone, but she is coming and I am going to welcome her and to say how do you do here. We have plenty of mothers sisters and uncles we have plenty are very distinguished relations. We need robins for seed.

I repeat to you I repeat to you these words.

Miss Katherine Ribbon and Mr. Evelyn Roberts had a very commonplace conversation about the future of Europe. They predicted cold weather and a revolution. They also thought it likely that there would be a lack of food. Pork they find delicious, game abundant, and veal of a very good quality. They do not care to eat beef or mutton. On the other hand they are very fond of cake and fruit. In the meantime we have acquired a great many habits. And do we agree about conversations. We do and we read them. I read of them here.

Can you sell a gentle pigeon, can you sell a relief from China. Can you sell birds and meddlesome horses, can you sell water, can you sell variations on voices. We heard them spell it.

I spell baby.

What do you spell.

I spell a ram.

What do you spell.

I spell ribbons.

And what do you spell.

I spell pussy.

And so sweetly she purrs.

I have an interesting impression of an American. I find that Abdullah, who spelled Abdullah, I find that Simone and this can be pronounced, I find that Cecile, and also how do you despise reading, I find that all the cloth is decorated by men and women. Men and women and children, girls and boys and aids and ribbons and pearls and chinese. How sweetly Americans love Chinamen Spaniards and watches. How sweetly they press themselves together. In inhabiting all the time all of the place they astonish neither themselves or their other friends. How can you be wedded to me. Oh so very easily.

Guess what do you guess you guess you are all my tenderness.

Make a sister be afraid. Make of her a serving maid. Make a sister wear her clothes. Make a sister sing.

Make a sister sing along. Make the most of a heating song. Make a sister make a sister belong to this order.

How do you arise.

How do you despise.

How do you not arise.

How do you not despise prayer.

How do you not arise from prayer.

I feel, I feel the very best way.

And as to candy.

Candy is not the word used to be used for candles.

And now let us mingle Harden, Kitty Buss, the Egyptian and the sister the Armenian and the sisters I never deceive anybody.

What would any sister say if they saw a fly fly away from the cross.

Any loss of a country, does a man lose a country does a country lose a man and his family. Any loss of a country and when he said they always resisted a little we laughed at clarity. We sang bitterly but we were not afraid of going further into civilization. Be calm be calmed.

The story of a hurried stay.

He would take care of her brother and lock her lock her in with clothes.

He would take care to plan.

A peal.

Peal.

Appeal to me to be pleasant to you.

This is his history. He came and was seen to be attractive to all who rested when they were not idle. He meant to care a great deal altogether. He was nourishing and more than that smiles and a loud voice have inherent stoles. Do Americans know that stoles are what priests wear.

How dearly clearly merely is she me, how dearly clearly merely am I she. How dearly is she me how dearly is she me how dearly how very dearly am I she.

In dealing with words worlds, with dealing with worlds words, chemise comes to our lips. We find an operation to be exceedingly difficult if there is an absence of the accustomed and yet whose custom should be regarded. The custom of those who give or the custom of those who receive. Accustomed as we are. Unaccustomed as we are we easily accustom ourselves to these threads.

And now as to civilisation. Harden, do not harden, harden and win from a woman, win a pin from a woman, and did they know who we were. We were their saviors.

A calendar.

At five I strive. At six I fix the prayer that is prepared. Pray at six. Pray for six. Pray for six a day. And every day. At seven there is a leaven, a leaven of ministrations and at eight, I ate. I ate and she ate, and children are not meant to be at all religious. At nine, a great many people have heard of the lonesome pine, and at ten, when do you believe me to be entirely yours.

A continued story. Civilisation begins with a rose. A rose is a rose is a rose is a rose. It continues with blooming and it fastens clearly upon excellent examples. After that it does not mingle it does not readily mingle with windows. It prefers to be colored by sweets. And how sweet are sweets. Sweets to the sweet.

Establish me at all to establish me at all is not difficult.

Canticles of the Saints. I consider that the perfect world is the one where weddings are easily seen to be wished for. I consider that the usage of letters words and conundrums are such as to inspire the irreligious to inspire the religious. I consider that willing willing sights are those that make humming formidable. What is the difference between humming to-day yesterday and to-morrow. The difference between humming to-day yesterday and to-morrow is this, it always means more. The difference between humming to-day yesterday and to-morrow is this. It always means more.

I did not think I ever could be cross again with love, I did not think I ever could be naughty as above.

In dealing with marvels, who said, you are a miracle and I do not like miracles, in dealing again with marvels who is astonished to find themselves enthroned on the throne. I enthrone, you enthrone, he enthrones.

Waves of heat in cold weather make steam, I do not know why they call it a dream. I really do not know how to dream. Do you. Fill the jew. With what. With butter. Thank you so much for all that good butter.

Now to resist conversation. Kitty said. I find it. Harden said. I find it again. And the other one did not utter his thought.

Michael the widow said, how do you dream of a mother and orphans. And a pair of flowers. The sun sets and rises on snow. Not readily although it threatens.

I remind you of saints. Here are many of them.

Cruelty to saints is not neglected. Cruelty to saints is not altogether neglected. Cruelty to saints is not altogether neglected by any of them. Pray for realisation.

Kitty Buss Cooperous. I have met a little jingle and I said. I treat I treat her very well, I own my own and I treat her very well.

I treat very well. I have said that I own my own and I treat her very well.

And now for no hurry.

Hurry to me restfully.

He found it very easily. He found it very easily the road to restoration. We restore doors, floors and fairs. It is only in New

England that they reverence fairs. Now what do you mean by that exactly.

I told you to be very careful of conversation. When you are completely rested you may mean to be splendid. You may mean to recognise merit.

Saints and saints and saints. Saints sing.

Do not deny what has been said. Do not deny your reply. Do not deny what I deny. I decline to reply. I deny that you have said more to me than I have said to you.

Many conversations begin with women.

Women said that saints and singing mean more than saints have sung.

Saints and singing.

I feel no distress at saints and tenderness.

Saints and tenderness. Ask me to eat what is eaten and ask me to have what I have, ask to welcome you.

I have good reasons for saying theirs. Here their prayers, their thoughts fly high and in eating loves love apples as tomatoes were once called in eating them and in leaving them how can I serenely say saints and singing, saints and tenderness saints and singing and tenderness.

Now to amuse me.

Remember what was said about us. Remember what was said about each of us. Remember what was said of us. Remember the Rhone.

And now wickedly wedding, not a wedding.

First a wedding.

He was married to me laterally.

Then a wedding.

He was reading, in his reading he read that a wedding was said to be spread before him.

In his reading he read that a wedding was to be said, a wedding ring was to be given as a revision. How many saints have prayed that roses and stones and birds and handkerchiefs be noiseless. How many saints have said, and have received their daily bread. How much authority have we for reasoning.

I find myself attached to very much that has been meant to be said to me.

How can you easily feel more than that.

And now we commence virtues.

When is an egg not an egg, when it is a sister.

When is a pitcher not a pitcher, when every one is very well.

When is writing and reading abundant, when embroidery is out of fashion and when do you despise churches. I do not despise churches at all.

Now let me mention every one I know. Mary Christopher, Mary Etienne, Mary Barnaby, Mary Reading, Mary Elisabeth Henrietta McIntire.

I have no desire to converse about any of these.

Another list.

Jerome Harden, Kitty Buss, Matthew James and the young Parisian.

We all pronounce their names.

And now how do you remember your name. We often wonder if your name has not been mentioned to you for a number of years and you have not mentioned it to yourself would you remember it.

I have said that I am intimate with my bed.

And what did I say. I said that the oldest sister did not go to stay. And how little they travel. And how content they are with gifts. And how kindly they remind you that they have that they leave no fear behind you.

Have you mentioned their religion.

I haven't and yet I do not blaspheme the saints.

How many saints have ears.

How many saints have fears.

How many saints have tears.

How many saints feel years.

How many saints are irreligious.

How many saints are there.

This is a litany of the saints.

To begin with.

Pardon me if I speak to you.

To go on.

Let me leave you to your thoughts.

And then.

And then promise me that you will remember everything.

And after that. And after that it does not matter at all whether they are willing to be individual, separate or painstaking. It does not matter at all whether women, white women, and children, red children, and women, white women, and children, white children, it does not matter at all whether men and women and children invent noises or oceans or cisterns, or ambulances, or ways with ice, or even reproaches, it does not matter at all what angle and with what speed every one is reasonable, it does not matter at all, I can so kindly understand human nature, and I do please myself with my recognition of the remark that all good things come together as one two, or one two three four five six, or as one two three four five six seven.

I have often remarked that invention and there is a great deal of invention, I have often remarked that invention concerns itself with inventing and, I, I feel no responsibility. I say read me, I say read him, I say read her, I say read them, I say very well do not follow my sister, I say my sisters, I make a mistake and say thank you sister.

In which wandering I feebly say do be rich. And then what does Jerome Harden do, he does as I say, and what does gentle Craven say, she say[s] my name is Henrietta Silver, and I have earned everything, butter and eggs and room. Thank you.

I wish to remedy wishes. She wishes, he wishes, she wishes fishes, she has fishes as a cow.

She has fishes as a cow.

I wish to earnestly inquire why do you do this. And she replies, I do this because in this way I get my effect. I say do you remember him. She says I remember him and he remembers me.

Once in a while I dash away.

And now how do you mingle with them.

Kitty Buss Cooperous.

Harry Jimmy Lee.

And white and yellow.

I remember exactly how I feel about races about races of men, and conversations.

Lilies feel white, and yellow lilies feel like Saint John.

Saint John and Saint Luke and birds.

When I miss any one I say to them why have you not come. And when they reply, but I have come often I say I find that very astonishing.

Once in a while I feel like caressing and what do I then, I caress.

Once in a while the sisters once in a while the sisters, once in a while the sisters are once in a while there are sisters, once in a while there are the sisters. We do not recover the word. Thank you.

Russet sing the sisters and say you cannot have the box to-day, and we reply, we will cry, and he will say, I obey, and we say we stay and he says do not go away and they say that will do any day. That will do to-day.

Noon or morning which is it.

Noon or morning which is it.

Now do not imitate me.

In winning saints and singing in singing in singing in singing saints and singing do they sing.

Now choose a birthday.

I choose Christmas and I choose an education. And I choose a robust jew. And I choose, I choose mending glasses.

A great many people choose their birthday.

Harden.

Come in Harden.

And William.

William Edgar Lane.

William Edgar Lane was born in America, he resembled Americans in that.

Allen Edgar means to produce America. Produce his birthday, her birthday, their birthday.

We remember, how do we remember we remember everything. In the first place we remember the wood we burned and the Chinamen we met and the splendid examples we had of letter writing and then we wished to replace dishes. We found it impossible. This is owing to the war. Now to be corrected. In the first place let us mention religion. Religion and hour glasses, re-

ligion and watches religion and an obstacle religion and a South
American. Let us mention religion and a South American. Let
us mention a South American. Let us mention religion and religion. Let us mention ferries that cross at the crossing. Let us
mention a South American religion. I feel that you have an excellent opportunity to be an authority on South American religion.

And now for my story.

I found it a great advantage to have met him and to have told
him that a great many thousands are men and a great many
thousands are women and that if they prepare their prayer and no
one refuses a wedding, how can stout people make a splendid
showing. But they do. They certainly do.

More than this we feel when we repeat the effect of these
words. These words tell me more and more. And now what. Can
you register your impressions. Begin now.

In the first place Harden, Harden has come. He brings honey
and flowers, and he brings his voice and his memory. He has no
memory of already around and he is so kind. I know that kind.
Why does he abandon her. Why does he abandon her.

Honest to God Honest to God Honest to God and true, Honest to God Honest to God Honest to God thank you.

And now to explain how easily we do not bother.

Here.

Honest to God we are not to blame. Blame rhymes with flame
and Dolly with folly.

Honest to God just the same we are not to blame.

How can she escape you.

And how can you escape him.

How can they escape her.

Now listen to this.

We met once and we said, honey we like honey flavored with
orange blossoms. And he said I am a judge of honey and she said,
we have been judges of honey. Do you find honey fluid or thick.
Do you prefer soup thin or thick. Do you prefer to increase or
decrease your sons, do you resemble yourselves more than you
did. Nigger nigger never die black face and china eye. Do you
prefer color or colors. And do you prefer sustained impressions.

I find a reasonable reserve of wood, I find a reasonable reserve of roses and I also find a reasonable reserve of mirrors. And more than that civilisation tempts attempts. Why can you wish that to-day that to-day and every day, why can you wish that to-day is easily longer than yesterday. How can you easily wish that negligence is prepared, is cared for is a memory of my earliest reading of my reading of the Indian Mutiny. While green, Harden, Kitty saints and sisters, singing and right, singing and right. He is right, she is right. Singing and saints, nobody paints, wool they paint, dishes and London bridges. London bridges falling down falling down falling down, London bridges falling down, my fair a lady oh. Which do you prefer, Honest to God, which do you prefer a diamond, a broom, a tumbler, an engine or a splendid page, which do you prefer, Kitty, which do you prefer Harry, which do you prefer Mildred which do you prefer Simone, Simon is a man's name and when you add an e it is a woman, Ferdinand is a man's name and when you add an e it is a woman. Leon is a man's name and when you add ie it is a woman, Harry is a man's name and when you change the y for iet it is a woman. Then why do you choose examples. Tell me why do you choose examples. Tell me why do you choose these examples. Tell me again why do you choose these examples. Tell me again what you have just told me. I told you that you would. And did you. You did. I have told you that I have just told you that you would and I have just told you that you did. Honest to God Mr. Brown I have just told you that you did.

EQUALLY SO

A DESCRIPTION OF ALL THE INCIDENTS WHICH I HAVE
OBSERVED IN TRAVELING AND ON MY RETURN

Equally so.

A description of all the incidents which I have observed in traveling and on my return.

Equally so.

As deniably equally so.

Incidents which I have observed in traveling and on my return.

Undeniably and equally so.

Undeniably equally so.

Descriptive as you please, and not noticeable.

As you went.

Did I notice that a woman was looking and a woman was looking I was deceived too.

Before traveling I had noticed some one looking and recognising I commenced an undertaking. Quickly finished. As quickly finished.

Satisfactory as unsatisfactory.

On my return once more as a cow now, on my return happening to wait I happened to wait and I intended to settle down to it.

One flag not a flag, one bucket not exactly more than one bucket, two two too and so facts establish themselves.

Counting, count very well. In this way many medals are useful. As useful.

Noticeably not only noticeably not only noticeably here and there. Noticeably here and there. In their in it happening in it in happening and in order to do so, noticeably.

Not particularly quickly.

Notice that in that direction notice that a given direction no more and no more and not any more nearly as nearly, this is to be noticeably besides noticeably.

Notice to stay there.

A notice to stay there.

And notice that and to stay there. Not nearly as unpleasantly so.

Can you conceal can you conceal can you conceal noticeably can you and can you can you conceal.

I remember now that I noticed that the house that was partly built was sold.

No not a street.

Manage the addresses.

I noticed I also noticed I noticed that there was nothing alarming about it as trouble.

No disrespect and no relief.

Pretty prettily.

Practically practically certain.

The rest do the very best you can.

Observations.

I notice that nearly all of them go very nearly to all of them I also notice that very nearly all of them are as you might say prudent. So much more than has to be committed. Committed to it.

The beginning of it nearly left over from the beginning of it. Left over from the beginning of it this is left over from the beginning of it. Jessie and left over from the beginning of it. Three and there, there three and three there. Here two and too here. Left left I had a good home and I left. Left over from the beginning of it. So then can there have been any intention in an impediment. How many impediments are there. Not really. I pass an afternoon. And they can be ready.

In or on or during or in the course of or more than at first it was necessary to remind them it was necessary to remind them that not at all so abundantly not at all not abundantly not even in preparation, we were prepared and so were they.

Needless to say she did not remember whether it was really the same glass whether it really was glass whether really may it really be said that silver, may it be made of silver, may it be gilded, silver gilded might it have been made of silver and gilded and in this way originally as she might say, originally it may it may be original and it might have been used on that particular occasion. So sweet. So sweetly. A very well known personage. As to that.

It is frequently it does frequently it happens frequently and as it happens they were nearly convinced that the situation chosen was the one that gave satisfaction. I do not care to settle down for less than a year. In this way. So well to do so.

One wants to be very careful that they remember presently that they remember presentably as they remember, presented as they remember as they remember and not presently and not at present as they remember. Many and most acceptably. Reunited. Rejoice. As stream. A nuisance too a nuisance to do so. I never wish to notice that in him because it readily makes me mistake it for this. For this.

I noticed that bibliography meant a great deal and also that arrangement in arrangement their arrangement, can an arrangement mean more of it. More of it. Can any arrangement make it accidentally plentiful. Plentiful to me. In order to pass it. Confuse me.

Awaiting an answer.

It is a great peculiarity that if it is not very well known, listened carefully understood it completely can repeat it word for word.

I do know what I say.

In exchange for this to be mentioned in exchange of this. When we travel to be mentioned in exchange for this. No one else covers them that is to say no one else that is to say they are covered in that way and no one else is. Full of observations as to this.

Eventually am sending to-day eventually no delay, eventually as we say and as we say eventually and necessarily observed. A great many observations satisfy me. Did you not. Nothing corresponds to it. As correspondence.

Do you think it makes it different. And very nearly and very neatly and in that way it does not reassert more than carefully.

What were you thinking of when you hesitated in speaking. What were you thinking when you stammered. Of what were you thinking when you were hesitating as if you intended saying something and found yourself impeded. Impediment.

May I sit here, may I settle here, may I. You may.

All the things observed, as the shutters were shut we always noticed that there was no rapidly increasing elegance not any rapidly increasing elegance.

We also noticed we noticed indeed we were to notice and we were to be noticed and notices as notices do they indeed dance as dances. As dances, not nearly really measured for it. It is needless to say that servants are clean and napkins have a surface and there and there. Here and here and there.

No need there is no need in need and need to need we need

when we need as we need and as we need who needed and how did it come to a question. A question is this. Can everybody establish themselves in this way and be prepared to inculcate to be prepared. And to be prepared. Gracefully. We have come for addresses.

A thousand welcomes to you and yours to all who have plenty of exceptional reasons for realising admissions. We admit that.

Once more all of them are inclined to go.

Not as exactly as we have been feeling.

A great many pleasures not as faintly.

Arouse yourself again.

Flourish now.

Estimate.

Estimates.

Sounds and securely.

As judgment. Her judgment was excellent and her reasons and more than that the arrangements and even these arrangements and more nearly feeling and expected. Who was it who was expected.

Excellent.

We find it better than the other. And excellent. As a stage piece it is better than the pudding. Not as satisfactory as the other. Excellent, excellent as a pudding. In this respect I am not in agreement. Longer and longer as long and as much longer and as so much longer and longer and longer.

Let me know the difference between a list here and a list there. In both cases the interest is sustained and in the one case the details can be added to at once and in the other case only very much later can the necessary additional information be obtained. For this reason we are not certain where we prefer to remain. We remain and we do entertain. Smile for me. What is the difference between old wool and all wool and what is the difference between ordered wool and extra wool and what is the difference between black wool and that wool and is that wool. So many people travel attractively. I observe. Can you remain and have you any feeling as to that. I know. Yes we know.

When traveling does one receive more letters than when re-

maining at home. In this way as answered can there be a reason
for it. Longer than necessary. Not any longer and as necessary.
As they say, begin now.

Not only introducing but reasoning reasoning with them
engaging engaging it for them explaining explaining about them
and rearranging rearranging it. As suddenly as they had it arranged, and as suddenly very suddenly. Not to find it at all amusing.

How often did it how often could it and how often did it
come.

Did it come.

Sticking closely to incidents. Not incidents.

This incident. Having seen that having seen farther, having
seen and having seen, not having seen. Collectedly. In the anticipation not really as in the anticipation and not so nearly and
seated, not to be seated and not only not to be seated. Do you
fondle recognition. I didn't.

An interesting not an interesting not as interesting not and not
copied. Copy copied copied. You can if you like.

I did not think that you would know what it was about.

See see see any one can see it. Any one can see it too.

A great deal of free space can be used by houses, houses here
are there houses here and is there a great deal of place for more of
them, more of them.

Not to and not to using advantages, and so much that is very
much longer. Resolved to buy brushes and mats as a necessity and
a charity. Newly as an article. An article is new when it can be
placed upon the table and in this way prevent the contact between the table and the heated crockery. And we can nearly
say so.

For frequently and they can be an addition to it. As soon as
that we are obliged we are obliged to be we are not sustained,
we are systematically furnished, furnished as if we could easily
understand that success. That success. It was very pleasant and
to us.

Nearly attentively as our slightly or very surely, needed it be.
So much for that and a crown. In this way the thing had no great
value. As great value, why great value for great value, more

value. Valuable. How valuable. How valuably do you estimate how do you estimate its value. For this. And in. Introduce. Introduces.

Now to continue histories and histories. As histories. Might it be so near might it be so new might it be so nearly, might it nearly be so new. Might it. Might it be so new as nearly as new. Might it be so. And it might be so. And it might be so nearly so.

In insistence. The text of a marriage in insistence. To notice eeney meeney miney mo catch a nigger by the toe. In this new sphere of liberty.

Now I wish to tell about the marriage of the daughter may we say illegally the daughter may we say the daughter of a man and how are you. Are you able to state that when there is all or nearly all when there are all or nearly all all present. They were satisfied. They were satisfied as they were satisfied and they had not heard of the other share. Share and share alike. Do for me do this for me, do this do this for me, do this for me. They did this for me. All observations which are equal to this one are equally so. Are equal to one and are equally so are equally and this one equal so. So equally, it is so it is equally so.

Exchange in this way exchange we are not successful, we are successful more by succeeding, this is to be understood as one succeeding another, not periodically but successively. I need not change this and I need not change this and so I do not need to change this, to change this, to change this and so and so do not need to change this. As exchange in changing this as in exchange and in exchanging and in exchanging this and not for this. We went to another one. Much better results. In fact results satisfying in every way.

A new title. I find myself unable to give it absolutely correctly. And yet in every way correct and accomplished she is in every way, it is accomplished in this way it is to be accomplished in this way correctly. As discussion and reward and reward and rewarded. The things that make me say so.

Announcements.

First as announcement. Not concerned with it and not finding it needless to say so nor needing it more than that. Much more than that. Needing it very much needing it as much needing it as

much as that and needing it as much and needing it as much as
that.

An announcement. An announcement of there being prepared
of there really being as prepared of there really being prepared
as they are to do so.

As an announcement.

Furniture.

As announcing.

No yellow.

Announcing.

Follow me and follow follow me.

As announcing.

Nineteen and a half.

An announcement.

Always had it they always had it.

Announcement of their pleasure in their day.

Just in time.

Every once in a while just as they find out that it is possible
to find exactly what they want they are apt to be disturbed by
the indifference and there never is any indifference they are apt
to be largely satisfied by the way that every one attends to their
wants.

Do they want to.

There are two days in every way, when are they prepared
and why are they prepared. They are prepared and they have
made the preparation which is not one that could not necessarily
be undertaken. In this way and in this way so much in this way
and so very soon. I find it soothing.

What are the changes that are to be noticed.

In the first place there has never been a time when it was not
possible to be recognised and to be as recognisable and to be
certain of such recognition. In this way there is no possible occasion for remonstrance. They have fully in their same satisfaction
the reasonableness of four. Four as in this return. Four as in this
return.

In turn fairly as they turn to turn and to turn in turn. When
can you, as you may say and when can you. You may say when
can you when can you you may say when can you.

It is not in any way a return to it. Return to it, as if and more than and they can, can return, can return to it and can return and return, to return to it. Leading to leading to more leading away as more are leading away as more are leading away and so and so. So nearly. Every one answers a description.

And just exactly, as exactly. We found it very easy to reason why. The reason why we preferred to go there rather than not was that in that way we avoided the kind of weather that we have concluded to find disagreeable. Able to change it. Is it very necessary. What does this recall. This recalls that I was always able to be unavoidably and this is astonishing. This is astonishing. In suddenness it is astonishing and not very nearly so. She was astonished to learn that it was not as warm as she had anticipated.

Had anticipated.

It did not impress me.

If we meet.

We did meet.

We did not meet.

And we meet.

For meeting.

Adjoining.

And for instance.

To be.

To be taught.

I wish now to describe how she comes in and out. She comes in and she comes out. I wish now to describe how she comes out. I wish now to describe how she comes in. I wish now to describe how she comes in how she comes out. I wish now to describe how she comes out how she comes in.

Much better.

All of it in sitting sitting there all of it admitting admitting it all of it admitting it we often ask do we need do and if we do we do. So easily have they needed it as they have needed it so easily. In the information as their information, as information can it have the same use have they the same have they used the same have they some of the same have they all of the same and so evenly moreover. All this resolves itself not so for indeed no resolution can make a postal or a mail service rendered, none of this inter-

feres at all, do I follow twice that is to say when there is need
of a return do I follow twice. Twice as twice. Formerly and
formerly not again to say so, formerly not as formerly, formerly
for these useful purposes there was no practical desire but now
all can it be who has no hundred and its more. Climax. Always
again. So much sooner. Are there ribbons, ribbons follow, ribbons
for naturally she knows when to have it very nearly too much.
If there is a place and place it there. Formerly they intended to
arrive Tuesday. Tuesday.

No one no one, and they you can tell that it is attractively
recounted. Recounted to count again. Recounted and to count
again. Attractively recounted. Attractively counted again. Not
in reference too in this way shall I count camellias. One camellia
two camellias three camellias four camellias, three more makes
seven camellias. Counted as counted again. At present.

Did they think did we think did you think, as it can be admired, admire it. Often you say so. Often you do. Baskets too,
baskets too often you do, as lightly very likely, a mistake very
likely to be a mistake and this year, yearly. As yearly as nearly,
nearly it is nearly so. To be used to mean newspapers as well.
It has been an opportunity for me to observe that next to it, they
are next to one another. Each one well not exactly next to each
other there is something in between. Added and not to at all.
Not to at all. No not to at all. So many visitors say so.

Titular and titles, titles to and titular, entitled entitles to this
entitles you, this is the title to, to it, to attention. In attention and
attention. They attended to it.

It is interesting to notice the manner of celebrating the holidays which occur which recur, it is interesting to notice the recurrence of the celebration of the holidays as they recur.

It was interesting to hear that of all of them only one of them
it was interesting that only one of them of all of them found it
obligatory in so far as he as all of them were were in a position in
the position of the ones doing as they were directed, it was of
interest interest certainly in the fact that mention was made of it
and there was no further indication of the choice there was no
choice as each one was in a different situation and so entirely
there happened it happened entirely as the result of the decision

of their decision that only one of them did remain interested. Interested in what.

As contradictory, as contradicted, an example of it as it is in here. It is in here and regardless of that, incontestably.

May we mention names.

How many ounces to a pound. And moreover how do they weigh what do they weigh and wait. Wait. Yes I have often made pleasant jokes at her expense.

Come and come and come to do so came to do so. Came to do so. He came to do so.

One article and two more articles. Pleasanter than that. Two more articles and three of the articles and pleasanter than that. Pleasanter than that and three of the articles three of the articles and pleasanter than that. Pleasanter than that and pleasanter and as pleasant and three of the articles and pleasanter than that and three of the articles and three of the articles and pleasanter than that.

Pleasanter than that and three of the articles.

Wait until we wait until they wait until we see it. It is very funny but almost every day I change what I say, I say wait until we see it and we do not wait. We do not wait until we see it. This is one of the things that can readily be understood. Not so much significance, not so much as significant not so much signifying not as much. Not as much significantly more and more signifying more and more, significant as more and more. More and more. Meadowingly. Laughable and not equal to it as an example. We have forgotten all about the article. An article used to be used in this way. As a weight.

He came in with rosy cheeks. He came in with rosy cheeks. As to coming in. Useful as useful as useful as that.

Interesting to separate dishes and wishes, fishes and dishes, dishes and wishes, it is separately it is as it is separately it is separately to interest them more than that is separately very separated. In this way, two and she knew, in this way two and as two. Two and let it, two and let it, to let it. This was the whole incident. As they were as they were, incidentally furnished for winter and summer incidentally as they were and incidentally as they were. Incidentally as they were.

Plans of taking out of there everything plans of taking everything out of there, plans of taking out of there of taking most of
it out of there. We whether we, we whether we whether we did
or we and whether we, did we they did what was more nearly
suitable for them to do.

We have had so many experiences and all of them as causing
no one any more nearly any more of it. Any more of it. Many
more of them. And return many more of them. In this way we
begin what is to be reconstituted. I guess so.

Observations.

Returns.

Many returns.

Return to observe.

Turn to observe.

Observations.

And amusements.

In the first place, three places, fruits, cakes, game, poultry,
leaves, buckets and returns.

Many returns.

And returns.

Turns.

And as turns.

Colored marbles make colors rosy.

In so far as they are far in a way far in a way as difficult to
distinguish.

Examples of subsidies.

Subsidies.

Examples.

Four and four makes eight.

Four and three makes seven.

Four and four makes eight.

Four and three makes seven.

We come nearly we nearly come, we come nearly to coming
as frequently as we have counted. We have counted it nearly as
frequently as that.

In case of in case of it what will they do in case they leave it
in case they have left it, what will they do in case that they have

left it. They will not need it very much and as they find it nearly everywhere they can easily decide to have it. Have it. They can easily decide to have it.

Plans for purchase.

In many cases all of them in all of the cases in all of them in many cases in case of it, in the care of it, as carefully as that is as carefully as they are, they are more carefully and so if the arrangement changes, if twelve times four if four times seven if more than twelve times four and not more than four times seven then there would be no need of waiting. Why wait then. So that when the arrangement is made more arrangements are made and as more arrangements more arrangements are made as an arrangement, it is a very good arrangement. Not as announcements and not as announcements. Not more than more. More more, four, for it before it, have it and have it also. Change also for most. To change also and to change most.

Now I nearly see, seated. Now I nearly see. Now I am nearly seeing, seated, now I am as seated as I was. This makes no difference when they lose when he can as spoken he speaks too. Too yes too. Not again especially.

So much for that and deductions. Deductions about whom you sympathise with. About whom you sympathise with. Neither. Very well. Florida. Very well. Florence. Very well. Chestnuts. Very well. Balls. Very well. I swear. As children. All of it. Frank's. All of it. Francs. All of it. Frank's. All of it. All of it. Francs. All of it. Francs. All of it. Frank's. All of it.

All of it. Thanks. All of it. All of it. Thanks. All of it.

Thanks. All of it. All of it. Thanks. All of it.

Moved around.

All of it. Thanks. Thanks. All of it.

When a collar as a collar, when a cellar as a cellar, when an inundation when, when is it. What is it. What is it. When is it.

When as when a particular story. A particular story is told. So nicely.

Now nearly nearly. Nearly. Once as at once, once once or twice not any more. Not any more. Once. Once. At once.

I wish to describe attractively what I have found attractive.

I have found this attractive. I have found it attractive. As I have found it attractive I have concluded that there is every reason, I have that reason. I have a reason.

I have described attractively what I have found attractive.

Three mentioned that. There are three who have mentioned that. There are three, not three, there is no more rain there than here. There is more rain here than there.

Add what.

The difference between counting and announcing.

If you have reason to be at all uneasy if you have any reason at all to be at all uneasy you should do what you can to do what you can.

If you have any reason at all to be uneasy have you any reason at all to be uneasy.

So much so.

As much so as that.

Have you as much reason as that to be uneasy. Have you as much reason as all that. As much reason as that.

All call.

So all call.

So they all call.

They all call so they all call.

And so they all call.

Finally that.

Establishment.

Exercises in secret.

Establishment.

Exercises in secret.

Exercises in establishment.

Exercise in secret.

Secret exercises.

Exercises.

In exercises.

Sent.

Yesterday.

Sent yesterday.

Not as well as sent yesterday and looking around.

Just the same as it.

Exercises in exercises.

When we mention when, when we mention, when we mention, when we mentioned, and as often as when, so often, when we mention when as often, soften. Or often. Eraser and as often. Not next to it, not and next to it, and not and next to it and not and not next to it. Not next to it.

A fancy to it. They took a fancy to it, we took a fancy to it, fancy to it. As a fancy, it was as a fancy. Nearly the same.

Some of the things to be noticed in traveling are these. When it is not difficult to please, please and please, when it is not difficult to please, as for instance in a restaurant, as for instance on a hill, as for instance at sight as for instance by and by and for instance. It is not as difficult as it is. In comparison. In comparisons comparing it, as in comparison. In finally and for that can an inclosure, nearly so, collect it collectedly and so forth.

So many reasons to say so, they have as many as they had and they had as many and they have as many.

They had as many.

Nearly are as nearly they are nearly there and as can they astonish and as they can see it now as they can. For instance if in coming there if in coming there if in there and they make they make most, they can make it, as they made it, they will not make it again. No more as means. Not any more as more as more it means more. More means more. So much is said as they say it. Not as suggested. They, we, we they are not inclined to go to and go there. Not as was as preparation. Let us describe each one in turn.

In the first place as enough of them, what is not at all puzzling is the re-creation. It is seen that closing and as opening, closing as as opening. Not too many as two are not too many. And three. For their three.

The next one makes no mistake. Mistake. Mistake it. Not mistake it and not to securely and not as securely and not securely, so securely.

In the third place no one can see the resemblance between them, no one can see the resemblance between them and no one can see the resemblance between them and no one can see the resemblance between them. I'll say so.

Funnily enough it is not only as authority but with authority and for the reason that they can they are they all of it prepares it. Say it with that kind of agreement which makes it not hurry. So nearly and one and two, surely. As surely, sure to be, consists in, and consists in. Thanks to you. Not surely. Surely.

We wish now to say that voices are as agreeable as they are when as many days and we can think of enough things. And we can think of enough things. And we can think of enough things and voices are as agreeable as they are when as many days and we can think of enough things. Superior to, superior to her, she is superior to her, and suitable. She is suitable. As suitable. She is as suitable. Suitably.

Indeed many can be.

Correctly as correctly as that.

If two steps were under water if they made another step if the third step was beginning to be under water what would be the next step. The next step would not be taken as the house would be evacuated in that case.

As it has been seen, as it has been as soon as it has been as soon as it has been seen, happily in there. As happily as in there.

Extra changes. Rechange corals. Examine it. She examined. As she examined it. As she examined it. As she examined it.

As she examined it, it was as if she examined it, as she examined it. As she examined it. At all.

It is marked sisters.

FINIS.

A HISTORY OF HAVING A GREAT MANY
TIMES NOT CONTINUED TO BE FRIENDS

1924

A HISTORY OF HAVING A GREAT MANY TIMES NOT CONTINUED TO BE FRIENDS

It was merely that after having been for what might be said unified and not forbidden it might be said of it that this follows in order that more are to be seen. How many more are to be seen. Just as many as if at once. Once at once.

How many are there who have often as can be seen literally. Literally makes listened to of it and name. Can sentences be wider.

The first one can remember some. Not as remembered soon or by a chance or slip or slips slips of wood and slips of wood. All slips of wood are what is not any more than spoken of for a president and a resident.

In bowing they begin now. Of that there is no memory. As to numbers numbers are either in one form or another and are equally easily numbered from one to another. Often there is candied imitation of nuts and cakes and even chocolate. It is decided that the best thing to do is what has been opened anyway. Further needed further and if there is no doubt about it. Changed to a place. This has no succeeding. Succeeded as if it were an estate. Commence cordially.

The first instance to be relegated is the one that makes settlers valuable. Settlers settle everywhere and feel it all. When no one said so.

If in the reception of what has been learned and really formed as a part of collections, if in pleading placing and application no more success has been refused than as fully as that, when can stretches and in as much as stretches have become primarily in their way, almost as much as was considered delightful. Following up seeing felt and causing. In this way in no delight can there be more choice. For the special sight and pleasure see it again as much. Do this and do so.

The first time and this is history as she said a king and woman killed, the first time and considering a rushing as a king and finally, more and more and have said more to him.

The first time and this is history, the commencement was finishing so that as to a part of it no part of it is hurried. How can again and again be said so.

If five five passing pass five six and missing miss six and one and missing miss one and missing.

Have all of them to be have all of them to be as yes and first and afterwards and new and now and by the way and shall and must and as it was and for and must and in that way and now and at last and more than this and can and did and rest and best and so much as so much and as and nearly not and now. Appreciably, returned by the direct agreeing and more so than so fortunately as in all the way who can see we see, we see him.

Supposing that the decision is made supposing that in accounting, counting makes no more regularly than, supposing that in accounting for it it has been received as principally serially and accepted. Accepted to have been so. To have been so or so. Or so for this to have stretches and stretches of intermediate and corollary in permission. As if permitted as if to be permitted. All of it has assemblies, assemblies has all of it more of it and more of the rest.

A situation established it concluded and it always does. As mentioning seventy.

The first exact case was this. After a certain number of years he never saw him again.

Was it a crime in his eyes was it a crime for him to have a second and a first and all the sixteen too. Two sixteen makes it that no one listened who had not been convinced. Convincing makes a satisfactory conclusion to a countenance. In not as much verbally as that he could be so. He said again and get it as it can be had for me. After this we concluded after this we concluded and as in writing no one had it finally as choice how can as not choosing make finally at best, finally at best, best and most, this was not to be pressed in any way. As not being pressed in any way if to establish, establishment meant meant and meant. After this an an example. By nearly eighteen and not again as around, around it say so, so and so.

Of having a great many times.

Please, please as please wind please as please wind it.

Not counting division.

Not counting addition.

Not counting condition.

Not counting wishing.

Not counting.
Not counting easily.
Not counting call it call it counting.
Counting count.
Promise of make it, make it soon.
The first followed as by a first.
The second as followed by and by.
The first shutting as shoulders.
The second more have it.

This makes all all to be all to be all all to be. Why in there and plenty of easily easily replied.

The next felt is this. Having forgotten.

What makes after whom after whom, and no one.

It is singular that the most and the most when not as strongly, it is singular that more than of use can be made by this as a refusal. Refuse to more than fairly nearly try and try again.

In not possibly so much and as much as not and desperately, in not possibly as much and as much and as not and not possibly as much and desperately in furnishing this there and more so to astonishingly and avoid, remembering branches how many branches are there and too, to be safely in their way. Not at all. And riches. Riches have not riches have not name of riches and riches. Have not in all this time do and who and makes it for having in that estimate a loser. Not to lose a towel too and other otherwise.

Feeling this and having frequently had recourse to existing creditably existing wood, woods are the poor man's overcoat. Smiles make much more certainly much more smiles, to himself, themselves, all but and butter and bread. Come quarrel so. Not continued to be friends.

Particularly as to part two.

Was Henry Rocker told about it by him or was he induced to say so by himself. As to that question. As to that question was he induced to say so by himself or was he told about it was he told about it, was he told about it. Was he induced to say so by himself or was he told about it.

Cannot do it if he says it if he says it cannot do it, cannot do it if he says it if he says it cannot do it, he cannot do it if he says it, if he says it he cannot do it, he cannot do it if he says it, if he says it he cannot do it. He cannot do it if he says it. If he says it he cannot do it.

When any one means to say he has forgotten what he looks like, if any one means to say he has forgotten he does not remember what he looks like, if any one means to say he does not remember what he looked like, if any one means to say he does not remember what he looks like, if any one does say that he does not remember what he looked like, placed where they were.

Comparing comparative and presuppose.

More and more as they were then if they were to be and ready, more and more if as they were then needed or not needed and first, first as first. Supposing it had helped. It would not.

Next in that position, next to that position, being next in that position as much as next in that position, at first if wanted, if wanted to if it was prepared as wanted to if it was prepared to be wanted to be wanted to what, wanted to not to and not to wanted to and either. Either can be pronounced both ways.

If in beginning counting counting can be made to have words as well as numbers, if in beginning counting counting can have words as well if in beginning counting counting can have as well, as well as ever.

Counting can have words as well as well as numbers counting can have words and numbers as well.

If there is to be a settled history of accidents and expected accidents, if there is to be a settled history of astonishments and expected astonishments, if there is to be settled history of choosing and expected choices if there is to be a settled history and if there is to be a settled history too of why when as nearly more nearly to be placed, cheered by it all.

They can remember a house a garden, a star a little boy a cloud an instance an instance of it. They can remember who was the one who was that one. Who was that one. In a question some have said there is a question mark. A great many say all faces have faced it. Can any one deny they do not see them.

They can remember that, that in that way for instance at one time having had it here and falling if more have had it it is best to arouse adding. Adding to adding and added. In this way no one has the means to benefit. It is undoubtedly of great benefit to me.

He never said, he never said no, he never said no to his wife.

How many cases are there of not continuing to be friends, how many cases are there of not continuing, how many cases are there of not continuing to be friends.

There are a great many cases of not continuing to be friends. As there are a great many cases of not continuing to be friends there are a great many cases in which not continuing to be friends in which not continuing not continuing to be friends in which there are a great many cases of not continuing to be friends. A great many cases of not continuing to be friends are those in which in not continuing to be friends, the cases there are cases the cases of not continuing to be friends. The history of a great many cases of not continuing to be friends is the history of having had a great many cases of not continuing to be friends.

Feeling it as best that those who have made a place in themselves and for themselves and in the cases and best of all for an opportunity to have Martha leave not earlier but how do you do it how do you do it how did you have to be told or more. More.

The next time having had it helped and hurried having had it hurried and heard having had it heard and at once all at once and pleasantly as the name. The name is this if when it happens that all of it places takes place and a place, cases of not continuing to be friends a history of having a great many times not continued to be friends.

One at a time two at a time two at a time one at a time, one at a time four at a time four at a time two at a time, two at a time three at a time three at a time five at a time five at a time four at a time four at a time three at a time.

No one mentions frames.

Frames are needed when not hanging here. When not hanging here when not hanging here and frames are mentioned one at a time, one at a time three at a time. Three at a time one at a time.

Having mentioned first, why do they need to see to sew.

Having mentioned why do they introduce persons and places.

Having mentioned why are exchanges made between an exchange of apples and apples are so much better than when they are so pleased. They are so pleased.

The next time that there is an in between season Algeria by

this one can mean a place where fruits and vegetables are found and sent the next time that there is an in between season Algeria is as useful.

The fifteenth case is the one in which suddenly and unexpectedly as if in no other way and as understood, it is very troublesome to be selected.

Selections have been nicely planned by those who feel best and most.

I did not know I had but I think I did.

Clara and Bell.

Coming back to ask and having coming either for or beside, fortunate as fortunate it is to place it.

As a list.

A list is made by those who having heard and seen and fairly and so often have declined to indulge in secretly favoring themselves. As this sounds and their safety first and their safety first and secondly all have a pleasure in places and in place of it.

In this way means.

It means.

In this way and it means as in can be.

Can it have it.

Can it have it made a difference.

Can it have made a difference to them.

Can it have can it have it can it have made a difference to them.

Take it or leave it.

Taking it to take.

Leaving it to leave.

Leaving it to leave taking it to take.

This is newly dated.

Taking it to take leaving it to leave leaving it to leave taking it to take is newly dated.

Taking it to take.

This comes yesterday.

Taking it to take.

This comes yesterday.

Taking it to take this comes yesterday.

Leaving it to leave.

Leaving it to leave has to be as that.

Leaving it to leave has to be as that for the same and in the way of even why and stretches.

Addressed to them for this.

Please wind this clock, in saying this it is not put in here.

This is the way that weddings met.

Allan Will came to say that in leaving himself he was going away. In going away and planning to stay they would hear from him regularly every day.

So much for that.

Next what happened was this. When he was there he was conquered by the appearance of what he wished and as it was all very shown was he disappointed. He was and blaming, he blamed what he felt on what he saw and in this way we quarreled.

The next instance of fanning came when a violence which had nothing to do with practices was enough cause altogether.

Partly this and partly more.

Nothing to do practically nothing to do with what was often told by word of mouth. Practically nothing to do with what was said and what was heard and very soon. Practically nothing to do with a couple and a couple more. Practically nothing to do with handsome is as handsome does. Practically nothing to do with equality and sternness and repeating that they can and will and all. Practically nothing to do with what has been told by blaming. Practically nothing to do with separate parts of stations and stationary and pleasures and rarely. Practically nothing to do with anything which concerns itself altogether with plenty of it. Practically nothing to do with any of it either as it is or nearly for a reason. What has, who has, who has had it happen, what has what has happened what has it to do with what has happened who has to do with what there was to have happened. What indeed who indeed who indeed and who indeed and what indeed, what has indeed happened.

As quickly practically as quickly as milk and practically as quickly as more milk. Practically as quickly as more milk practically as quickly as milk. Practically as quickly as milk. Practically as quickly as more milk.

Oddly enough oddly separately enough separately separately oddly enough.

As decision.

A great many times.

A great many times having said and said it. Having said and said it having said and said it a great many times, if the places are as if they are and if they are as if the place is, is to be placed and advancing advancing to see a place changed to change a place to change places. Admittedly so.

Act as though and acting as if, acting as if and act as though, act as though, act as if, and act as though not in meeting and admitting.

A special case.

The extreme case of it is disappointment, another extreme case of it is refusal another extreme case of it is admission another extreme case of it is plainly more and more at once and very advantageously. All these together make by no means make an additional distribution.

Engaging and now engaging to be as easily pleased again.

The first time the first time that the first time that of that of that in union there is strength the first it can not be given as an instance and for this reason there had been no friendship before there was enmity, and was there enmity and was there enmity before there was friendship, was there.

Again and again amounting amounting to that.

Nearly everywhere and earlier nearly earlier nearly and earlier nearly everywhere and nearly earlier, nearly earlier and nearly everywhere and nearly everywhere and nearly earlier nearly and earlier nearly and everywhere, nearly earlier nearly everywhere nearly everywhere nearly earlier the advantage remained an advantage it was to be an advantage. Fairly recognised as to more principally.

This is pleasantly thought.

If slower and more slowly, if more slowly to be certain, if to be certain, a certain day can replace regular a regular direction. The direction was this. Come as soon as you can. In this there was no adequate to this there was no adequate and because of this and fairly to please it was easily mentioned afterward. The experience and in returning not as much as sensible of an increasing habit of settling everything once before. It had needed it had afterwards as has been it has been as if it were not needed, in no case as needed and needed why and preferably.

Did not go again but she came. They came. We came. And they did not go again but they came. We came. She came. Easily placed and places. Places are needed and added and added and added so. So and so. It never need be suggested. This and more. Read and lead and afterwards on time.

May she easily answer that the reason is that she is not often more nearly and happier. This does not make any difference at all as outburst. The next time is useful. That ends that.

How many in a year how many in one year.

As happy as one may say as gay as one may say as gay as one may say as happy as one may say and leaning.

The next time that afterwards as it has to be in every essential, the next time that it has afterward to be and in every essential and afterward and as it has to be and afterward as it has to be, as it has to be afterwards in every essential too to be remembered too. It had to be fifth.

Almost and most and occasionally occasionally almost and most almost and most and occasionally and after a time and in between and for more than that and as to in advance and formerly and so forth. This is next to a division. Divided by five makes twenty and most most of it. Sending this.

Can at once and follow can at once can have it can have it at once can have it at once can and at once can have it and at once can have it at once can have it and at once.

Fortunate in securities.

Can fifteen divided by twenty-five successively coming again successively.

Every one I have ever known.

One I have known.

Every one I have ever known.

In keys in threes in please and in please, in please and in case and in case and in favor. In favor of it.

Plenty of extra and even inside and more, and even inside and more.

If in remembering the last if in as unexpected too if in the appointment and fortunately blaming if in hearing that and more than motioning in or out, as it has to be in all the exact ceilings which have to have been made aware aware of the best that can be thought and said so. This has to have it at all.

Can force can force to force to force it to and in and countable for not in the same and astounding. To change a use to be sure. To be sure used actually. Needless to point to these and so and so much so. Can having had it arranged for annoy him. It does.

How long can it be needed as arranged for and annoyed. And annoyed. Many times and as tortoise shell too. This is introduced.

If one had three, if one had three if each one had three, there would be something wrong in nothing. If each one had three there would be something and there was as if they left, left it about, left it out. This was the result of selecting, they selected two and three and as it felt very well and was so much as that in afterwards.

Happily in the past and at once, and it was as if he agreed. And to be accepted and to have accepted and to prepare in an accepted pleasure and so for a part of that in a way.

This meaning beginning this meaning in unending attention to the rectification of so much as in sight. The sight of it.

As it is. It is is the case of intention honesty honestly and to more as and sent so. He needs him. He came again and greeted he was greeted attentively. The next time and a long time and a long time and by next time and by the next time he was greeted attentively. For and fortunately and at once every part of all day and more than fortunately, fortunately and two, two and in reasoning, they reason as well as leadership, this made a change in their doing it all the same. Thank you very much and in attention.

The next satisfaction fortunately was as much so as that. And in insisting. The result was that in advance it was as a protection and not in advance not in advance it was as a protection and not in advance. Next at most it was as if there was easier more easily and in result, and a result, conditions and interallied and union. Fortunately and best. After that on that and that and that on the return not as at first and and best. Would it make a difference if it changed. The next was very satisfying and helpful and just as it was. He was asked and gave it all and very well, very well was

there was it, was it old. Was it at all measured. It depends a great
deal on everything and where they went. Twice and as they say.

Fairly names.

A list.

Arthur

Ellis

Edith

Edna

Clara

Herbert

Edgar

Philip

Adrienne

Herbert

Edward

Joseph

   and

Adolph

The rest are mentioned.

A list of names.

Fairly names.

Jenny

Carrie

Lily

Hattie

   and

Ada

The rest are mentioned

Antony

Abel

Louis

Howard

   and

Hilda.

After lists afternoon.

If they came and are seen, if they are seen and have come if
they have come and have left if they have left and have heard,
if they have heard and had shared if they had shared and had held

if they had held and had hurried if they had hurried and had counted if they had counted and had changed if they had changed and had placed if they had placed and had and it had amounted to that and as much more.

A disappointment merely changes one into six. The result being that she has that satisfaction.

He had chosen. Chosen it.

He had chosen with undoubtedly a delay.

They had been chosen with their consent.

They had been chosen and there were no replacements and yet they later did not perform the activities for which they had been chosen. The reason for this being that gradually as they needed and not as they needed they rather refused. How pleasantly do fathers and mothers say so. After this there was as it might be added religiously.

If readily is assured if readily is assured if it is so and so and so.

In no case have they been used to this use. Useless and whether. Whether altogether.

After that after that makes it certain.

There is more habitually.

They know it too.

Two and aloud.

Three and four.

Three and aloud.

Six and four.

Three and aloud.

To fasten and a floor.

To fasten.

And a floor.

What was said when he what was said when he had when he never had been when he had not been here before.

The next time means that particularly often and finally as soon.

Reading cases.

The first case.

To change and kind and as kind.

The second case. To ask to be remembered.

The third case. As soon as it was arranged as soon as that they resembled all who were mentioned.

Out aloud.

Out of, out of it, out of it nearly all out of it.

The next present is the present that is given just the same.

And at present.

The next present is the kind of present for which as well as no preparation there is no preparation at all.

Can illustrations be as useful as that.

From time to time.

And a repetition.

The first time that it ever happened that there was a cessation of intimacy was one in which they happened not to be there. The second case was the one in which it having lasted all along there finally arose the excellent interest which each had in not further happening to hear it said. In so far as there was this occasion and afterwards as it was nicely visited no one not either of them said so.

The next case which presented itself to the attention of the one reading writing and counting is one which has been as attentively destroyed as anything else. In this case very many returns of the day have been wished to one another and very sincerely and mentioned and with authority. In this case there have in consequence actually repeated renewals of description separately retailed. And as much so.

Parts and parts and parted. Parted as a case can call. Call and call and call and see and safely safely as it has a shawl. A shawl is used when it is intended to have it used at all at all at all thereby and called in to see.

It has been said that the interest is not the same when the name is not the same as the name of the one who has returned it securely and left it there and thereabouts. Come to have it so.

Is no one interested in quarrels no one at all is no one interested in the quarrels no one at all is no one at all interested in quarrels no one at all.

One two three four five six seven the seventh was not counted.

Easy to see and easy to have and easily.

Continually in front continually in front of them and meant as having at no time not an opportunity to see.

Not continually in front not continually in front and meaning that only once and a while and then as often as not.

Not continually in front continually in front and as often and as frequently and as it is to be meaning to do and so of course not at all. In this reason, in this and a reason in this in resting in resting and no and not and not and now and not at all. Thanking just as much as ever.

Supposing he said I would and would. Supposing he said I will and I will and I will. Supposing he said I would. Supposing he said I would. Supposing he said I will. Supposing he said I will. Supposing he said I would. A supposition.

Finally a Negro too.

Supposing he said finally, supposing he said and finally supposing he said as finally supposing he said finally supposing he said finally supposing he said finally supposing he said finally.

After all not at all not at all very much very long and not often and not often and as yet.

This made a joke.

The next having it is the one who when another who was rarely seen said he was to ask to have it as a pleasure added that in that case if it might be advisable. To this there was no answer.

The incident in question.

Having is faster having it as fast having it as at last having it at last having it as fast having it faster having it having had it and undoubtedly always forgotten having always forgotten it. Almost a description in a minute. No names. A part of the way. In no time and a title a title to it entitled to it. If it is interesting if it is as interesting if to go and if to go and say so if it is as interesting to go and say what did some one do with it. Three cannot be a list.

A great many times.

An aid an aid an aid, and if an aid and if in aid, and if and if and if in aid and if an aid and if in aid, and an aid and if it is an aid, and if it is in aid, and if it is and if it is an aid and in aid. If it is in aid of it.

Consuming at least twenty-seven and consuming at least twenty-seven.

Happy in stretches happily stretches and for stretches and happily at a stretch.

So much for this and for the other.

If in and at at first if at first and in and at at first, very often and so many and as often and very many nearly all of them and most nearly all of them and most of them nearly and most of them thinking from having seen and heard and had it happen, had it happened and by this as of course, of course is more in that as at once and by and very likely.

Forgetting to refer it to that more than to this and at once. Does it make any difference if he said so.

He needs me, she needs me, she needs me, he needs me and especially. If it can if it can be remembered that one half of forty is twenty. Is one half of forty twenty, and is twenty one half and one half and one half of it. If it is more than one half of it is it more than one half of it.

Having heard it here.

A history of having a great many times.

After and before.

After and before.

After and before and emphasis.

After and before and after and before and after and before.

The next time after, before the next time, before the next time after the next time.

After and before.

Continue after and continue.

Continue after and continue.

After and before.

It is as plainly as that it is as plainly as that and it is as plainly and it is as plainly.

As that.

Continued after, continued before. As plainly as that.

One instance of having had a certain time one instance of having had and having had of certainly having had of having certainly had a certain time. One instance of it.

Blue and blue and blue and new and new and new and to offer and to offer and to offer it to them.

Jennie or a wife's affection being the history of later and then marriage and then travel and then wishes and then wishes and then having had a house and a garden having a house a garden and enough fish and chicken and then as rich and more rich than could have been expected continue to engage herself to wool and fur. Having had an interesting enough voyage to the home of her husband.

This did not come this did not go away this did not go away this did not come this did not go away.

When with its when with its white when with its white and black when with its when with its white when with its black, and in no particular case anger or indeed coming again. Make it plentiful and really chosen, make it chosen, make it plentiful make it plentiful and really chosen, make it chosen.

It has been decided that there should be a division the kind of a division that is to the advantage of everybody.

Mention ten, to mention ten, to mention ten to him, to mention ten to him to mention ten, to mention, to have to mention ten. Mention ten to him. Mentioned ten mentioned ten to him to mention ten to him and not to mention then, then to mention ten and to be carefully pleased. In this way and not in that way and not in their way.

He mentioned he mentioned he mentioned it of him. He said that it was believed to be more nearly true than ever.

He mentioned it of him. He mentioned it and he said that it was more nearly true than ever.

Divided between him, it was divided between him and this and not accounting for it this did not account for it.

And the value of it.

Supposing they had been friends, supposing he had been a friend supposing he was a friend supposing he is a friend.

In supposing and having remained and having remained and curiously having remained comparatively recently and success-fully and at once and as in reason for a certain time and more than apparently. In this case and not at all because of the fact. The facts are there, they knew and he did not know, he did not know and he had the explanation he had the explanation and he had the habit of that event, he had the habit of that event and he referred to a discovery, he referred to a discovery and in the presence of those who meant to appeal he appealed and they were as much so as before. Classes, classes listen when the classes are large and small. Classes are large and small when classes listen. Classes listen and classes are large and small. Classes are large and small and classes are large and small and classes listen and classes listen and are large and small.

Continue to think of more than the other.

Came in came in come on.

Continued to think of more than the other.

Come in and think of more than the other.

Came in and thought of more than the other.

In plenty of time.

Came in and continued to think of more than the other and in plenty of time.

That and enough of it.

To start from the beginning to start from the beginning and start from the beginning, starting and from the beginning having started having started from the beginning, starting from the beginning and waiting starting from the beginning and waiting waiting and starting starting from the beginning beginning from the beginning starting from the beginning waiting from the beginning, waiting and starting, starting from the beginning it is at once begun. Begun to be and not nervously.

The next and satisfied the next to be satisfied and next to be satisfied and to be satisfied next.

How many can you confuse with the one who was prettily accurate.

How many can you confuse with the one who determined to leave.

How many can you confuse with the one who had established it.

How many can you confuse with the arrangement of it all.

How many can you confuse with it at all.

How many are confused with the others so that in part and partly so that partly and so that partly at all.

How many are confused with there being that and there being there and there being no difference between and in between. How many are there further and how many are further and how many are confused and how many are confused by that and how many are confused with the others, and how many others are there. How many others are there confused with others.

At first, the first, the first, at first, at first, at first the first, the first at first. Confused with the other.

Afterwards confused with the other.

Told and told and told of it, told four people that in doing it there would be a description of a great many different kinds of differences.

Each one heard.

Each one each one who heard each one each one not noticing each one each one and each one to one, each one to one and not noticing. Not noticing each one and not noticing and one and to one and not noticing and not noticing and each one.

He said to stop it.

We said to stop it.

We said to stop it.

He said to stop it.

We said to stop it.

And if in having gone away and not in that way and it might be admitted that if everything had been bought it would have been as favorable and as favorable and as favorable to all. All who have and all who have and all who have and all who have to have that and where where all where all who have where all have have to have and favorably as favorable.

Please to be pleased with habits and independent of answers.

Will you let me know now, will you let me know now. Will you let me know now.

In this and not as in attention, in this and not as in attention in this and not as in attention.

Will he let them know now, will he let them know now. In this and not in attention, in attention and in this and in this and in attention. Now altogether, altogether now.

It is not in and as estimation that a reason for most of it is at once added.

He knew it.

It is not for and in case of betterment that there was likely to be that in use.

It was not on account of individual reasoning that an acceptation of an industrious decision was asked for.

He said that he would not and he would not if he did not if he did not and he did not if he did not everything else let everything else go.

To go.

There is absolutely no possibility of there ever being an element of surprise in it.

It is easy very easy easily it is easily very easily and not what was favorable to it then and always.

If able and a boat a boat and birds if able and a boat and birds if able to have a boat and birds if to be able to have had a boat and birds advice is just the same and not telling it too often and not having had to exaggerate and not having had time and all of it carefully.

This has no more to do with it than that.

She will see.

He will see.

He will see

She will see

Me.

No more to do with it than that.

Nothing to do with friends.

Nothing to do any more

Does she do it nicely

Does she do it very nicely.

Does she do it very nicely does she do it very nicely does she do it nicely.

This can come to have evenings after a while occupied altogether as if there were in no way any advantage. Disadvantage.

In plenty of time they went away in plenty of time in plenty of time there is plenty of time. Once or twice. There is plenty of time once or twice there is plenty of time once or twice. Familiarly.

In exactly separate and satisfied examples. And example and

it was added and it was the habit of the difference of the difference between if there was plenty of added initiative or in blame. And uncounted.

To count makes it at once faster, to make it at once to make it faster at once to count makes it faster at once to count makes it faster makes it faster makes it faster makes it once makes it at once makes it faster at once. And counted. Three is an addition right away.

Was or was it was it so. Was it so and was it.

An agreeable feature.

It is to be remarked that being alike that it is being alike, it is to be remarked that it is to be as much alike as ever.

Having handed it to him and having had it first and last and having had it at first and having had it at last and if so, was he nearly there when he mentioned geography and when he mentioned geography and when he mentioned geography. To wonder, a wonder.

Had it for them.

Meeting them and having it for them.

Meeting them and having had it for them.

Meeting them and having arranged to have it for them.

Meeting them and arranging to have it arranged for them.

Meeting them and arranging it for them and having had it arranged for them.

Personally and personally and personally and personally and personally, and personally and personally and personally too.

In and call, to call, to call and to call it and to call for it and to allow it and to allow it to call it to call it and to allow it.

Initials too, initials and to be used too to be used to it, to be used in place of to be used for it. Initials and to be placed and to be used to it and to be used and to be placed and to be used to it.

Over again.

As much over there was as much over there was as much of it there was as much of it over there was some of it there was some of it left over.

Supposing it was perfectly simple supposing it would not depend upon the last time nor upon an other time suppose it depended upon at first and what naturally happened to have been intended when there was no delay.

No delay at all.

Three and four entirely different.

If there had been following in succession and at the same time apparently no interruption and in part, leaving earlier and no earlier and having followed separately as before. In this way it would always happen that they would have it given.

Always do a little more pleasantly and fortunately and ineradicably and in mistake. Has it happened to be always the same and at once. And at first and with them and in exchanging and to follow her. Always as much assistance it was always as much of an assistance and in this way and in this way, that has that is the same as that and decided. Decidedly makes it another third. To commence when and to refuse it.

She said now she said now and not new, she said now and not new and not before she said not before and now she said now, she said now and not new she said now and not new and not before.

This was the same and not now.

This was the same and for him and not now, this was the same and for him and not now and this was the same and not now and for him and this was the same and for him and not now.

He stood in this way he sat it in this way he stood and he sat in this way. He sat in this way he stood in this way he sat in this way he stood in this way and for him and not now.

He stood and he sat in this way and for him and not now and this way.

It all depends.

Having heard that many are the ones older than that having heard that many are the ones, having heard that many having heard that many are the ones having heard that many are the ones having heard that many are the older ones having heard that many are the ones. And in the meantime.

In that case there was no difference.

In little places and the same in the same place as that, in little places as little places as if there was more than enough prepared in time.

Next to it for them.

Having easily and easier, having easily and having easily and easier and practised for itself by having seen to it in their place.

Recognition.

In many parts in place of all of it as it had happened and a chance and once in a while and admitted.

Partly understood to be and left over to have as it can be over estimated and partly and more than added and rejoined.

Not in this way and at once.

Having laterally that is to have a part in following and coming faster having established and relieved and often and meeting coming to have it so at once and not used as it was. In having four and four makes three in having four and as much as especially reasonable.

He knew that he had heard it said.

Once in a while and often.

Partly and as a question.

Once and twice and three times and all as it has been called at once. At once fortunately and it makes having it have it have it at once have it as having it as at once and there. They had a plan.

He knew that when there was this and as early and wishing to see and settle it for themselves, settle it at once all along.

It was astonishing that they met twice.

Having a fortune just the same.

Why are there enough at once because every one has used it. And thanked and thanks so much.

Able Mable Mable able Mable able too.

No names mentioned.

Mable able able Mable Mable able too.

It is understood that and not coming to be when and in between.

He was easily stimulated

He was easily relieved

He was easily prepared

He was easily and he said so.

If in leaving word did there come an answer at first. And later when there was a request did there come to be an appeal or more of an instance of it.

A history of having, a history of having.

It is in spite of it an arrangement that has not had to have it.

All names.

All names too.

All names too and too.

All names and not named.

All names and not named and in respect to the following.

It has been said that names are important.

It has been said that names are important for the biography.

It has been said that names are important for the biography it has been said that names are important for the biography.

It makes that difference and to come and come at all.

In making that difference and in coming in making that difference and to come and in making that difference and in coming and in coming at all.

In making that difference and in coming at all.

It is to be.

When there is when there is and there is and as well and there is when there is when there is when it is as well when it is as well that there is when there is when there is as well and when there is and when there is as well.

An example of what was it.

She started there and it was only later that she left. She started there and it was later and it was later that she left. She started there and she started later and she started later when she left she was there and she started later and she was there and she started later when she left.

She started there. At that time there were at once and as it came to be nearly as much so there came to be an occasion they came occasionally and soon oftener and again. This happened to coincide. As it was to be hearing and a doubt a doubt of that. Did hearing and as all of it made it better and as much so. Afterward there was as much enjoyment and in that case having it with them with them and there. This makes it more easily at once. No one can disturb and no one can disturb and no one can disturb and passes it passes it. Remember harder longer and the same remember the same and at once and in the way and not in the way of it.

At once, not interesting.

At once, not interesting.

At once.

Not interesting.

At once and not interesting.

Did he remember to say please wind the clock.

Did she remember to say a quarter past nine o'clock.

Did they remember to say what time is it.

Did he remember to say there are as many as that here.

Did she remember to say there is enough of that left.

Did they remember to say then there is not any necessity to order any more.

Can it be a little more so.

At once and after it and at once and after it and at once. And at once and after it and at once and after it and after it and at once. Two mention two. Two mention two.

In this way all who wish have to have to do so and say so. This does not make a difference.

To make a beginning by arrangement.

He remembered all who said there are there and each one and having in the place of it and carefully. He remembered each one and having in it and at once and not eagerly as is a question.

To and to question. In that way as easily. After that in a minute in a minute or two. That is and two and the noise, they have asked as if to be and having had it for them at once. This makes the first time the first time or two. Not a question.

It is awfully nearly and at best and answered. This answer.

It is ordinarily an advantage and compared to it up and down.

It is more than most and in effect and having in question the father of the child yet unborn. Should questions follow the absence of it at once.

What did she do when she satisfied herself reasonably. What did she do when she had not refused to admit and admit.

What did she do when there was more admiration than ever.

Let it be considered.

First in at once.

Sound as if if she has known that under those circumstances that would be best.

Third. If she said I might and if in leaving if in leaving more were expectantly adding that it would be best, would there be a more added.

It is quite useless to have opposition after that.

It is quite useless to have it at all.

It is quite useless to be at once and measured.

It is quite useless.

It is quite useless and destroyed.

If a mother and a father, if a father and a mother, was she sorry that it had been said.

If a mother and another mother if another mother and a mother would she be sorry that it had been said.

If a mother and another daughter, if a daughter and another mother would she be sorry that it had been said.

If a daughter and another daughter if another daughter and a daughter would she be sorry that it had been said.

A cousin and Douglas went about together. By and by they went together they had plenty of occupation and plenty of accumulation. As it happened he acting quickly was able to add rapidly and in consequence they both at once continued to be the same. After that in order to be attached they found obligations very pleasing and further they established themselves admirably. As it happens they never saw anything of each other later.

Mention three. The first one a surprise because hitherto there had always been devotion. The second one a pleasure because after having established the habit of once in a while it came suddenly to be permitted and as it happened after she left no one asked for pleasure. Please it to please it. Please and pleasure. This is what she was reproached for.

The third case is one that happened as it came to [be] known. As it came to be known no one could be careful. Carefully. This can be had by having had it once more. Now it is time to get dressed.

I did not think I did not think I did not think I would.

I did not think I did not think I did not think I could.

Could do it.

Parts of plans.

I did not think I could do it.

This is the way that they keep it and this is the way to keep it and this is the way to keep it and this is the way to occupy it and this is the way to keep it and to occupy it and this is the way to keep it to occupy it.

Having had to have to ask and if the hat is just the same and if they say that in their way they will at once and soon and why will there then be that after it when they have said and done it all will they then send and after that will they then have and had it in it for it just at once and so forth. He expected it.

There is no reason why anything is undertaken.

Asking him again asking for it again asking him for it again.

Always to have and easily passed in that way. Would he be willing would he be obliging and willing. Would he be obliging and willing would he be and will he be willing will he be obliging and willing.

No one can guess this, I am the only one who can guess this.

No one can guess this.

I am the only one who can guess this.

Not a while.

He was right when he chose and chose it. He was right when he chose it. He was right when he chose when he chose it. He was right when he chose it.

When was he right.

When was he right.

When was he right when was he right when he was when was he when he was when he was right when was he right.

When he was right when was he right.

To begin with it it has to be presented to him, it can be said it can be said to present well.

To begin with it has to be presented to begin with it has to be to begin with it has to be presented to begin with it has to be presented. It presents well.

To begin with to begin with it has to be presented to begin with it has to begin with to be presented. It presents well.

And in that case and following suit and following suit, in that case and following suit. Following suit and in that case following suit in that case following suit in that case. The first thing that has to happen is that it has to be presented and it presents well.

After that and as much and after that and as much after that as much after that and as much and as much after that. After that. As much after that. It has to be presented as much after that and it presents well it presents well as much after that it has as much after that it has to be presented as much after that it presents well it presents well as much after that.

Next preparation is of course. Of course the next preparation and of course and of course and the next preparation and of course. Of course.

The next preparation and of course.

The next preparation and of course and it presents well. The next preparation and of course and it presents well and of course, and of course and the next preparation and it presents well and of course. Of course.

And it presents well. And of course.

Did he ask it for me first at once.

Did he ask it for me now at all.

Did he ask it for me as at once.

Did he ask it for me for this now.

Did he ask it for me.

Had he asked it for me at all.

The next time in planning.

Plan and plain and expect and complain and not attached to a division. Attach and explain and not attached to a division and to a decision. Attached and a plain and not attached to a decision to a division, attached and contain and not attached to a division. To a decision and attached and explain and attached and contain and attached and to a decision and attached and to a division and contain. Contain and attached to a division and explain and attached to a decision and contain and attached to a division and contain.

It need not be so easily said at once.

It need not be so easily said at once.

It need not be so easily said at once.

If forty fifty and thirty if forty fifty and thirty at once if forty fifty and thirty at once it need not be so easily if forty fifty and thirty at once it need not be so easily said at once.

Not at once and to spare. He meant to have and hold a house a house that needs to have an arrangement made for it.

If two two two and not mentioned but shown. If asked for and reasons and there are reasons. How often have all all of them.

It needs more than this for that.

He knew best.

To begin to ask everybody is nothing to begin to ask every one is no sin, to begin to begin is nothing to begin is no sin to begin is no sign, to begin is a beginning of asking every one the same thing.

Ask every one the same thing.

Begin. Begin to ask every one if they are able to be of assistance. This makes it critical.

This is one thing and Bridget is another thing. Bridget may be either Scotch English French or Irish and in each case she will appeal to Janet. And to you too.

Let us act as aloud.

A wife. Never had any.

A husband. Never had any.

And they were right. My son John and his wife us four and no more. And they were right.

And they were right, myself and my wife my son John and his wife us four and no more and they were right.

Let it be considered relation. A relation is one who either living or visiting may be known as not at once. And they were right. This can be said biographically.

Parties and parties and they were invited to their parties.

All who had had and had been held to be at once interested interested at once. Would we be interested at once.

Ask him why he had it to do, ask him to do it too, ask him what he could do ask him when it would be best to do it. He would answer that he would be very glad to do it.

In leaving it would be best to decide about it, after leaving it it would be best to decide that it would be best that it would be best and that it would be better.

Not likely to have an answer not at all likely.

It is very disagreeable to dislike and it is very disagreeable to dislike and it is very disagreeable to dislike it.

A long time in which to decide that although it is a slate a slate used to mean a slate pencil. And to use it to write. She said I could not use two at a time.

If he came and was at once inclined inclined to have heard that how many places are there in it. How many places are there in it. This is at once the cause of it.

It is not true that no one is invited.

He met him. It was very difficult to remember who was here alone.

This has decided us to consider it a trait.

After that if only one of two and the two are there that is not enough to force it enough not enough to space it enough not enough and enough still enough so that it is not all alone but still not enough so that the others are as wanted. Wanted wanted wanted to be wanted to be and wanted to be and wanted to complete want to complete and anyway.

She reminded me that I was as ready as not and I said I will not say that I preferred service to opposition. I will not say what or what is not a pleasure.

Let us think of the battle of the Marne.

Not at once.

Let us not at once think of the battle of the Marne. Let us not think of the battle of the Marne at once. Let us not at once let us not think of the battle of the Marne.

Next. Let us not think of the battle of the Marne.

Next. Let us not think of the battle of the Marne at once.

Let us think of the battle of the Marne not at once let us not at once let us not think of the battle of the Marne, let us not at once think of the battle of the Marne.

In that way and as tens. They tried to change tens to fifteens.

When he troubled him that is when he troubled him and aid to use that is when he troubled him.

Matter of time and in aid to use when he troubled him and in aid to use.

Happy and happier.

If how do you do and afterwards if you are welcome and afterwards this is where to put them.

Where to put them past past and where to put them.

She might have been if it had been that standing openly there was no there was nothing darker. Nothing is used and used to. As it is we have kept Maggie.

As it is.

Yes she has to have a Saturday and Saturday and a precaution. Precautions make more noise than ever. Precaution and not in a fear. No one is afraid that is to say not when not when and always not when absently enough and heard and said.

He needs all of it she needs all of it, she needs all of it he needs all of it.

As he needs all of it.

She needs.

All of it.

It has never been known to be it has not been known it has not been known at all.

When do they is not the same as why do they.

Five times fifty is fifty times as much.

And resuming.

He has to stare. And afterwards in an addition. Supposing at best and advice. He needs no advice. Any advice is good. Any advice is good if it is given strongly enough and any advice is good and he needs to have to have and ahead. Ahead too and may be hears too.

It may be said of Henry Kate that after he had been introduced and that was by addition afterwards and in no case two and one, and in the past and at this time, two and one to turn too and one too, in having two and a whole, two and a whole. One might be satisfied and to believe that if he were satisfied would there be a difference between that and right, that and bright. He had the pleasure of being able to have a home and as and and for. By them not to be them, to bewail does a wall to bewail and a two brothers, two brothers as if he asked and you meant to be hearing it. How nicely does Brenner do so. Who mentions whom.

If you please I make the best of it all.

We are very pleased that by the interposition of Luxembourg which has always been known we are able to avoid a decision in regard and without regard to the weather.

As likely as not.

An entirely different matter. It always happens to be what
and where and for whom.

And to be very careful.

Pears pears say so because of pears we have decided differently we have decided even if it is late to go at once to the other
place and once at the other place we can easily decide which
place to leave. Leave and to guessed. Guessed at once.

His having had and had to hurry.

In the middle.

What happened to it. What is the difference.

He knew nothing.

And she was with a dish a dish of fruit.

And in that way.

Very very much.

Fortunately he paid for houses. Fortunately.

With institutions and with arrangements.

Persons play.

Answer and back.

He respects a witness.

He expects a witness.

In language for that.

If only coming to stay as younger and to close.

He knew first and last.

All the mention and intention all the mention of it.

Surprised to find.

Accepted for them.

Not annoying to them.

No one can understand butter. Bread and butter, no one can
understand bread and butter, bread and butter and eggs no one
can understand bread and butter and eggs, no one can understand
bread and butter and eggs and it is defended. Defended just as
well.

It is easily believed believe it is easily believed. How many
times in one day, and refused and refused to go to know, and
happened to them. This is included in questioning and in having
heard, heard the bell.

As there were two three times and the fourth time and as there
was to be one at once at once temporarily.

She will be so pleased to hear it. Can it be had can it be had for them, for them indifferently and division, division means that twice and even twice as often.

Nicely on time.

This is a history of having a great many times not continued to be friends.

Friends and as much as having heard it directly from Spain.

Friends and having heard it directly having heard it directly from Spain. Friends and having heard it directly from Spain.

Much more.

Indifferently to carry to carry and it was as attached as ever in place of it. And very often.

Could it be possible that she and not to remember it at once. Once or twice. In time.

No one has angrily.

It is. It is a difficulty.

Seeing separately sealing separately separating, separately, able to safely say so and as much. As much as ever. Together.

In these a list at once.

First. As slowly.

Second. As much.

Third. As at once.

Fourth. We expect a fourth at once.

First. He measured it for us.

Second. They had it ready.

Third. At once and for this and for their use.

Fourth. He could have it.

Animals as if at once. As if at once and animated as if at once. To decide and to have intended to see to it at once. At once.

Furnished for them.

Meeting Abel. It is very interesting that this name which means reasonably waiting, preparation, advantage and really expectation means that at once and at once and at once and north and at once and at once and at once. No one needs to change. No one at once. No one at once and no one needs to at once. No one needs to and no one needs to at once.

As well as ever.

As convenient as that.

He changed his mind about astonishment.

Having had and having been and it having been an offense to receive and destroy and refuse and return and handle and avoid and appeal and engage and it having been an accepted intention. Could she ask any one to join.

Indeed and to say so.

To exchange distance for distances.

An advantage for them.

An account of virtue and virtues, of at once and a little further and in time.

To say and to saying.

And if and at once.

Right and as right and contain.

How to remember why there was an occasion to exchange writing for writing. The lady writes so beautifully.

And knowing that.

And never has been.

Two sentences too.

If he has invited if she has invited if she has invited too if she too has invited if he too has invited let it be considered in the middle. He and the middle, exactly they were three.

They did not come and they did they did afterwards they did, included they did and literally.

Have a name have Leonard as a name, have Leonard as a name have a name.

He comes here and at once he comes here.

To change one with two and four to one with none.

It is so much easier to see than to hear to call than to thank to cover than to arrange.

Come along.

She said yes to come along.

How differently to forget and to please, please come along.

After each time time mine line. After each time.

To announce two and the two who had come were not only later but at least at least as it happened it happened to be not only but also astonishing. If surprises change to surprise, if to surprise changes to surprising if surprising changes to surprised as surprised as that.

He interrupted her.

At once to them.

No one need does it at once no one needs and does it at once as if if they had been and to be there. Wanted to and reproach as well.

As differently satisfied as that.

To begin explaining.

Have to have and happen to have and happen to have it. To begin explaining.

Partly as much as for a reason and at this time visited by preference, prefer to delay and after all is it easier to have it all, as easily.

And in plenty of time.

Have to have protected all of it in order to repress what is not exactly recently renewed. And to renew.

How do you do.

At one time.

Plans to relate related as at once and perfectly perfectly and so much, did he learn that.

And to remind.

In crowds and crowd, to crowd into them, and into the crowded and wood who said it of woods that the woods that woods are a poor man's overcoat and having had it for them for them and really, really all about it.

All about it makes it indeed more than looking like and like units units looking like and like and like and looking. Who needs changes. She says that she says that she has and has and has to hear it although indeed admirably.

An explanation of only one instance that was peculiar and more quickly. On top of this and not and it was not it was not unfortunate and he came after all had we not already gotten tired of associating associating and associate. Associates too.

Should should be repeated.

And now for assistance.

On and about the time when it was easily arranged.

On and about the time when it was easily arranged he refuses she refers to this and in reference to it may have happily placed their wishes in such a way that previously and as to predictions,

predictions and previously, previously and predictions, previously as much as that.

How many more can as a fact how many more can go how many more as a fact, as a fact how many more can go.

Ought to.

How many days are there in it.

In where.

Referring to some one else.

He imagined he had that as an object. Referring to some one else.

At all.

Plenty of the best of them all.

Inclined to have a reason for all of this later.

When was he lost when was he able when was he able to be told about it.

When was he able when will he repeat when will he feel it and prepare two or three. When will he prepare two or three.

How many times when they begin again.

Suspiciously of four.

Can any one see the resemblance.

And so obliging.

After this they had they did, they decided for themselves alone.

And how very carefully to be even kinder.

Twenty times and in a way.

And they met them.

Please find it out.

She said it did not do them the least good.

She could easily tell all about it.

And I promised.

How can keeping be kept as it is.

To decide that almost a year is enough and to decide that almost a year is quite enough. Quite and quiet.

To need to know.

As is usual when it has happened.

Unused may be explanatory.

Did he attach enough importance to it.

And has it explained just what we like.

To have easily forgotten to ask for it and to have easily for-gotten to ask for it in return.

Who can furnish more of it to those who are intending to be able to arrange for it.

Not as easily angry has never been mentioned.

I know this will please her.

Balanced means a book.

Parts and parts.

Do they do this to them.

And she laughed as heartily as if it was pleasantly and care-fully, carefully explains it all.

Increasing it for me.

Come to and come as a part and come as a part and carry. Once more an obstruction. An obstruction is made and one might say this is true of snow and ice and water and wells and snow and ice and cutting. Cutting makes no arrangements necessary. Sup-posing frankly supposing he knew as much as could be known about why she left. She left in the first place because at that time was there an advantage in adding twenty-five to twenty, and twenty to a hundred and a hundred and twenty to all who have it to do. This can be learned just in time and all of them have plenty of tables. At table.

She asked for it and just at first, not as if it had beside more than was understood to be better. Whether it makes it originally a plan. If he and he and he if he and if he had a son how many sons are there altogether. Three. And how often may the mistake be admitted. As often as all of it has been actually meant fairly well.

Do you describe white and wider, do you describe as well and better. After this they made many explanations and if following and following following it at once. If they followed it at once and at once and restless is not the same as resisting to be to be resisting, having had a reason for it. The reason for it is this.

And starting.

All who mention mention very properly mention that it was nearly as much as that.

And all who do too.

As best and best.

Is it best that it should be altogether or not.

Do they get the better of it.

Opposite to stopping.

And houses can be just as well.

She was never any trouble at all.

Does he bring himself lucky and does he add that he wishes that which he wishes, is that he or she can attend to it attentively.

Next to it.

Nearly as nearly and does it occur often.

And by and by.

Not as attractive.

He looked at me yes, she looked at me yes, she looked at me yes, he looked at me yes. Yes and yes. Yes he looked at me yes, she looked at me yes she looked at me yes he looked at me yes.

The chances are that they are very attractive.

In answer.

Left in makes more of it.

An excitement shows it.

Adds and angrily and if it is undeniable that with the exception of disappointment there is no case of it and afterwards afterwards and in that case, in that case they have antedated antedated it.

Large and divided into as many as can count quickly.

Targets.

No interruptions and who knows where they are.

And a pretty collection.

Very prettily or so.

To whom does it belong.

And I like it.

Does one realise that in summer they use them in summer and in winter they use them in winter, is it all realisable.

This will never make her and startle her and startle her and startle her and make her angry.

Every one forgets about it.

Legs as long and legs as strong. Strength. Legs as long and legs as strong. Length. Legs along.

What a color.

Fortunately in places fortunately a story. Suppose an addition, and a subtraction and registration, supposing there is pleasure in

shining and in question and in purchase and in exchange. This is
meant to be an actual refusal. Does any one pray less.

Immeasurable

Accountable

Useful for stockings.

Useful for it.

Nearer and nearly.

Nicely and now.

If any one were to guess would they guess what it is that is to
come next.

A history of how they did it. They stop again.

Of easily arranged

Easier and later

Does she know it.

The fourth one was unexpected.

Even at best.

He would so much rather.

And now all at once.

To repeat in exchange.

If each one looks.

Privately

They can easily and across they can easily cross.

Know and known makes it there all day all day too.

To accompany.

Up there where where is it.

Do they resemble each other.

Two to arrange it.

She knows what is open and what is closed where they see
and where they look, where they go and where they stand and
where there is more appearance of division than ever.

How much room is there.

How many more are there.

Particularly as they were so very well placed.

And not at all alike and repeatedly not at all alike.

In looking up in looking up. In looking up at it not in looking
up not in looking up and at it.

Every one without it. Each one but one without it.

How nicely as a street and expectations and gratified. For

instance gratified by having Etta and Etta is a name. Also gratified
by having hurried. Also gratified by having at once and most of
it in this way. Did a boy did a boy did a boy dare. Did a baby
did a baby need it at all and did occasionally did they occasionally
further and further divide it as they said it was more nearly appropriate and in this way. However.

Part of it all the time.

The first time and not the first time.

Did it seem a surprise.

Arthur and all of his relatives.

No one should mention it either or at all.

And almost very little.

That is a name.

Why does Paul want to see John and where do they attach it
if it is to be and to be as to be pleased.

Why does she laugh at once.

And not being at all tired of it.

At least faster.

Indignantly and to tie it too.

Paul said that he had found them.

So did he.

The next time.

The next time there was just as much to use.

Days and days and all all ought to be ought to be occasionally
further than as much.

A Paris cousin who married an Alsatian.

And at once.

There are plenty of occasions equal and equally arranged so
that there are plenty of occasions so that they are equally arranged there are plenty of occasions there are occasions in plenty.

Why does it effect everything in just the same way.

Who said who said and who said it occasionally.

In the difference between announce and announcing, about to
be and an attraction.

Attractive to them.

Having asked and having admitted that for the future that in
future differently admired differently admitted admittedly and
so forth and appointment.

In their way may easily mean an interval and an accustomed decision. It is not dishonorable to mention and to more than afterwards assert the separate authority which has replaced all of it for them. For them indicates that originally there was more distance than happened to be carefully calculated.

All the same how do you do.

He said he knew when, when did it happen to interrupt.

Three times or fifteen times this and that and before following. Let it having been before fastening it as well as when it was mentioned in the meantime and before joined and to join. Have you had it.

Having all of it as allowing it and beside mentioned as a friend indeed.

Would it be better to happen to have seen him or to have asked to see him or to have offered to see him. Would it be better to object to seeing him to recover from seeing him or to arrange not to be seeing him. All this never takes place and never has had an arrangement made. After this many have to be asked for this and with it. Saturday does make Monday and by and by it has been changing changing just as much. Oftener make it as much as that. Is it necessary that she buys some more.

Oil is fatter.

And when all of it makes it all makes it all. Please recount piles, piles of it. This makes it have to be as satisfactorily as if the daughter the son or the daughter was at one time was at once all of it gladly. No one of them makes many of them many of them and most of them. She admired me.

In plenty of time to see him too.

The first of the twenty-four, twenty-four makes it easier practically to account at once for one, the first of the twenty-four and seen and I see you. Would any one prefer it, preference easily and afterwards as much as as much as needed if for himself too.

Full of preparation and in no case in memory. Curtains and shelves and chairs and imitation of making African Africa and other things other things. In which way did he agree.

How often are these the results and the result how often are they the habit and the habits and in use. Used to be very well attended. Perhaps not.

It was a surprise.

How to surprise.

An enquiry into how to surprise everybody at the same at the same time as at the same time. At the same time they all preferred it very much to anything else that they intended to do and afterwards they might easily afterwards add and divide and disturb and mostly all of it all of it and mostly, mostly meaning that it as detail and considered and regularly as to pressure and advice and even accidentally an intermediary. All of it has this as a gift, first an account, second a delight, third a decision fourth admiration fifth as much and sixth in plenty of time for each and afterwards all the best that has been that has been that has been and largely largely changed. In the rest and snow, snow or say so, violets and say so, say so, their say so, snow and say so, violets and say so.

To please attach this to that and Monday, Monday makes it afterwards a pretension. Afterwards a pretension and in this case added and divided and this because more easily in and invited. No one joins labor to repose. She and she and as she and as he and as he and as he and as she and as they and as they understood as they as they and as they, he and as he and as he and understood and undertaken and as they and as he and as he and as he and understood and as he and understood and undertaken and as they and as they and undertaken.

FINIS

A THIRD

1925

Have half.

Accordion.

Have a house.

I do.

If they do as well, then as well.

This and there.

It is pretty nearly a chance to do it.

Come climates and practice.

Ahead now.

In play on a day and in and ahead and at and at least and on and on it and for and favored.

It makes and it makes and it makes a detachment.

One wonder.

Two tried.

And a third.

Aloud now.

Pretty place and put it there and there and here to hear, pretty put it there and place and there and have to hear. Put it there and there and here and pretty place and hear. And this made and decide quickly.

If no one had said look around entirely and let, let it and very much like it.

You must be very careful that there is no difference between waterfalls and waterfalls. Very careful. Where was the sun when was the sun bright.

It is new and newer and leave it and attach it twice.

Wonderfully so.

PART TWO

A real noon.

A real noon makes twenty-four and half and hear it. To return to hear it.

A real noon makes twenty-four and half and near it return to near it.

A real noon makes twenty-four and half and ate of it. To return to the weight of it.

A real noon makes twenty-four and half and the state of it. To return to the gate of it. Gate should never be used as an entry and a gate should never be used as a gate. No indeed a gate should never be used as a gate.

How very entertainingly do they arouse noise. And trees. And once in a while.

Consider it better. Consider it as better.

It never follows as it never follows it as it never follows before as it never follows. It never follows.

It is especially so that it is best to know, that it is always as it was when it was the one after the next and so not chosen but instinctively one may say instinctively allowed for and as a result and a result it is undoubtedly an exact and rightly organised victory and a correct satisfying and pleasurable arrangement. Who can and does and why and for it. For it is included.

Not having heard of a place for them and for it not having desired to find one residence more attaching than another one argument more attaching than the other one agglomeration more attaching than another in order that in a decision having been envisaged as a desirable result that if not there then here in this way in this way led that way and having at least rested in an entire accord with a previous occasion it might be and as it did indeed result it resulted in as much as it would always be preferable. And preferred. One may say and preferred.

How did it come here and how did this come to be here and on both sides at once or one after the other and remained in each place altogether. In which way was this arranged for and will it gradually grow smaller. It will it does.

A little differently at once and pointed pointed is not used concerning brushes. A little differently at once and not rapidly, rapidly is used concerning leaves. A little differently at once and gently and gently is not used concerning thirds. A little differently at once and suddenly and suddenly is not used concerning that.

She says that of all days that she likes best the best is the one that they find very obliging and with a day and all day prepared to be careful. Who could be as it will. And she has and easily and easily.

Renowned is not the same as found and found is not the same as sound and sound is not the same as around and around is not the same as round. Round is not the same. Not the same name as came. Come here.

Feeling her way.

In this way they hurried.

It is very remarkable that in the morning sometimes the arrangement is by minutes and sometimes the arrangement is by hours and half hours. To understand it.

When it is decided that the morning is from the use of it practical then it can happen that there can be found written, from ten to ten fifteen, from ten fifteen to ten twenty from ten twenty to twenty-five, then it can be found to be written from ten to a quarter past ten from a quarter past ten to twenty minutes past ten from twenty minutes past to twenty-five minutes past ten from twenty-five minutes past ten to half past ten.

Daily habits naturally, naturally daily habits naturally and naturally daily habits naturally and satisfactorily and practically and naturally and actually daily habits actually daily habits naturally daily habits naturally, daily habits.

Daily habits are these these are daily habits.

These are daily habits naturally actually actually daily habits actually. These are daily habits these and daily habits these daily habits. Every moment at some time waiting and after that attending to arranging it at once. At once and as again around. Was she ready. Very ready. And were they ready not so ready and will they be all there is of attention and intention. Nobody can do more than so and so. After that the hour was changed.

Finally a pleasure.

Immediately finally a pleasure.

Finally immediately a pleasure, not immediately not finally immediately not immediately finally a pleasure how can it be how can it be averse to it. Finally immediately finally a pleasure.

Altogether immediately finally a pleasure.

Not the least bit verifying. Not the least bit verifying and why because having observed having observed it being observed and making it as a movement rapidly as rapidly found it to be out in a different way out and about. They move quickly there. It moves quickly there. It moves quickly.

They never knew who told them that they were in the distance.

Divisions and divide and wide beside.

Divisions and divide and wide and beside a half of a place. After all she was right not to want it.

What is it that is easily and rapidly done when it is once begun.

To transfer one and two to this and to transfer two and one to this and to transfer one and two to this. This makes happiness to those and this makes happiness to those and makes it extremely well, supposing they were very happy. Supposing they were.

Not as not as not as at all and not as at all as they were when they had had it around and around and out. Out comes out, and as out comes out and as out comes out, comes comes comes out. As out comes out, so that in as diminish diminish means extra and extra means at all and at all as at all. And so inclined. For this to-morrow. Raspberries strawberries and raisins. Raisins strawberries raspberries and raisins, success is followed by successful and successful is followed by one side and side to side. That is it beside. As afterwards constitutes and how are you. How are you when you do when do you do this. To-morrow morning after six and to-morrow after six when you do this when do you do this. It came as much as if they had horned horned is on their head and out beside and on their head. What should cream do and what should they do and what should a cow do and what should she do and what will she do, what will she do, will she do will she do will she do, faster, what will she do will she do will she do, will she do.

Stop and to stop and to stop as started and to stop as started and as well as started connected with and by and as easily as easily not having been relieved by recognition and for this and they are as pleased. They are as pleased and they are as pleased.

When they have had a habit of easily saying they had had a house and a house and would they and they would please them. We please.

How do they act when they please they act with what was the

sweeter and smiling for it to have it and wishing wishing when
it is the first and what do they say they say that the star is bright
and what do they say they say that an orange is usual in the day
and what do they say they say they can happen to say that they
prefer it every day. What. Every day. What. Every day.

When they do do it, when they do do it, and when they do do
it. She likes it when they do do it.

And when she likes it when they do do it it is when they do
do it that she likes it. It is when she likes and she has the way of
having heard that she was satisfied with what had been heard
earnestly. And then she disagreed.

She said that she much prefers this to that and she much prefers that when it is satisfactory that she is accustomed to it. She
very nearly has meant to be attached to what is not accustomed
to it and if it is not accustomed to it if it is not accustomed to it
and what did they by way of and that afterwards and no one can
expect what is after all finally decided. Who decides what. When
she says that she prefers that they are accustomed to it she says
that she does prefer it she does prefer that they are accustomed to
it.

There they have it, there they have it. There they have it,
there they have it. A third. There they have it there they have it
there they have it, there they have it. A third. There they have it,
there they have it.

To change two to two and a third. There they have it there
they have it. There they have it there they have it. Two and one
third, there they have it there they have it. They did not startle.
Rocks roll down and they do not startle, they see the rocks roll
down and they do not startle they see the rocks roll down and
they see the rocks roll down and they do not startle and they see
the rocks roll down and they do not startle. Change this from a
third to two thirds.

A third.

Is a little chicken tender. Is a celery tender is a raspberry
tender and is a salad tender. Is a third tender.

Not losing and leaving. Not and losing and leaving. A third
to-morrow. Promise me that some day you and I. A third to-
morrow.

A third.

Third.

What is the difference between third and a third. This is the difference.

A little difference to them all at all.

In all.

By all.

A little difference and asleep. By all with all. A little difference and to concede by all at all. A little difference and as all.

It is a very great pleasure to watch it now. It is a very great pleasure to watch it now. And now it is a very great pleasure it is a very great pleasure to watch it it is a very great pleasure to watch it now and now it is a very great pleasure to watch it now. A very great pleasure.

If a third is covered by stages stages and pages page one seventy-two and responsibility if a third is covered by stages covered by pages page one seventy-seven and repaging of not it if a third is covered by stages is covered by pages page one eighty-seven and left in in feeling if a third is covered by stages is covered by pages page two thirty-two and they and then certain, when do they do it.

In a frightened tone and what do you think if a third and instead of in front instead of every where any where, if in front if instead of in front instead of in front instead of anywhere. They are very likely to be included. Very likely.

A third makes what what and what and a third makes what, what and what. A third makes it matter to them.

She needs to see that a day for a day a day for a day all day and to change from three to three and from the three to the three to change it as easily makes it decide that on top means the top means raisins apricots and orange oranges. This does good. Does it does it do good. This does good. Having decided that each time afterwards each time afterwards. No one has exactly known the difference.

To begin a third to intend a third to pretend to a third to dispose of a third to announce a third to allow a third to accustom a third to adhere to a third. A third of what to please me. A third of what to please me. A third of what to please me. Two thirds of what to please me. Three thirds of what to please me. Two thirds of what three thirds of what one third of what, a third a third is nearly a third, two thirds are nearly a third three thirds are nearly a third.

Who makes three, not Henry. Who makes three not Nellie, who makes three not Eddy who makes three not Susie who makes three, three is made by circumstances. Who makes three and a third, Henry who makes three and a third Charlie who makes three and a third Lucy who makes three and a third Daisy. Who makes three and a third who makes three, at once and surprised. Who makes thirty-three every three and every thirty-three when they are asked to be different.

It is nearly four at once two now and two how, how is it placed as to as wished. For a wish. A cow for a wish and not told for a wish and for a wish and how for a wish and a cow for a wish.

Just a little word to say sacredly just a little word to say, orange raisins good conduct and cows there should be no mistake made as to which is which.

When she does not live where she used to she has moved.

When she does not live where she used to she has moved and she has said so dozens of times.

The cow it shakes it out and as it falls it slaps and spreads.

Neat and nets have it yet nest and yet have it yet, have it yet net and yet have it yet neat and nets and nest.

A net needs fountains and flowers and hats and chairs. And so does geography.

A little third a little heard a little heard a little forty-third. A little forty-third a little heard a little heard a little third. So thirdly.

Reward and toward inspired by deep distrust and must must and two. She knew how to and when to and why to. Why by fourteen. Four and fourteen makes twenty-four and how to eat and a spoon and how to eat and between. Between to-day. She likes to hear me speak.

It was at last and very fast and very quickly and by that time and how to have four placed at different distances.

It is always in the meantime and added.

Altogether different to have chosen to have found and chosen an altogether different setting. To rest before and after sleeping before and after eating before and after staying before and after losing and adding and adding. She can make it do.

Not at all as much pleased with this one as with others and sweetly. A third and sweetly a difference in kind and color a difference in milk and cows a difference in delight and places a difference in Connecticut and altogether. Every one is pleased to have her show it.

Heavy hangs over her head what shall she do to redeem it, have a cow have a cow have a cow, now, not now but later, later means sooner and sooner means better and better means fuller and fuller means altogether and altogether means altogether. Every day, altogether.

When they and they and wandering and wandering and I and they and they and they and I and wandering. Why does where does it lose where does it lose it. Where does it lose itself a river or a noun. Surround makes it a share.

Pretty nearly pretty pretty dear me pretty, pretty pretty pretty nearly and pretty and often. Often is introduced and often and often is introduced and when the best that ever was for sale was sold how much was it sold for it was sold for as much as it was intended to get for it. We have decided that we prefer hope to hoping and they will come back soon evening and noon and she will say well and he will say as well and they will say thank you. Not more than two say thank you and rest now.

Never neglected never never neglected never never never neglected. Every name never never never neglected, every name all the same to be exactly all the same to be exactly all the same never never neglected never never neglected, all the same never neglected all the same never never neglected never never never neglected never neglected, all the same all the same never neglected and the name never neglected all the same. Never neglected.

If I am shown how I can do it. I can do it if she is shown how. If she is shown how I can do it and sea-weed. Sea-weed. Sea-weed can readily be changed into a tonic and a tonic can be changed anyhow and anyhow can be changed into longer and longer and longer and longer anyhow. To mention a cow. Longer

and longer anyhow. And now. And to mention a cow. Next to
that that is sat and sat is having exchanged this for that. Now have
you had hills. Not any more. And still. Not any more. And will.
Not any more. Now any more a cow any more a door any more
before any more and how any more. To repeat longer and longer
and do this sea-weed can be changed in the morning at once in
the morning for once in the morning and after that more than
once there is very much success about it after all about it at all
about it all very much success success follows succeeding and
succeeding follows needing and needing follows follows at once.
At once makes nights and morning at once at once at once succeeding at once when it is finally finally means more when it is
finally attributed to him and to her and they both have this advantage every time at once. At once at once and at once at once.
Once and then regularly.

If to look and fan and if to look and than if to look and see if
to look to be to be protected from the sun. The sun is not shining
on her head yet.

A third makes motions and kissing. Kissing can be said of here.

It is not necessary ever to think of anything.

To very rightly know why he loved her so and persistingly.

A third makes mountains and eye-glasses and the rest and
covered.

It was done one day it must be done to-day it can be done
she can say she can say it can be done to-day. And call it a day.
How do you do when in the distance and you can see and it is
not distressful to see that almost all of it has not had it as if it were
and had their different names, a summer home a winter home and
as well. She does not believe nicely that she has heard him say
now do you understand. Wishing to assist them to come and go
and to say so very politely and in love. Loves to. She is very
beautiful.

Part one and two. Beautifully too.

A very nice one of choosing a difference is to always prefer to
be left to have it done. Anybody can follow.

If a baby is a baby how many pairs are three three and no
question, he said she said she said that that in any circumstance
he would ruin his over-coat under any circumstances and as

easily as ever and then they were just as contented with all of it as if it could possibly be earlier. How many houses are there in every village. A village is a place where to pass through it must be as carefully done as before. And are there villages and will Jenny know. This makes it just as natural that villages are agricultural and agricultural always means the same thing not night and morning but morning.

A third is what is said. And she has it to do and so do you.

He never knew how much he said yes. Happy to say. When they say that she sleeps well they are happy to say that she sleeps well. In exchange.

The third time how many times are there and there are. She prefers Bourbons to Jews, wives to weddings and it happens that it happens and not as well as finished. There are two things that are dangerous roads that are dangerous and wools that are double. If wools are double and roads are dangerous then we agree. Dutifully and accepted.

In which knitting is told about and initials and plenty of time and suitable and also as if often.

To be sure of all of it so that he knew she knew she knew it.

Did it almost and then not that as an idea.

They easily arranged that it was as early and they easily arranged that they liked to withdraw and they easily arranged that if she did he did not do it and in that way they were never and need never become accustomed to any derangement. How to say that from the beginning wool was made.

If there, if it is there if I am surprised if I am surprised because I was interrupted if it is there and every time it is there, and every time it is there and every time it is there. Who can need grey blue and so blue and blue and who can concede it as it has to be oily. Corals are oily.

Only so sweet. She did she did say, she did say she did say she did say she did say it and it is just as if there had been no mistake.

There is more than two but not as she is not but not as for two. As for two and as for two too. A third is always first. That is for you to find out my fat wife.

Not the least of all that all that that all is that that makes that might in what respect does the tower of Magnes resemble Chambotte. Because in the one case they go away and see it and in the other case they stay and see it.

She was happy to do so, very likely and very likely she was happy to do so.

There is at once there are at once there are at once there have been two twice and one once and times and at times what happens at times when this happens at times what is it.

What is the reason, the reason is that mended is mended and pretended is pretended, and sent and send and leant and lend. So nearly. Can she smile. Can she awhile awhile so and so and so much. How many kinds are there of each. There are a great many kinds of each. How many kinds are there here. There are not very many kinds here and of these kinds there are not very many here not very many here.

Just a little word to please a little third a third is just enough and it is come and come and come. A third as well, very well.

She does it to fit and very nicely as because if he was chosen three times there would be no comparison and so usual. How much longer is one stocking than another. A great many wear stockings. How much longer is one stocking than another. Three times three twenty-three four times four twenty-four, three times three twenty-three two times two twenty-two. She meant to be adding that to that.

Climax no climax is necessary.

And so near soon.

Who and what wives.

Please and pleases.

Extra for them.

Now they have mountains.

She came easy.

Not as if it had never been said. She came easy.

What came it came.

You see I see.

You agree I agree.

I agree you see.

You see what came it came as you see. Three is more than most.

In the morning, more than most.

In the morning at most.

And understood.

A third more.

Two thirds more.

Three thirds more at most.

What came it came at most.

Thank you.

A third thank you.

She meant to know.

The difference.

She meant to know the difference and variety.

She meant to know the difference and variety as french and english llama and alpaca. Each one can be untinted and undyed and unified.

When it is careful careful makes three carefully three carefully be careful when it makes three. We have decided not to be to be as we have decided to be. She and if three three and if she carefully she to be careful to be three to be carefully three. She has decided not to be carefully three and this makes a third. She changed her mind long ago.

It is as best and find and it and is as best and with and see it is as best and have and can it is as best and as and yes I did it.

I see.

Once again and then irresistible and then see and seat and then irresistible and then see and seat and then eat. After that early. After that early, after that as early and see how it is. Once could easily dispose of it.

Who has a little who has a little who has a little who has a little who has who quietly has who has quietly a little. A little fish. Can a little fish float. It can and it does. Can she have a result she can and she does. She does very well. And if it could be mentioned without a be without a be be mentioned and if it could be mentioned and if without and if it could be mentioned then it would often be respected and received. And this time. Who said that time. And this time. Who said this time. And that time. Who said that time. And this time. Who said this time.

It is a very great pleasure altogether.

Softly in a hotel, softly and in a hotel softly in a hotel softly in a hotel.

Next.

Softly in a hotel softly.

When she is through there is nothing more to do when she is through everything is done. Well begun and paper well begun and paper and later.

To say it here to say it here to say it here, to say it here. Here to say it here.

Very good.

She counted two hundred and eight two hundred and nineteen two hundred and six one hundred and one hundred and two and one hundred and thirty-eight and altogether it made one hundred and fifty-eight and over. When they say over they mean they mean they mean that they have continued the counting on the other page. And do say so.

Having returned having had it returned having returned to the one we have here.

Agnes all the same. And all the same Agnes all the same and when he came when she came he said to her not to Agnes but Agnes hearing heard him heard her, he said to her did you or did you not and she said if I did and he said I did too. Agnes as it is said made a distinct decision. She decided to abide by it. And so forth. Did she. And so forth.

Having placed and tasted tasted and renewed renewed and appointed appointed and who who who could hear it.

Twenty-third.

We saw five.

Five are forty too many.

Yesterday.

Yesterday was day before yesterday.

Forty are five too many.

Yesterday was the day when there were only two.

To-day was the day when there were five.

Listen.

Yesterday was the day when there were only two.

To-day was the day when there were five.

To tell it to tell it to well as tell it. It is very easy to prefer this to that and Bertha. Anybody can say Bertha.

As soon.

Gratifying.

At once too to me.

Succeeded by whiling.

Shutting up the satisfied and satisfying naming. Name me.

Josephine. Name me.

Helen. Name me.

Anthony. Name me.

Edward or Edwards. Name me.

George or George. Name me.

What did you say.

There is no need to accentuate bird.

There is ever need to leave Susan alone, to do what, to arrange, to do what, to arrange.

To do what.

Not a little not at once and she not a little not a little at once not a little not at once and she and me not a little and she not at once and she not a little not at once and she. She said that she thought that nothing made a room more gay than flowers and youth.

And three.

Yes let us have a third.

She told about William.

He told about Helen.

They told about William and Helen.

If she is well to do.

Who.

If she is well to do.

Many wives are wives.

Many many many wives are wives. Whose wives. Many wives are wives many many many wives are wives.

And now announcing.

Announcing.

Announcing that he had let her hear him.

And now and now and now and now.

Plenty of intended to be told. Told them.

She does read and knit. So she does.

She does see and sit. So she does.

She does.

So she does.

It is easy to decide between one and one. One is the same height the difference is as to being round or not round. Also what should be around it around and over it. What should be around and over it. What should be used to cover it. And how much longer would it take. To please me.

To look around.

And decide.

And prefer what is preferable. And return and measure it. And not to be disturbed and to be really anxious to have it as it is. Thank and thank you.

She has nearly she has now and now is how and how is cow. Just as new.

She makes me makes and having heard not having heard humming oh so happily. And now very well. Very well indeed for me. Having had to hear having heard and here, having heard and having here, having having it having it having it here. Here and having heard makes it divided makes it divided having heard a third. Makes it divided having heard a third makes it divided. Makes it divided having heard having heard a third. Hear it. Having heard a third makes it divided having heard. Changing if and and and changing this and third and changing this and with and changing with and at and in and well. Changing with and third. And no neglect.

Always as much.

Fifty fifteen sixty-two and who who is it. It does not deceive her. She is not easily deceived by changing silver to gold and porcelain to glass and rubber to ink, and lead to rightly. Rightly after after all. She is neither stupid nor unwilling. She is not. She went in to see to it. She saw to it and returned. When she returned she had seen to it. When she had seen to it she had returned. In this way to-morrow can be Sunday and half past one can be too early but after all why not show her the house.

PART II

Three parts make part two. Did she write to Janet. Two parts makes part two. Did she ask for it. Three parts makes part two two parts makes part two part two makes two thirds too and she had only paid for part of it.

As well be it as well. She is not mistaken.

She says she needs a word a third.

She has to undertake bunches and grapes figs and apples and after all and then satisfactory. What does a disguise mean. I mean.

She has that. She is do not she is. See to see. Sea bells, hare bells and ring bells. Nicely. When this when this and to me.

Little now and then who said here. Little now and then and who said here. Who said here. I said here.

Every minute when they sit sitting.

Now and not who has said got got it. Who has said what what. Who has said not not it.

Now and then who has said what what now and then who has said got now and then who has said not. Not makes a third remember makes a third.

Will he will will he will he will he will.

Any way of anyway. Changed too any way of changed too anyway any way any way of anyway changed too.

He could hear her her name hear her name hear her name all the same hear her name hear her name them name them Edgar. Oh Edgar.

Finish with a time on time in time.

This makes it happen often and I thank you.

Pretending to pretending to be a jew pretending to.

Pretending to who mentioned it pretending to who mentioned it pretending to.

After answer.

Now and see see what see where see there. See there and pretty soon pretty soon and no time and questioned. Do you like silver, do you like weeks do you like dear me do you like do you who has had you. Who has had you here. You. You too. You too who to two to one one one is too little. And little all who makes pets pets. Pets pets and would she give it up for there. She would not.

Never leave out a third.

Always put in a third.

Always have to arrange what is there as carefully as ever.

A week a day and will he say yes too.

He will really say that.

He will really be that.

He will really see that.

He will really and that attend to that.

First. She and he will have had it very well arranged for them nicely. Fortunately.

Now to return wood to a cow. Wood is for wood and a cow is for a cow. Now. Now here now there now and there. Politely makes me more at once more. Afterwards. It is easy to believe in salt cauliflower cake apples meat sugar and newly. After that provinces every thing as provinces. As provinces. Basque can be used as clothes. There was a time once upon a time when they once upon a time once upon a time.

In exactitude and Gertrude, have it so funny.

This is the first time to have mentioned mentioned mentioned repeat mentioned.

She went in and out. Every time sometimes it was sometimes salad sometimes it was sometimes it was for salad.

What is the use what is the use what is the use of this what is the use what is the use what is the use of this for that. And this. Once in a while.

If she goes on as she is going she will continue to be pleasing.

If she likes what she is doing she will continue to be always to be occupied. Once again.

If she is as quickly used to it as ever she will plan three things.

This is this when this is as well as ever if it is as well as ever if it is as well as ever.

Can a dear delight be as they had changed. I mean from what to steel. Steel is beautiful. And it all depends when you to follow this this which should be changed to the and the ridge. There is no ridge there now.

Third. There is no ridge there now.

Should a third be first should it with a hat. Should a third be a third. Should a third by three thirds and should a third really a third as really a third by really with really and really from really a third. And so incline. They made this noise three times. To be told that they were easily seen. And he said if they had asked me I would have said no.

She looked as if she did, she did not and she looked as if she did not and when she did to not, not when she did not she looked as if she did she looked as as if she did when she did when she did when she looked as if she did when she looked as if she did. That is another day from yesterday and last night too and this morning too and this morning. What was this morning. This morning was the morning when she came to say and to stay. What is the difference between say and stay. None. A little better yet.

That comes to this. That. Remember that. Does she know without the trouble to leave it off at once before and answer. This is the hat. Too. Two one changed and one changed. One not changed. This never can make three. Individually. Has been at once. And now an entirely different subject. This is now neither as big or little around or around but it has reference to higher up and all out. Yes and pleases.

She will refuse to.

How do you do and little and pears. And after that little and pears. I will refuse to. There is no likelihood that after it part of the time they will have it every little while as they do. And then thanks.

She needs me. She needs me too. She needs me to as well. And kindly should he signed and kindly and thank you.

I can only repeat that I expect that finally not finally but ably and ably so to speak in the morning they will not moderate more moderately as that is at first a word is at first a word is at first a word and finish is at first a word. Who knows this. When they can when do they when they do and intended intended to do.

Do they have it as it is just now. She said they had it and now an entirely different subject. The subject is this please be careful and give to her what is it give to her have her have it. So nearly fifty more charges fifty fifty just as well. She will not have what she had this morning but what she needs. Thank you.

Let us say in this way that a dove a dove does a dove does anyway.

One set and settled.

Let her say in that way that originally anyway.

Let them say that they may may be they will but they doubt it.

How do you do preferred to.

The next time that there are smiles.

A little later.

To-day.

If hair could be made who made. Next to pleasure please and next to please and yes and next to yes to expect and next to expect after it. In their climate it is often very warm and very often very warm and very often rainy. In their climate it is very often very warm and very often rainy. Thinking to agree.

Now and then.

When.

Did she have.

Yes.

Did she like.

That.

Did she hear.

Me.

Shall she sit.

There.

Shall she have.

Care.

And quiet.

And will she as a result recognise the egress.

Yes.

And will it be sufficient.

It will.

Then and now have a cow.

Then and when have a hen.

Then and there have a pear.

Then and now have a cow.

How.

Very well I thank you.

The most beautiful and she said it was the most beautiful and she said it was the most beautiful the most beautiful that it was the most beautiful. She said it was the most beautiful.

Apples and figs burn.

They burn.

It can be admitted that there can be made an exception it can be admitted that an exception that there can be an exception that there can be made that an exception can be made.

She had tried.

Establish and disestablish.

Very well she has tried.

And now luckily.

If they feel and it feels like it then it does and then it will relieve it recover it replace it rely on it and renew it. In this way well in this way.

And never that is hardly ever.

Once more once more.

She was when she went in talking to Agnes she was when she came out going in and then it was a relief. Then when she went in she came in and when she came in she stayed in and when she stayed and it went out and that is all that there is about it. Now. About it now.

It is usual under these circumstances to talk about it now and it is usual under these circumstances to please themselves and it is usual under these circumstances to better it and it is usual under these circumstances.

Very well I thank you.

If we are invited if we are delighted if we are delighted if we are if we are if we are invited.

Next to roses read next to roses she is very well I thank you.

After all she has another another set of ear-rings and after all she has another another way of holding grapes and after all she has another another way of saying it with corals.

My only wife and mother.

When this you see she is all to me.

It is not expected of it that it is intended, it is not expected of it. It is intended. So then seen. It is expected of it that it is intended and so then seen.

No doubt about it tube-roses no doubt about it.

When next when they were interested next and turned around. She saw Bruce and he saw her.

After that three figs and many grapes and after that satisfaction.

Third comes after after three. What are three three are she and me and a standard a standard is at it were fish and fishes and a standard is as it were a cow both regular both to be regular. She was what she was as she understood everything.

When she heard of three she preferred two. When she heard of me she preferred me. When this you see remember me.

When she went out and asked how many are there she was told that there were twenty-five when she heard that there were twenty-five she was satisfied that more would arrive and they did.

Then this was what was very well considered. It was very well considered.

Always return to round about and in their way. It might be questioned whose way. It might be answered her way.

Back to three when this you see when this you see back to three. Back to back when this you see when this you see back to three back to three when this you see when this you see back to three back to back and back to three when this you see back to me, back to back and back to me when this you see back to three back to back and back to me when this you see. And now to explain back to three back to three means that they will they both will they both do they both can refuse nothing and so they are very well as to brown color and odor without. Do you understand.

Every day there is a third this way this way to the third.

He knew he was a minute or three this way. This way to the third.

Having meant to remain and all the same having meant to remain.

Having meant to have the third this way this way to have meant to have the third this way. Having meant to remain having meant all the same having meant to to have the third this way all the same.

I wish to describe third third wish to describe.

It is notorious that they have nearly finished in a minute and by the way by the way they do. To always remain at once. She knows the difference between three. Three three everywhere. Elsewhere.

Now now nearly and have it as well as that. Now now nearly my dear my dear nearly and nearly near near is as well as a fish and more than a fish is fishes and now is nearly and nearly is near and after that reduced to squalling and if undisturbed and undisturbed then as well as much. Much much much is never an insult.

See to it.

To see to it.

I see to it.

Can examples be described and as described be as sensible.

To change her mind.

Do change her mind.

Can examples be described and be described and be description. Description of their being obliging. Obliged to come again. It is obliged to come again to come every time and in the midst of it and the most of it.

She does not.

And now nearly one half different not nearly one half nearly one half. Half and half.

Who knew Angora.

Three.

Who knew three.

Angora.

Who knew three who knew Angora.

Who knew three who knew Angora.

One two three Angora.

Then there is this awhile.

To always return to meeting with cows with cows with cows.

What makes not flocks but speckles and speckles are in their place. And if properly admired the result as result is admirable. She is not very likely to be equal to it and meant he.

He once he twice she twice she twice that makes it certain to be to-morrow. Always understand that it makes it certain to be to-morrow.

Seriously earnestly to repeat now seriously earnestly to repeat how seriously earnestly to repeat how now seriously earnestly to repeat cow seriously earnestly to repeat how and now and cow.

She did have it at once and now twice twice at once and thank you.

Lead can be useful in many ways and as she knows it can be used in replacing and so when she announced that she had succeeded he said it is pleasure but in a way regretful. She was more than satisfied and so was he.

One two three he she and necessity. Necessity and necessarily and necessarily and nearly.

Always having mentioned that mention this.

She knew how to be so and do so. Thank you again and again and I see.

Not at all neglected at noon and so then when the answer could be at once all ways. She made it seem likely likely means just alike and just alike has this for a reason did they know ends and bees and also look like it. Look like it and looks like it. Always to say that it is best to have it every day.

Nicely to begin and he was never ashamed of anything. Nicely to begin and he was never ashamed of ending anything. Nicely to begin and he was never ashamed of anything.

One two three all the men are there and they say that a man is nearly as often ready as not. One two three and they say that half the time they are very able to be happily aimed at. One two three and they say that they have all always all of it.

One two three they may neglect what they see. One two three exactly.

He might not she might not she might not he might not she might not say so to him and to her and to them and he might not he might not say so to them to her and to him. So they might.

One two three for me and six and twenty divided by three makes two. To who to whom and excuse. Cunning it is very cunning to be able to remember what was said.

Having been and having been she will be he will be thank you
so much.

Yes two a day yes yesterday.

See smiling.

Now and this.

She makes this be as much as it was and he has been inclined
to much more so much more and now more and more and now
more and more two and three.

One two and three.

One two and three.

One two and three.

Then there is as can be said for it.

One day I said to her I like it like that and then I said to her I
like it like that and then I said to her I like it like that and then
I said to her I like it like that. One day I said to her I like it like
that. She likes it like that and so one day I said to her I like it like
that. This is the reason why she said that by and by she would
wish to be ready to sit down earlier. One day I said to her I like
it like that one day I said to her I like it like that. This is the way
that they enjoyed everything.

Once every little while they had to be easily satisfied. Once
and as much as they had and did and by finally as once and arranged. One two three four she needs four one two three she
needs three one two she needs two one one she needs one. They
have certainly asked it of her. She can be almost once in a while.

She needs me.

They said simply.

She needs me.

In that way they say there are distances distances at once. To
put it in very simple language. Very simple language at all. They
may be mentioned as three sizes and frequently. Every day at
once every day. At once every day every day at once. Once every
day every day once. And sizes sizes depend upon kind color and
that, all three are as needed and needed is as succeeded and succeeded is as expected. I expected it all and she as I expected it all
expected it all and as she expected it all it was all as it was to be
once and all all and always and that makes it not only original
but necessary not only excellent but understood not only under-

stood but useful. I can say in very simple language that she will have her cow.

Announcements.

She did.

She will.

She can.

She does.

Other announcements.

When they have arranged for it he and she she will be very nearly ready and have everything ready and then he have everything ready nearly everything ready will very easily see to it. And she. She will be very nearly as ready as ever and so when there is an upper and a lower all the upper will be above reproach and very well. In this way not alone women and men but even women and men can be more nearly employed than as much so. Touch here touch there touchingly and not ever forgetting that very nearly a cow is inclined to be very nearly a cow and so it can be combined with a very useful member of the race who is and has been known as Mr. Lindo. Mr. and Mrs. Lindo at once and as twice. And so now. To be generous and delighted.

PART THREE

There are many parts of part three and a favorite distraction. There can be instituted blond with black hair blond with dark skin blond with blond dark eyes blond beside. What is a blond a blond is one who is courteous careful reasonable right and anxious. And she has it as well. There can be added to it as fishes and now to know. Teeth and now to know. Where and now to know. There and now to know.

It can be very attractive.

In plenty of time.

And by naturally.

To exchange.

To wish to state actually what he thinks.

And then.

To wish to state actually what he thinks.

And then to indulge that.

And then to be perplexed.

And then to be accounted for.

When she is as nearly there how many are sleepy.

When she is who says Lindo too when she is who says Lindo too when she is admirably prepared.

Very well.

And as she did say that it was true.

Well if that fell.

Very well.

And as and in wishes.

They made themselves as they were there that is wool that is hair that is hair that is wool and by it and she wished she wished for her. Following again a throat following again a tooth following again a cow following again and a pigeon never a pigeon and deer here. When a deer then a deer when a pigeon then a pigeon and when a purse then a purse she arouses smiles smiles at that.

She said she was.

This is the way we feel about it.

That we can.

This is the way we feel about it.

That we can do it.

This is the way we feel about it.

That we can do it and we can do it.

This is the way we feel about it.

That we can do it.

She needs to be.

And moreover.

Moreover she is to have attributed attributed it to her.

Moreover she is to have it attributed to her.

And so there can be no organisation. Organisation is when one around won around organisation and when and when organisation and won around and organisation and when and when and when and won around organisation and won around. In the morning and at noon when they have to have it soon in the morning and so soon they found it out.

Walls stoutly resisting. And they remind it of walls stoutly resisting. Now an entirely a different matter. Our mind can linger on the subject of cows and fishes in abundance.

She said she knew when she was who and to-night separately there will be three to four as before and they will include directions such directions as are followed by this one this one and that one and that one and something returning from that. She knew. And then when she sees these she will be by and by as in order to enjoy by this time what always can be any morning introduced introduced in the place of out out and it follows just as with that and she knew. Always incandescent means delight and always right and when she settles settles and sits then there can be what has been meant by yesterday as to-morrow because they have meant it for that purpose and it succeeds.

MORE GRAMMAR FOR A SENTENCE

1930

PART ONE

The Almonds

Buy me with this.

Will you be well will you be well.

A lily smells as green as when it is annoying that it is right about it.

If for long she had been with or without them. That means that her name had not been changed but not known about. She had been with the and without it making a matter with at all. Why then. She is the mother. Her father. Her brother died a young man so did her husband. He was a young man and the house was bigger. Without it to do. She was very well very well to do very well to do with them. After they are a while. Like that in a sound.

There is no other family with at all.

To go on with going on with it.

It makes it safely with them and who.

Wordly worthy worthy worth were they were or were they with be.

Worth bitter.

It is better or are they better.

It is better or are they bitter.

She had held spend when she was sent.

In and uninvited by the mention of that.

Think of their weeding. They were cutting without it at last.

Not only not it but not it.

Try it out. How do you do. Do they love you. Or curiously. When it is different to be agreeable or agreeably older. There it is not to be mistaken.

They made it a danger to have avoided a door which they meant to have had and a hinge in undividedly an attention.

Remark that a recalled pleasing having for them makes it immediately known which is theirs. They have to be without doubt well known. He likes to have him be hired for that in that

with their care named Bradley which made whenever they do
more than that deliberately making a mine of use of their acknowledge meant for them a reason assistance made curious and
by and nearly which is that. Make without call. It is very beautiful
to have the winning language.

This a paragraph in substance.

Of course it looks like it in that shape and they always remind
it of it. This may be spoken of why. When they are alike they
resume a plant which has that for them that they did which was
theirs because of ordinary less than white. Ivy leaves resemble
harbors. He harbored added it as in order having had it in detail.
This makes a paragraph attached.

What is in amounting. Who is in power with having find.
Now or then there never is a need of having nine or mine in a
name, a noun with thinking of currants makes it different alright
but without their say so they will even will with an account so
that there is namely that if they turn they will please do with
hesitate. Finally they refuse. All this is how they cannot use
the name currants after they were women. This whole paragraph
is explanatory.

It is very true that it is of use to after to you. With you they
will withdraw with which they have to do with you. After all
why will they meet with which.

It is very likely that they tell that they liked when they liked
it which was which they have as much as an instance of which
it is as well. Known as paragraph.

He fortunately was as playing with him. They need know
that he thought with them. With by which it is remain and remained about in by with in having they made it have them with
and to do. This is a paragraph that plans of thinking it with as
Etienne.

It is at adding in remaking tens. Every little way of calling
May away from them. With whom were they careful. They will
have been thought well of without. Every little nicely by a paving
with when by this in and announced. She let fall something which
made a little racket. There is why they need now and know their
paragraph. A paragraph is not natural. Who knows how. A noun
is nature personified. Alike. A sentence which is in one word is
talkative. They like their moon. Red at night sailor's delight a

vegetable garden which is when there is a cage wherein they add with add withheld with string. A paragraph is not natural. Peas are natural so are string beans all sausages are natural, butter is natural but not cream paragraphs are not natural, quinces are natural even when they are late and with them they are natural without cherries they are natural. A period is natural a capital with a capital with and with a capital. It is beautiful. A word which makes basket a name. If it is a name will he be confused with whatever with it they make to name. There is no doubt that a mine is natural that always is natural that appointment is natural that nearly is natural that will they have their board is natural. It is natural to remain once again. It is natural. A paragraph is not natural but needful. There are more needful with what they do. Think of everything that is natural. Now. It is very beautiful to have a birthday. In which they invite prefer. With them. A paragraph is not nature. Not unalike.

If I leave with them now if I leave it with them now if I leave it with them. Now. A paragraph is not a division it does not separate. Because if they must go they will not have gone. Not now. Be with a wife. Wifely. Enthusiasm. Natural. They will think about who says. She liked their coffee but she does not like it now.

A paragraph without words. Why are mainly made in comparison.

With having lost. He was not discontented with having lost. By that means he was received without having mine and then it was nearly by the way of fastening. With in union for they made it do. Without them as they could for which they were in an opposite reason of a placement. For their attachment. Which made it be by the time that they could diminish. Upper. and more.

The difference between natural paragraph and moving paragraph.

A little at a time.

It is as good as exercise.

A paragraph of why they will apply theirs to this. Infinally acute hire that they can. Appeal that it is very times to be.

A natural paragraph is not waiting.

They will it is not natural to speak of them. It is not natural to speak. It is not natural to have them. They have them come with them. It is natural not to have them come with them. Reduce remaining without them. It is very natural to have returned with them. What has a paragraph to do with it. They are not having it to do it as they wish. Providing they are coming with which they made it anyway. There is no use in a paragraph which is outstanding. A paragraph has not naturally as an encumbrance without which they are with wither a blessing good which is as good. What can a paragraph do eventually. Do without but he minds it. A paragraph is naturally that they are disappointed. a paragraph is made in between continuing which is that they will have it bloom. How can you tell the difference between eat it all and a pea. Which they mean. It is not that they are without equivalent.

To think well of any paragraph they must have affection.

There is no such thing as a natural sentence but there is such a thing as a natural paragraph and it must be found.

It makes no difference whether he gets tired first or whether I do if we continue to go on it is not necessary that we have both went and rested without there after made it be a different in the way. This is not a mistake in wasting which when without theirs as they do needed all alike which if it is a part of inclusive that they make in agreement and after all it was hers I used.

There is no such thing as a natural sentence and why because a sentence is not naturally. A sentence. With them they will detest without whether they will belie it. A paragraph in when there is a little valley in noon or as it is in the way of a little of it as soon as there has been is a moon. That makes it not naturally be a paragraph. When he is afraid he is after afraid and if it is then that it is that it has been might it be in with which it is in return. Rarely afraid. After afraid. A paragraph is naturally after. Afraid. After afraid. To look after. It is after.

There is a difference between after and after afraid. A paragraph is not a sentence after it is a paragraph after.

Supposing three things a will they be having met and at a time with while and after without not at a time with which to trouble with advising why they weeded without grass. Because they prefer separating salad. This and they come alternately again. It cannot be naturally a paragraph because they are there and they have left one shovel so they will be willing which is why two hundred salads are as small and will be larger. A paragraph is an hour.

After every day they think.

About their wheat. Which is coated with bread. And they like grapes. Because a dog looks at it as a ball. Why if they are currants and made it with it.

If a dog looks like it does with them.

It is very nearly a paragraph to cry.

She knew who whose when they lent. It is a basket which they covered with a and with in it. It is very actually fine.

A paragraph made a mention. And Nora or no or a dove which is widen.

Partly relief.

Nobody knows what I am trying to do but I do and I know when I succeed.

Plainly attaching the string to keep they string beans within. This is nothing.

They know very well how they stand and are thinning but did they. Very likely they always did. It is not a representation of unified attaching to them. Now then she always knew she would be everything. He always knew he was becoming. They are accepted as being in very mainly if intruding. They will accept as well. Well enough alone. They know how they are standing with without moving. I do not think that they never didn't. Well and. Just as very well. In hive and in him. Every and one.

Forget how beautifully Marin has his hours. With his hours. She with out him with her son with out him. He may sail. Not with his same as with a name. If he has not asked him she will come and call of him with of her son. He has since been with women and named them attaching inclining for it to be other than their name. A fox which is that it was right basket was a name. There is no need of a paragraph without amounts. This time a paragraph was not natural because he said. If they had three men then they lose it with his good-bye and an offering. There is no use in an unnatural parting. Pears and apart. And will they leave with pillows. With them. This paragraph is not natural. To-morrow is not natural. Without with them. Is not natural.

May full of weights a darkness all in declare.

What is thought about whether with will they go.

Resist having a natural sentence. There are a great many ants in apricots but they can be blown off without very much of an effort.

A natural sentence can not remind one of startling.

It is of very little use to like to walk.

With them.

It is of very little use to like to walk as well as be with them.

A paragraph is why they went where they did.

A sentence made it be all when they were through indeed how are they after all may it be for their sake and ridges. With may if it makes more than at most will be for in for instance. Now a sentence can come and be no disappointment. She criticizes. But which week.

A sentence is natural. He did not come. This is a joke. A sentence is natural. He did. Which is variable and they will offer him liver with and without oil. A sentence. Made against. His will. Will he do it. He will. A sentence made with his meaning.

There is no difference between a paragraph and at once.

If it is better than ever. If it is finished. This is no paragraph. They will remember like that. This is inviting his confidence which is not withdrawn mainly but with it.

A paragraph does need a two by three. Without doubt. Which it does. By the time. They will deliver. With adding. More than they can. In need of a reliance without a difference in their name they have it a name. With them.

A paragraph is mentioned as silly. As silky. As a silky saving that he had.

That is a good paragraph. Thank you. He came. It was so good. Which is that he came. May be he did.

There is no effort in without a paid relief.

What is a trait which they have. They made more.

Forward and back.

Sashay forward and back.

Think quietly of how to do with out a way of which they were well out of it.

Folded wrong.

The salads have been wet.

The salads have been made wet by water. This is as useful as a doll.

Now this is the sort of thing that she would write. I know what a paragraph is after all.

What is he willing to do. For you. As well as for him and they will be asked to come if they answer. They will wave it as many could have made change in a firm hoping for it now. Why are nasturtiums natural which they have as which they are. Awhile at a time. It is our they hope. But they will see. To it.

Did he drink out of his water because of well well. Who can be cured cared while they may. Who while they may. Now do you see how wrong that is.

Leave sizes to paragraphs.

Paragraphs are one two three one two one two one two three paragraphs are sizes.

That is without what paragraphs there are. Paragraphs are sizes.

They began with using me for them. Will they be well and wish.

Paragraphs are named.

They name a paragraph without with this.

Why is a sentence natural if it is not in disuse. A sentence is not natural. Why is a paragraph not natural. A paragraph is not it is not not natural a paragraph is not it is a paragraph and it is not as that that is as a paragraph to tell. Do tell why is a paragraph just as much as ever natural.

A paragraph is natural. They will mend by the time it is mended by the time. A paragraph is natural by the mended that it is by that time. This is not in used. A paragraph if they were occupied which they were there and care. It was foolish to care. Have to take care. Which they have to care.

A paragraph is natural that is it is that it is is very well to know is very well known. Thank you for forgiving with them to with him.

A paragraph is natural with forgotten. That is with may and said.

Think of a paragraph. Reminded and remember. Remembered.

A paragraph is natural. They will be a paragraph will be a paragraph will be as natural. As should never be used for likely.

A paragraph. Which is natural.

They will know that each sat as they lay there. A paragraph is not with drew.

William and who. This is a mistake.

A paragraph is natural.

What can be expected of paragraphs and sentences by the time I am done. With or without. What do we do. We do without. Why is she stout. Because we do do without.

It is perfectly easy to make a paragraph. Without a sentence. Because they like it better. So.

If they do not tell them what they have. That is a natural sentence because it is without this which they finish.

If they do not tell them what they have they will be able to have it as often. This is not a natural sentence. Any more.

Need they be always one of without that. They do have. To like it.

They made it be naturally. Without a place. With theirs.

Think of a natural sentence in religion.

As we went along.

She made it appoint them. They will like which they had being alike.

One of which.

You can have a natural sentence if you look alike.

Reliable they made a bee.

A bee hive is made for once and with is kisses.

Will they cry with their with their with thin with. A sentence made from anxious.

I am thinking a great deal about which sentences are, left over, asked, and leaned, made for it in easy. They made it walked around.

With which do you think me.

That is a natural sentence without Baltimore.

What is the difference between and with made easy, that they came, made why in their amidst with in them, they are tallied, in remainder after soon. That changes it to all of their time. It is very easy to miss a sentence.

But not a paragraph.

It is very wrong to miss a sentence.

If they move they will move with welled and they did not like it for them as fish.

That makes it change readily from Baltimore to Belley. In with when. When announced as added then.

They can refuse paragraphs.

It is.

Baltimore west. Belley east. Boston.

They made it different to have tears.

Let their be paragraphs why or not.

They are no paragraphs. Belley. They are paragraphs. Baltimore.

It is by this wish which is.

What joins which is and which it is. Boston.

There are no paragraphs.

Paragraphs they will bequeath weddings.

Thinking thanking.

A solace.

Natural sentences do exist in arithmetic.

If we both say he threw that tree away.

It does not make any difference how old they all are.

These would be natural sentences if they were at all to call harder than for her.

She does use that which will there oblige it with either at very heard for advent in refer to a sentence.

She does not make it a paragraph.

No nor at all likely.

There is a difference.

There can be natural sentences if they are halting which whichever that is with renown that without that waving that if they or through. This is a sentence.

A sentence is halting with but as a cow gives and is gives it is sent has calves.

The Almonds have women.

A sentence leaves cows out about left where with all it takes.

This sentence is around.

I think naturally not with have their things they like with their shone as add or fancy.

This sentence more and more grows wider without carrots.

A sentence can be natural with wheeling.

With can be natural.

Some say forty. And some say one.

Now make all this into a paragraph without me.

Bend ended wagon. This is no sentence nor a pastime.

A paragraph is natural but not to be amused.

Bend ended wagon here nearby they will paper with comforting in rejoice.

A sentence is without their dear. Dear me with.

A sentence means too much a paragraph doesn't, therefore a paragraph is nature nature we we are averse.

Assent. Recent. Assert. And question. Do stop. When you do. It was a rotation. In regard to their fixing habitual arrange meant.

A sentence needs help. And she cries.

A sentence is why they were folded. Please have it folded.

Who helps whom with help. Withheld help yourself.

That is or or hour.

A sentence will come.

Chiefly. Will come.

That is a natural sentence. A sentence will come. Chiefly. Will come.

It must be wonderful to hear about these things and then see them.

The difference between not reading and not inviting may do.

It was opposite wholly in directing.

What is a paragraph when they predict rain.

There used ordinary sentences to make it apply.

Really not to care really not to care makes it a hole with a well. A well is not used any more. That is an ordinary sentence and is it satisfactory.

Count again. Fifteen.

This is in a tradition. They will be as careful.

To make it do.

This is a paragraph.

What is it. A paragraph. Grenoble. On the way to Grenoble you pass a hill without a town where you might stop which I see it is used by it in a main while in the way. A usual sentence is placed anywhere. What is a sentence. Without a trouble. They will be just as well aware. Without it. This is a paragraph without delight. They are after it. After awhile. An ordinary paragraph. Which they have.

How is a paragraph. Taken by themselves. Or right away.

What is a sentence. With them a paragraph.

Think carefully about a paragraph. Nobody knows whose is it.

All of which makes how is it. Now think about that. How does it have a help without them they will in relight right away.

A sentence is not in naturally made in part. It is easier.

What is it.

I see what is the trouble with a sentence they will not be two a day. That is the trouble with a sentence. Now try to make a sentence with this experience. Not to care. But with whom by the time they have finished. A sentence by the time. No thank you not to thank you. A sentence by the time who has been named with them. It is nice that they do now.

It is easy to know that a sentence is not a paragraph.

With will with them do. Will they do.

What will they do with them they will want them. They will do what they want to do.

Is this a paragraph or are these sentences. Who will know that about them.

Sentences are not natural paragraphs are natural and I am desperately trying to find out why.

Neither for as turkey which in ended May. She tried to get a sieve in many towns.

It is easy to sound alike and to diminish with their welcome that they state.

What is a paragraph, no place in which to settle. Because they have been moved.

A paragraph is different that is it affects me. That is it it is why they are relished. As for a sentence in what way do they stop. They stop without. And why. With is noon. It is with them it does not make a difference they will wait.

All this leads to me. I can be careful of what I do. That is a sentence. If it is repeated and for days there can be hopes that Florence will marry which she will. A sentence is a plan. It is never plain. Think of a sentence by its birthday. What is a sentence. With or without an ado. A paragraph is why they will at with their other brother. And they are hurried. They like the best of all when they made it a part of which they can do. If they feel well. What is a sentence. No. Nobody.

All of it. Content to be obstinate.

What is a sentence. He may mean that he is very nearly his cousin and that he has been made fortunately for him with a tendency to remain thin. That would be a sentence if one did not use anything to have him tell them.

There is this named him. This is a sentence with his name. Feeling the same.

A sentence is a hope of a paragraph. What is a paragraph that is easy. How can you know better if you say so. A sentence is never an answer. Neither is it. Who answers him. He remains with them. They have to have him because they took him. And they with this are what they are saying.

What is a paragraph. Right off. Write often. What is a paragraph. He drinks as if in wishing. He drinks of if in washing. And so and so they will be out of mind out of hand. This makes no difficulty. Have they thought of that.

A paragraph is naturally without a finish.

A paragraph is alright.

With or without a chicken fish or vegetables she came to pay for a harness. This is what they were taught.

A paragraph always lets it fall or lets it be well and happy or feels it to be so which they never were themselves as worried.

What time is it.

A paragraph has to do with the growth of a dog. They talk about it. She says. No. A paragraph is never finished therefore a paragraph is not natural. A paragraph is with the well acquainted. It languishes in mediocrity. It makes it doubtful if lips are thick and the eyes blue and the blonde which they have it might be

cupped and alike which whenever a reliable made to order as
plainly. There is nothing troubled with how about them. They
are ordered to make it more for them. A paragraph ceases to be
naturally with them with cream. With them they are enthused by
holding it off. A paragraph is natural if they walk. It is natural if
it has not come. In order. Which was given. And no blame.
A paragraph reads why do they like where they know why they
have gotten all of it back not all of it because a part of it has been
missing. This is a paragraph naturally.

There is a difference between natural and emotional.

Who can sing. Sing around and about. If one thinks of a paragraph without thinking one does not think of a paragraph or anything. A sentence is why they like places. He replaces it. She replaces it. She replaces the amount. They place and replace and re-
correct their impressions. They do not change. They do not
with how do you do. How do you do. How are you. A paragraph
never is restless. That is easy. What is a paragraph.

I like to look at it.

What is a paragraph.

She likes it better than Granada.

She likes it.

I like to look at it.

A resolution is a paragraph.

What is a paragraph. I thought a paragraph was naturally a
paragraph was naturally a paragraph and now I did please my
retaining a paragraph.

What is a paragraph.

She will be with women. She not. She is places where they
can hear it which they wherever it is replied. Will she open the
gate. She will in spite of an appetite which she has. This is a paragraph and it sounds strange. They may be made to have a calf
that they feel which that it is for them to sell. They make all of
it well will it do. A paragraph need not be a finish. They will be
and think with what they said. A paragraph has changed hands.
A paragraph made a noun. A noun is the name of anything. How
in a paragraph. I like a name use and lose. They will use the name.
Some will use the name. A noun is a name. Basket is a name. Will
they come for him is a name. What is it is not a name. Why do

they like me is why they have it as a name. They change from some.

It is a change for some who come. This is a sentence that is unreliable. A paragraph is of sentences that are reliable. A sentence is very well when it is as if they had sat and waited. Do you see how they sew. This is a sentence of which it is for which in part of the time they will see me. This sentence of which I speak. Made in pairs. Maidens prayers. Made in pairs. With which they are placed. With may which is mainly. This is a mistake. As spelled. It is very beautiful and original.

Now any word made an impression. They will in three make Mrs. Roux. We always speak of her. Mrs. Roux. This is without an opposite with her.

Withdrew, they withdrawn have withdrawn, they withdraw.

It is unbelievable how many sentences have a mistake. Unbelievable. How many have. Very few have. They will do well not to have a mistake. They will do well not to have a mistake in competition. They will be very careful too. Which they are. Whatever they do. Now this is an example of just as well. A sentence is very often more than added. A paragraph is in that case not just a paragraph not at all now without this. What is a paragraph. Who is with to blame. Change meant to mean. A paragraph has been motioned away. And now sentence is natural if they redivide it.

Redivide. Who will be winning by their half.

It is alright that a sentence and express what is it they will see to it. I know what a sentence is or is not and a paragraph is not a sentence even if it is all one because they shrink from it. Not from it. This is a paragraph for them.

A paragraph is if it is natural that they will change it too. This is a paragraph which is natural. It is a sentence which if it were a paragraph would be natural. If you introduce as natural you do not make it too.

A paragraph is natural because it falls away. A paragraph need not fall away to be natural.

A sentence can not be natural because it is not rounded that is round is natural but rounded is not natural. A sentence is not natural. They will go on. A sentence is not not natural. If a sentence is not natural what should it be. If a paragraph should not be because to help it is to go away, she said he would be busy. This is neither a sentence nor a paragraph the country says no. This is neither a paragraph nor without it. A paragraph is natural because they feel like it. A sentence is not natural without that with that. And now think about damage. It is no trouble to wear green, thank you Len. This is a sentence which they know. If they know. Thank you if they know. This is a sentence. Thank you if they know. What is the difference between rounded.

In other words a paragraph is not naturally a natural thing but it is.

I have suddenly gotten not to care. This is an old sentence. To say so.

She knew she was right by the way that he said so. This is simply that.

There is no distance to come. With them come is came. She came.

No sentence when they were careful. A sentence when they were careful.

It is why they were aware that they were carried away by her. That is a nice sentence but not a natural sentence because they were divided in a sense. They were divided by leaving them about when they were ready. A natural sentence has nothing to do with how do you do. A natural sentence is vainly made by butter. It is in vain.

A natural sentence. A yellow peach may be ripened. There is a kind of a pear that has a rosy center which if felt is not in itself. What is it that made her know with a measure, she said there had been enough.

What is a natural sentence. A natural sentence they need not write. A natural sentence. After all. Who is here. After all who hears him. If they can.

None of that has anything to do with how a sentence is held. A sentence thinks loudly. Why must must is by me. Nearly beside made by then. A sentence cannot be natural. It must be returnable. To be returned. As well. What is a sentence and why cannot it be natural. Because it is a sentence. A sentence is not unnatural. A paragraph is not made of sentences. A paragraph with a precious sweet with eat. A paragraph is not pressed for time. Ever. A sentence if it returns or if it is added or if it is ended or simply in each way they make it do. They always can. Make a sentence do. You see why a sentence is not a part of it. A sentence should be ours. Now listen if he makes believe loving and eats in playing he eats in resumption, this is the same as anything and this is not a margin they make either stopping or not it is a paragraph with how and treasure. A sentence should be within a lope, that is why they had with him. Now think of these things. With them. A same with in all either shawl. Nothing to do with it. What is a sentence. There is no use in telling a whim. Nor in he sews. It is alike. Everything they show is piled alike. There should be a sentence in some arithmetic. But with fair they had it as may fairly hand it our like. No nor should it be my fish. A fish can be taught as a lake. What is a sentence it used to be that they liked it. Without a notice. That they liked it with that they had to be mine. What is a sentence. Often I will make a paragraph.

It gives all the effect of a mountain but it is on a plain.

Make it have it. It is a part and a part is not where there and have more. A part is not that it is belonging to the same plans.

A sentence if you thin then you thin sauces and sauces have need of Leon and Rosa. Every time you end will you have a refrain. Refrain can only mean that they wind and leave. He has disguised his action by his delight. He is delighted with it. Now these sentences do not make a paragraph. Nor do they make an end without it. Without doubt. That is a sentence but two words cannot make a preface. Is a preface a sentence. Very well. Send it. A sentence is a present which they make. In that way a sentence comes without a paragraph. Do you see. To say, do you see, is finally without employment.

Think of a sentence in two places it is not natural but engaging and very frightened. That is a sentence with waiting for them. It is very disagreeable to be waiting for them. This is a cadence. A cadence does not resemble a sentence it looks like it. A cadence does not resemble a sentence it is partly without a paragraph. Without is vainly made true. Mainly, mainly is the idea. That a paragraph is returned. It is not. It is mire which is not where they used. A paragraph is our, signed William. What is a paragraph, a paragraph is not a partition. A sentence never can be set apart.

A paragraph is this she discovers that the lake which is far away is not absolved in a partition. That is to say the land in between does not belong to them. It is very kindly of them to be back.

This is not completely a paragraph because of hoping that they will hear it alike. If it were a paragraph listen they would be told. How are they. Now a sentence is made by happen to distance.

They will be called anyway. This is neither a paragraph nor a sentence.

After a while.

I feel very differently about it.

Is conversation sentences. Is it paragraphs. Is it seeing them. There is an advantage.

When is it taken the advantage.

By them. Made by them. They will be willing. A conversation changes to paragraphs. With hope. Will, they be pleased. If they go. What is a conversation. They have learned all of it.

A sentence it is so easy to lose what a sentence is. Not so easy with a paragraph it is not so easy to lose what is a paragraph. What is a paragraph. Who loses a hold on him. That is a paragraph. That is not a sentence. Why is it.

What is it.

What is a paragraph.

I can come to know.

I have been known to know and to say so. A paragraph is not varying with the summer or anything.

This is a paragraph because it says so. Do you see. It says so. If you do see and it says so. Yes we do see and it says so. A paragraph says so. A sentence if it could would it say so. Would a sentence say so. If it said so would it have it as if it had it as said so, no. A sentence has not said so. A paragraph has said so. Think of a sentence. Has it said so. Yes it has said so. Two to a sentence. Yes it has said so. A sentence has not had it. It has not had it to say so. A sentence has not said to say so. A paragraph says so. A paragraph has not to have to have it say so. Easily say so. Too easily say so. A paragraph not too easily to say so. What is a sentence. A paragraph is not a sentence exactly not many more. There have not been sentence whether they say. A sentence always returns if they are happy. A sentence always returns if they were happy. A sentence is a sentence. This may be but it is not with arrive. Arrival. A Rival Sentence. Will Dan come and meet me. If he is meeting there. Think of a sentence. They will part. A sentence can not exist if it does not come back no not if it does not come back. A paragraph finishes.

This is it.

SHORTEST PIECES

COLORED AS COLORS, A GIFT

1924

WHICH ONE WILL

1924

TITLE, SUB-TITLE

1930

COLORED AS COLORS, A GIFT

She gave, he gave he gave she gave, he gave it as he gave it she said she would consider it as her gift.

Colored as colors, a gift.

White a pretty way to say it four times.

Blue a celebrated way to have plenty of decision.

Green a pleasant way to be perfect.

Grey a way to place it out of the way.

In the meantime all of it is furnished to make five.

In the meantime what has been put away is not more useful.

In the meantime recreation is not commonly expected because at once and now and again it has not become a habit at all.

Feeling it before feeling it for feeling it before a beginning.

As much as in having after and a pair.

Supposing in their place.

Supposing as a place.

He knew how to predict.

In prediction.

He knew how to predict.

To-morrow.

At once.

To-morrow.

Not at once.

To-morrow.

And at once.

To-morrow.

It is decided.

To change the subject.

Brown.

To change the subject.

Yellow

To change the subject.

Yellow brown

To change the subject.

Abundantly

To change the subject.

Change it again

Change it again and again.

And then prepared and then prepared and then.

Change it again.

Change it again and then prepared and then.

This makes listening.

Listening like that.

This makes listening like that.

Prepared again.

This makes listening like that this makes listening like that and prepared and again and again.

Prepared again.

This makes listening like that and prepared again.

If it did and obliged to if it did and obliged to and obliged to if it did.

As added as it was.

In the next addition and white and wetting, if it is not wet and wetted, if it is not wetted.

In the next addition and exchange, exchange one for two this is done practically.

The reason that it must be and had to be the reason that it could be and it could have had it all the reason that it can nearly and nearly and at all, at all and at all.

In no time.

In time.

In time.

In place in time and out.

In time and out in place in place and out in time and out in time and out in time in place in place in time and out. There is no need to admire more than the result.

If it is of use, if it is of use to use, if it has been of use, to be used, and to be used. Excellently and to matter, what is the matter, what is the matter with it. This is the matter with it. Up to just now it should be longer as well as fuller and fairer. It should be. As it should be. As it should be as it would be, and it would be, and it would be better that it should be. Should it be longer and fuller, should it be fuller and larger, and should it be more abundant. Should it. Would it be would it.

Would it be should it be more abundant and longer, would it be.

As often as inconvenient.

Preparing to prepare nice [rice?].

Preparing to prepare all of it and establishing it for instance.

Having had it mentioned here.

Beautifully and naturally.

Naturally and beautifully.

It can be had and had it.

If in consideration if in considering.

Considerable and expenses and having returned to colors.

The first color.

And their color.

The second color.

And their color

The third color

And their color.

Their color too.

Returning more and more naturally and beautifully, beautifully and naturally, returning more and more beautifully and naturally.

It was as pleasant as it was, it was it was it was it was, it was as pleasant as it was and it came out too.

It will be carefully prepared it will be shared it will be spared, it will be carefully compared it will be all it will be as it will be had it will be called it will be made it will be as it is declared, complete, to-morrow to-day just like at noon in the morning, just the same as habit and have it just the same as if it could never be and not at first and as often as if every day and not a bit and all and for it and how it is and covered and often and always and at a glance and so much and in it and by and by and when where and this and as much and more and obliging, very obliging.

At once.

WHICH ONE WILL

Which one will which one will which one will which one will, birds. Which one will.

In exchange.

She had offered and she had accepted she had accepted and she had offered she had offered so and so and because of this she undertook to ask she did not undertake to answer she undertook to ask and write and she did not undertake more and more, she and in at least as much she undertook and more was undertaken.

Which one will.

And not either.

Either is admitted admitted here, either is admitted here in choosing.

Which one will which one will which one will which one will either.

Either is earlier.

Either is earlier than that.

And not so quickly, after it had happened.

Divided by a pleasant day.

What is the difference between faith and faithfulness what is the difference.

A little novel it is a little novel.

Cast of character.

Inez

   Which one will.

Herbert

   Which one will.

Edith

   Which one will.

Felicia

   Which one will.

And Jonas

   Which one will.

And Emma

   Which one will.

If she writes this and that, if she writes that if she writes that and this and afterwards, that made it easier to be a mother. To be a mother that made it easier to be a sister to be a sister that made it easier to be a daughter to be a daughter that made it easier to be a father to be a father that made it easier that made it easier to be a brother to be a brother that made it easier that made it easier to be either.

If if it goes on.

If if it does.

If it does go on.

If it goes on.

And if it does.

If it does.

Anna Hannah, Hannah has to come.

Anna has to come.

Anna and Hannah have to come.

Anna and Hannah have to come, Hannah is younger. Hannah being younger and having successfully had and invented a horse, in this way there was no cause for any difficulty. If she wished to continue and stop finally and at once and after that.

This has been left behind altogether and finishes and fastens it to the admission of large numbers.

Supposing a set a separate set each separate set contributes. Supposing it does and there is more than enough and no addition. Adding is easily felt.

Having had a half of that having had as it were having had it as it was having had nearly having had it, what is the difference between Harriet and Anna.

Having had it for the rest having had it with the best of all having had it as the rest have had it, having had it literally having had it, there is more difference between Joe and William. Having had it alternately and exchanged exchanged some of it advantageously what is the reason for all of the agreement that undoubtedly exists between Frank and one or the other. Having had it explained and having had it carefully undertaken and having had it followed up as in opposition, why and where are there interesting questions such as are raised by the inattention of all of them and for this.

Fortunately husbanding husbanding what are resources fortunately what are resources are plentifully appraised fortunately what is appraised is practically organised and fortunately organization and restitution makes all of it plainer to value and to remove. Fortunately there are no exceptions and fortunately for them.

This is a choice between between this is a choice between waiting this is a choice between waiting for it.

Handsome is as handsome does.

There is a choice between waiting there is a choice between waiting there is a choice between waiting for it. To be pretty makes no difference to them at [all], to make no difference to them at all makes no difficulty in arranging for it in arranging for it it makes no difference to them at all.

It makes no difference to them at all.

Which one will make a Tuesday earlier, which one will if he says he can which one will if in spite of widows which one will if they do or if they do not find they can. Which one will answer all and better which one will place it well apart which one will be seizing it as property which one will which one will have it at the start and which one will fairly well.

TITLE, SUB-TITLE

Grammar in relation to a tree and two horses.
a title
a sub-title.
Grammar in relation to a tree and horses.
Grammar in relation to a tree and two horses.

I have invented many titles and I have invented many subtitles. What is in this sense the meaning of invention.

In grammar have to think why a fugue and also why exercises are expected and delay nothing. They are more interesting than a tune to any one. Now are they. Yes they are. You are ready. Are you ready. No I am ready's brother. Are you ready yet. Not yet. This is all an explanation of why to do so. To like cows better. I like cows better.

Now the whole theory of choosing change is this. When they sigh I reply. The whole thing of being right is this. Ask him if he likes it. It was quite good. This is his reply.

Now it is not nearly happily that she repeats the word and the meaning of the word butter.

Every one likes after that to have been right.

These are the foundations of grammar.

After all any thing will do if there are two. The same is not true of three and so forth and yet it is fairly easy to be loquacious. Mrs. Rue walks adequately. In reply.

They are at their name sake now. It is like this.

A little to resist entitle.

Now whose name is it when they forbid it. Somehow they do come when they are to come when they are to come. Now the reason that that is not finished is because there is a hesitation between at call and called. They could end come with call but not to excuse please. On the other hand called is impossible. And why. Why is impossible. It is not possible. In this way teasing is a pain as well as pleasurable.

A man stands on a watch that is if she is placed there. The title of this piece is a watch has a little sound. Watch is a name for which we do not like it any more at all it is scarcely used.

A title may make windows be the place at which they sew.

With a little noise of exciting he found his ball.

Ball ball. That is not a title.

It is insistence.

A title is never insistence. It is not even a pleasure. It is a necessity because it comes after or before. A sub-title is a pleasure always a pleasurable diversion.

A title

Carrie came here.

That is a title. I can remember so well. That is a title. I will go
    where they are.

That is a title

Thank you so much. That is not a title.

Why is thank you so much not a title. Thank you so much is a title.

I will go where they are. That is not a title.

Why is it not a title because they will not make it a title.

I will now tell you everything about leaving them with them.

They felt at home. That is not a title. Where they went. That is not a title. They like what they do. That is a title. A sub-title is not a title because anybody likes it.

Howard a title.

Pennsylvanians did not want the tittle title.

Please prepare the bed for Mrs Henry.

This is a title. Dear dear this is a title.

I would like to have been met by them. A title cannot be too long.

A title because after all all numbers are beautiful.

I undertake to overthrow their undertaking. That is better than a title.

I undertake to over throw their under taking.

This is a perfect piece of neither title nor sub-title.

Thank you very much.

For the moment the end of grammar.